Genius and Lust

GENIUS AND LUST

A Journey Through the Major Writings of HENRY MILLER

by
NORMAN MAILER

Grove Press, Inc., New York

ISBN: 0-394-40946-9
Grove Press ISBN: 0-8021-0127-5

Library of Congress Catalog Card Number: 76-14556

Second Printing 1976

Manufactured in the United States of America

Distributed by Random House, Inc., New York

GROVE PRESS, INC., 196 West Houston Street, New York, N.Y. 10014

Acknowledgments

Henry Miller, *The Air-Conditioned Nightmare.* Copyright © 1945 by New Directions Publishing Corporation. Reprinted by permission of New Directions Publishing Corporation.

Henry Miller, *The Colossus of Maroussi.* Copyright © 1941 by Henry Miller. Reprinted by permission of New Directions Publishing Corporation.

Henry Miller, *Big Sur & The Oranges of Hieronymus Bosch.* Copyright © 1956 by Henry Miller, © 1957 by New Directions Publishing Corporation. Reprinted by permission of New Directions Publishing Corporation.

Henry Miller, "Sunday After the War," from *The Henry Miller Reader.* Copyright © 1944 by Henry Miller. Reprinted by permission of New Directions Publishing Corporation.

Bern Porter, *Observations from the Treadmill,* as related to MY, editor of *Observations from the Treadmill,* February 16, 1975, at 22 Salmond Road, Belfast, Maine and appearing in the Winter Issue from RFD #1, Union, Maine, 1975.

Henry Miller, *My Life and Times by Henry Miller,* reprinted with permission of Playboy Press.

Henry Miller, *Tropic of Cancer,* copyright © 1961 by Grove Press, Inc. Reprinted by permission of Grove Press, Inc.

Henry Miller, *Tropic of Capricorn,* copyright © 1961 by Grove Press, Inc. Reprinted by permission of Grove Press, Inc.

Henry Miller, *Sexus,* copyright © 1962 by The Olympia Press, © 1965 by Grove Press, Inc. Reprinted by permission of Grove Press, Inc.

Henry Miller, *Nexus,* copyright © 1960 by Les Editions du Chêne, Paris, © 1965 by Grove Press, Inc. Reprinted by permission of Grove Press, Inc.

Henry Miller, *Plexus,* copyright © 1963 by Henry Miller, © 1965 by Grove Press, Inc. Reprinted by permission of Grove Press, Inc.

Henry Miller, *Black Spring,* copyright © 1963 by Grove Press, Inc. Reprinted by permission of Grove Press, Inc.

Henry Miller, *The World of Sex,* copyright © 1959 by Henry Miller, © 1965 by Grove Press, Inc. Reprinted by permission of Grove Press, Inc.

to **Henry Miller**

Contents

Foreword

After living with the difficulty for a couple of years, Lawrence Durrell put together an anthology of Henry Miller's work published by New Directions in 1959. The Henry Miller Reader, assembled with Durrell's keen eye for ornament, was a collection of Miller's least obscene writings. Durrell had his reasons. As Miller's friend, possibly his best friend, Durrell must have been aghast at the gap between Miller's large European reputation and small American readership. Known to the American literary world as a phenomenon, acclaimed by a fraction of that literary world as a giant and a genius, Miller was still relatively unknown and ninety-nine percent unread by that larger world of reasonably serious readers who camp in the fields just outside the literary world. His most renowned work, Tropic of Cancer, was unavailable in the U.S. except for copies smuggled in from Europe, and his succeeding works, Black Spring and Tropic of Capricorn, were also banned. His later works brought out in the Forties and the Fifties by New Directions were considerably cleaner. They were also not exactly as magnificent. Durrell, putting the anthology together in consultation with Miller, came to the well-researched conclusion they could not touch Miller's best writings—in 1959 they were much too obscene for the U.S. Post Office. So The Henry Miller Reader is obliged to do without the powerful prose of Tropic of Cancer, Tropic of Capricorn, and The Rosy Crucifixion—precisely the heart of Miller's gargantuan talents and vices as a novelist.

Under the circumstances, Durrell must have looked for the next best solution: he could at least introduce Henry Miller to a good many serious American readers who hitherto had had only a limited idea of Miller as a pornographer. That was a marrow of readership Durrell's friend deserved to reach, nay, it was his right to reach such people and their duty to read him, and Durrell may have been looking for the way to make a proper introduction. So our literary best of Miller, the Sunday best, the most attractive collection which could be dressed out of the quarter of his least offensive work was gotten together, and there is a wealth of exquisite writing in Durrell's collection. I recommend The Henry Miller Reader to anyone who loves the work of Flannery O'Connor, William Faulkner, Tennessee Williams, Thomas Wolfe, Eudora Welty, Saul Bellow, Nabokov, Updike, Cheever, Bill Styron, Thomas Pynchon, John Hawkes, Nelson Algren—it is rich literary writing of the best kind, and proves in passing Miller's collateral right to be regarded as a distinguished literary talent full of character and evocation.

Durrell therefore did the best job available to be done, but now a decade and a half later, with all of Miller's work available, the choice of an anthologist may open: one can look to come a little nearer to the heart of the work. Of course, that is not necessarily simple. There is so much of Miller, and the very best (after Tropic of Cancer) is so intimately coupled with the worst in him (that is, with any particular anthologist's idea of what is worst—few readers are ever uncertain of what they like and don't like in Henry Miller), that the job of putting an anthology together becomes tricky. Miller, his work embraced, which is to say swallowed in four or five weeks, and then re-read over another month or two, can sit *in one's mind with all the palpability of a huge elm lying uprooted in your backyard. The nobility of the trunk and the relations of the branches are all on the ground for you to examine and try to compare, not to speak of the rich nightmare of the roots and crawlers offering all their separate intimations of the peculiarities of tongues, as though we are about to learn how voices belong not only to the wind but to earth being pulled apart from itself. How slippery are some of those roots, and ripped up. Fibers of root-hair emerge from the soil like ideas drawn into wires. One hallucinates: every scent comes off every crotch of the roots—wholesale corruption may beckon here along with organic integrity.*

To read Miller in so short a period reopens the old question which is always too large: What is a man? Just as that uprooted elm would take on constellations of meaning as it lay in the yard, until finally it is reminiscent of a battleship, or a forest of caverns in Hieronymus Bosch, so might you be forced to ask: What the devil is a tree? Just so does Miller return us to the first question of humanism. What, finally, is a Man? Nothing is settled after all. We have been given the illusion that we know Miller, know every one of his vices, peccadillos, hustles, horrors, cadges, gifts, flaws, and transcendent generosities, are, yes, familiar with that man who is by his own description "confused, negligent, reckless, lusty, obscene, boisterous, thoughtful, scrupulous, lying, diabolically truthful man . . . filled with wisdom and nonsense." Nonetheless, when we are done reading, we wonder if we know anything. In My Life and Times *published around 1972 when Miller is 80, he mentions that he was plagued by piles for all the years of his young manhood. A stud with piles! He never gave a clue. Not one description of his anus suffering through a lacerated shit. It is a reticence tucked away in all the extravaganza of his exhibitionism. So, too, will he mention at 80 that he never wrote about any of the women with whom he was in love except for his second wife June. His seven years with her form the ground of his autobiographical writings, and of course, as we shall see, he could never quite write at his best about her. In the middle of his triumphs resides his failure to create her. None of the other loves was even attempted. Then we learn from the diaries of Anaïs Nin that Miller is an impeccably neat housekeeper. In all the stench of the Paris scenes he depicts, we are now to picture Miller tidying up his personal quarters. Compulsively! Yes, he reopens all the questions of literature—reopens the first question: What is the nature of that truth we find on a page?*

It is not that he bears no relation to the Henry Miller who is the protagonist of his books. (That Henry Miller is, indeed, the ultimate definition of the word protagonist.) No, the real Henry Miller, which is to say the corporeal Miller certain writers knew intimately and wrote about well, Anaïs Nin being the first, is not a Henry Miller who is so very different from his work. He is more like a transparency laid over a drawing, copied, and then skewed just a degree. He is just a little different from his work. But in that difference is all the mystery of his own personality, and the paradoxes of a great artist. And the tragedy. The failure. For it is impossible to talk of a great artist without speaking of failure. The greater they are, the more they fail to fulfill their own idea of themselves. Dostoyevsky failed to write The Life of a Great Sinner, and Tolstoy failed to bring a religious metamorphosis to man. Miller was never able to come to focus on the one subject which cried out to him: D. H. Lawrence's old subject—what is to be said of love between a man and a woman? Miller saw that Lawrence had come to grips with the poetry of sex but none of the sewer gas. Miller would light matches to the sewer gas like nobody who ever lived, and he set off literary explosions, but he never exploded himself over to the other side of the divide. He could be poetic about anything and everything except fucking with love. While nobody can be more poetic than Miller about fucking itself—two hundred beer-hall accordions might as well be pumping away as he launches into descriptions of the more heavenly engagements he has played, the writing is invariably an evocation of some disembodied and divine cunt and what it is doing to him—maybe it is even equal to a critical appreciation of a great symphony; he still cannot write about fucking with love. (Of course it is fair to ask: who can?) Miller nonetheless pounds away on the subject like a giant phallus trying to enter a child's vagina—in the pounding is one simple question: How do you get in? So we are forced to contend with the contradiction of his character. He is at one pole of his personality "a mystic in the wild state" (a characterization of Rimbaud by Claudel which Miller eagerly appropriates to himself). At the other, he is profoundly Germanic, and his people are tradespeople. Sooner or later we find out that his mother is strict, intolerant, penny-pinching, string-saving, petty-bourgeois in her righteousness and unrelentingly humorless. Insanity is in his family—just so close as his sister—plus all the iron cages of a lower-middle-class milieu drenched in rectitude. What a journey the man has taken.

Now, at our leisure, decades past the years of his fevers, we can begin to see how much of his life is illuminated by his work, and yet how much remains that is obfuscated by the writing itself. If all the writings are now available, they do not always provide a clear path into the unique heart of such a writer. He is after all a great writer and that heart is not so casually revealed—this "diabolically truthful man" can be diabolically sly. Still, he is always there. It is the center of the power of his writing. Whether comprehensible or subtly and self-protectively out of focus, few writers in the history of literature speak with so powerful a presence.

In a passing entry in her diary, Anaïs Nin offers this:

> Henry talks about Saint Francis, meditates on the idea of saintliness. Why, I ask him.
>
> "Because I consider myself the last man on earth."
>
> *The Diary of Anaïs Nin*

He writes that way. It may be what accounts for his presence. He has such an extravagant sense of mission that his presence is palpable. What is in his mind is more real to him than himself, and vastly more real than any of the people who come and go in his life. Episodes seem to exist just long enough to build up the reader's momentum for a plunge into more of Miller's mind. Perhaps that is why there is no transition between his superb realism and that all-out mysticism so volcanically cosmic it jumps through the galaxies with no more for a launching pad than a new paragraph.

Yet the worst thing about Miller is the best thing about him. He is there. He is there like few writers, there like Paris is there or meat on a hook in a butcher shop (at least as meat was hung on a hook in his day). In the most powerful, the most obscene, and even in the most godawful stretches of his most impassioned and chaotic writing, that presence is upon us. Finally it becomes one's guide, a criterion at last for the anthologist's powers of selection, a way to choose among the sweetmeats of his work. So a feast of perception and a fireworks of energy become the very least any anthologist can now offer. One need only lean on that literary presence.

To come to grips with more, to offer an insight into the unique character and exceptional psychology of a twentieth-century man so special as Miller is another matter. Jean Malaquais once remarked that through his imagination a writer may comprehend every kind of human being but a writer greater than himself. The brunt of that maxim is upon us now.

c/o British Consul,
Villa Agazini,
Parama, Corfu
[August 1935]

Dear Mr. Miller,

I have just read Tropic of Cancer again and feel I'd like to write you a line about it. It strikes me as being the only really man-size piece of work which this century can really boast of. It's a howling triumph from the word go; and not only is it a literary and artistic smack on the bell for everyone, but it really gets down on paper the blood and bowels of our time. I have never read anything like it. I did not imagine anything like it could be written; and yet, curiously, reading it I seemed to recognize it as something which I knew we were all ready for . . .

. . . Skoal to the stanchless flux
Lawrence Durrell

18 Villa Seurat, Paris (XIV)
Sept. 1, 1935

Dear Mr. Durrell,

Your letter rocks me a bit too. You're the first Britisher who's written me an intelligent letter about the book. For that matter, you're the first anybody who's hit the nail on the head. I particularly prize your letter because it's the kind of letter I would have written myself had I not been the author of the book. That isn't just sheer vanity and egotism, believe me. It's curious how few people know what to admire in the book . . .

Your letter is so vivid, so keen, that I am curious to know if you are not a writer yourself . . .

Cordially yours
Henry Miller*

---

* The letters are from *Durrell and Miller—A Private Correspondence* (New York: E. P. Dutton & Co., Inc., 1963).

Genius and Lust

1. Status

Literary criticism has left a space around Henry Miller. Fanfare in plenty has come his way, some grandiose, some opalescent—Miller would draw his share of critical rainbows—yet it is as if his reputation still lives in a void. Years later, Karl Shapiro would write to Durrell that they should "put together a bible of Miller's work" to be substituted for the Gideon Bible in every hotel room of America. Durrell, in his turn, would state, "American literature today begins and ends with the meaning of what Miller has done." Anaïs Nin began her preface to Tropic of Cancer by declaring: "Here is a book which, if such a thing were possible, might restore our appetite for the fundamental realities."

Yes, Miller has had his share of praise, and such literary maharajahs as Eliot and Pound and Edmund Wilson made their contribution. Pound contented himself with a remark from the fundament: "Here is a dirty book worth reading," and Eliot, who found Shelley satanic, nonetheless became a closet devotee of Miller's, and even sent a letter to the author (if no public pronunciamento). Wilson wrote one of the earliest laudatory (and starchy) reviews to be printed of Tropic of Cancer. George Orwell, in a fine essay, said, "it is the book of a man who is happy"—how close to the first virtue was happiness to Orwell! He added: "the only imaginative prose writer of the slightest value who has appeared among the English-speaking races for some years past."

That was in the Thirties. Miller has not lacked for adulation since. A small but accountable part of the literary world has regarded him as the greatest living American writer for the last four decades and indeed, as other American authors died, and Hemingway was there no longer, nor Faulkner and Fitzgerald, not Wolfe, not Steinbeck, nor Dos Passos, and Sinclair Lewis long gone, Dreiser dead and Farrell in partial obscurity, who else could one speak of as the great American author? Moreover, Miller provided his considerable qualifications. One had to go back to Melville to find a rhetoric which could prove as noble under full sail. Indeed one has to ask oneself if Miller could not out-write Melville if it came to describing a tempest at sea. Miller at his best wrote a prose grander than Faulkner's, and wilder—the good reader is revolved in a farrago of light with words heavy as velvet, brilliant as gems, eruptions of thought cover the page. You could be in the vortex of one of Turner's oceanic holocausts when the sun shines in the very center of the storm. No, there is nothing like Henry Miller when he gets rolling. Men with literary styles as full as Hawthorne's appear by comparison stripped of their rich language, stripped as an AP style book; one has to take the English language back to Marlowe and Shakespeare before encountering a wealth of imagery equal in intensity.

Yet it can hardly be said that the American Establishment walks around today thinking of Henry Miller as our literary genius, or one of the symbols of human wealth in America. Born in 1891, he will be eighty-five by December 26 of 1976, an artist of incomparably larger dimensions than Robert Frost, yet who can conceive of a President inviting him to read from his work on Inauguration Day, no, the irony is that a number of good and intelligent politicians might even have a slight hesitation over whether it is Arthur Miller or Henry being talked about. "Oh yes, Henry Miller," they might say at last, "the guy who writes the dirty books." There is such variety in America that everybody ends up being understood by a tag. Dirty books is the tag for old Henry.

Of course, there is the objection that one does not go for sound literary measure to a politician's judgments. Even in the literary world, however, Miller's reputation survives in a vacuum. It is not that he lacks influence. It is even not unfair to say that Henry Miller has influenced the style of half the good American poets and writers alive today: it is fair to ask if books as different as Naked Lunch, Portnoy's Complaint, Fear of Flying and Why Are We in Vietnam? would have been as well received (or as free in style) without the irrigation Henry Miller gave to American prose. Even a writer as removed in purpose from Miller as Saul Bellow shows a debt in Augie March. Miller has had his effect. Thirty years ago, young writers learned to write by reading him along with Hemingway and Faulkner, Wolfe and Fitzgerald. With the exception of Hemingway, he has had perhaps the largest stylistic influence of any twentieth-century American author. Yet still there is that critical space. Miller has only been written about in terms of adulation or dismissal. One does not pick up literary reviews with articles titled, "Ernest Hemingway and Henry Miller—Their Paris Years," or "The Social Worlds of F. Scott Fitzgerald and Henry Miller," no comments on "The Apocalyptic Vision of Henry Miller and Thomas Wolfe as Reflected in Their Rhetoric," no little studies about the similarities of place and time in Orwell's Down and Out in Paris and London juxtaposed to Tropic of Cancer, no, and certainly no biographies on Miller or the women in his life. If Scott had Zelda, and she was undeniably equal to a formal biography, so Miller had June Edith Smith and she may also be worthy of such treatment. No one seems in a rush to go near. Nor is there bound to be a work titled "Henry Miller and The Beat Generation," or "Henry Miller and the Revolution of the Sixties." Young men do not feel they are dying inside because they cannot live the way Henry Miller once lived. Yet no American writer, not even Hemingway, necessarily came closer to the crazy bliss of being alone in a strange city with no money in your pocket, not much food in your stomach, and a hard on beginning to stir, a "personal" hard on (as one of Miller's characters nicely describes it).

The paradox therefore persists. It is a wonder. To anthologize Miller is to read just about all of him. To read that much of his work is to take in willy-nilly his dimension. He is a greater writer than one thought. If Tropic of Cancer is far and away his best work and nearly everyone who has read Miller has read it, that novel nonetheless offers a highly imperfect view of the rest of his future talent. Compared to Melville, Miller's secondary work is more impressive and considerably more varied. There is not one Henry Miller, but twenty, and fifteen of those authors are very good. Of course, when Miller is bad, he may be the worst great writer ever to be bad. His literary criticism can be pompous and embarrassingly empty of new perceptions. His work on Rimbaud, The Time of the Assassins, is disappointing. He may have nothing memorable to say about Lawrence or Balzac. His polemical essays read like sludge. At his worst, he sounds like a small-town newspaper editorial. He can even be corny.

At his literary best, however, as in "Jabberwhorl Cronstadt" he can do a parody—"vermiform and ubisquishous"—of Finnegans Wake which may as well set the standard for parodies of Joyce. In another year—it may as well be another life—he can write an undemanding account of trying to take care of his sick car in various garages in Albuquerque which has all the charm and publishability and perishability of the sort of piece The New York Sunday Times Magazine is always trying to find and never can. Or he will write a sustained memoir, The Devil in Paradise, about a complex and not unevil astrologer which is superior to Thomas Mann's "Mario the Magician" and nearly equal to "Death in Venice." He can create a gallery of characters in his trilogy The Rosy Crucifixion who match any equivalent group in the work of Thomas Wolfe, and the vividness of his creations need never give way to Balzac. He is a virtuoso. It is possible we have never had more of a literary acrobat.

In fact it would be tempting to say that he writes well about everything but his enthusiasms, which could explain why the ventures into literary criticism are not as good as one might expect. When Miller applauds, he is empty, he is loud. He is always putting his friends on his shoulders. For want of a new idea he is too quick to repeat the last one. Unable to develop a thought, be certain he bashes into the next. It is even tempting to say that he writes well about every situation in society but sex, except it is not true. One has to know where to look, but Miller has superb descriptions of sex. Even his standard writings about fornication, those accounts so famously empty of relationship, and stark, ergo, as pornography, can at least be read as pornography. He could have been a giant of pornography if he had chosen, right up there above John Cleland and Restif de la Bretonne; he could also have been the greatest writer The New York Times Magazine ever found; could have been a jewel of an avant-garde pen, the most poetic and surrealist protégé New Directions ever published; or a great travel writer; or a species of Beat Mencken—nobody hated America with better language than Henry Mencken unless it was Henry Miller; he could, with a little luck in his personal life, have written one of the great picaresque novels of the English language—reference is to The Rosy Crucifixion—somehow, he did not quite have that luck, something went wrong and large parts of his most ambitious work were written in years when he was miserably married and dragging his life uphill, far from the years of his exuber-

ance in Paris after Tropic of Cancer *was finally published. On the other hand, you could take any one of the paragraphs in his more surrealistic writing and recognize what an instinctive sense he had for film montage. In another career, he might have been an extraordinary movie director. He sees with more astonishment and savagery than most film artists.*

> You step out along the Atlantic littoral in your cement suit and your gold-heeled socks and there's the roar of Chop Suey in your ears. The Great White Way is blazing with spark plugs. The comfort stations are open. You try to sit down without breaking the crease in your pants. You sit down on the pure asphalt and let the peacocks tickle your larynx. The gutters are running with champagne.
>
> *Black Spring*

The extent of his talent is that he has exhibited all these literary modes and styles in the thirty-odd years he kept writing after Tropic of Cancer, *yet he had not even begun that book before he turned forty. Near to middle-aged and just about penniless, he was a middle-class failure who had used up his credit among friends. Leaving New York for Europe he was barely able to borrow ten dollars for pocket money on the boat. That is failure backed up in all the pipes. Yet living in Paris by his wits, living in Paris with the operative definition of what it means to live by your wits, he succeeded in putting together the manuscript of* Tropic of Cancer, *and it is one of the ten or twenty great novels of our century, a revolution in style and consciousness equal to* The Sun Also Rises. *You cannot pass through the first twenty pages without knowing that a literary wonder is taking place—nobody has ever written in just this way before, nobody may ever write by this style so well again. A time and a place have come to focus in a writer's voice. It is like encountering an archaeological relic. Given enough such novels, the history of our century could never* be lost: there would be enough separate points of reference fixed forever in focus.

It is close therefore to incomprehensible that a man whose literary career has been with us over forty years, an author who wrote one novel which may yet be considered equal to the best of Hemingway, a better novel than anything by Fitzgerald, an author who at his richest gave us sustained passages as intense as anything in Faulkner, a writer who could probably produce more than Thomas Wolfe day by day, and beat him word for word, a wildwater of prose, a cataract, a volcano, a torrent, an earthquake—at this point Henry Miller would have fifty better words to string—a writer finally like a great athlete, a phenomenon of an avatar of literary energy who was somehow, with every large acceptance, and every respect, was somehow ignored and near to discarded, ignored indeed most—the paradox embeds itself in new paradox—in just those years when his ideas triumphed most, and the young of America, for the large part ignorant of Miller's monumental collection of writings, were nonetheless living up to the ears with his thoughts or spouting his condemnations. Turn on, tune in and drop out was old hat to Henry—he had been doing it all his life. Ecology came as no surprise; he and Lewis Mumford may have been the first to write about what was being done to the American landscape, and plastic was the stuff of nightmare with which they covered those air-conditioners he wrote about. Still, nobody was breaking down the doors to get to him. On any given night in any lecture hall of America, Buckminster Fuller—another genius—would draw an audience five to, would it be, ten times the size and Fuller cannot write a sentence which does not curdle the sap of English at its root.

We must assume there was finally something indigestible about Miller to Americans, something in his personality and/or his work which went beyond his ideas, for his condemnations are virtually comfortable to us today. No, it is as if there are authors whose complexities are in harmony with our own. Hemingway and Fitzgerald may each have been outrageous pieces of psychic work, yet their personalities haunt us. Faulkner inspires our reverence and Wolfe our tenderest thoughts for literary genius. They are good to the memories we keep of our reading of them—they live with all the security of favorite old films. But Miller does not. He is a force, a value, a literary sage, and yet in the most peculiar sense he does not become more compatible with time—he may be no better beloved today than twenty, thirty, or forty years ago—it is as if he is almost not an American author; yet nobody could be more American. So he evades our sense of classification. He does not become a personality, rather he maintains himself as an enigma. It is as if he is virtually disagreeable to confront—a literary ogre. There is something faulty in our comprehension of him. His work at its best is marvelously in focus, indeed that is the first virtue of his greatest work—he is one of the first to be forever telling it like it is, here and now, just like it is—yet his own personality is never clear. It is too complex and too vigorous, therefore too worrisome for us, too out of measure.

It is as if Henry Miller contains the unadvertised mystery of how much of a monster a great writer must be.

"There is only one thing which interests me vitally now, and that is the recording of all that which is omitted in books."

2. Genius

Part of the crisis of the Twentieth Century is that nothing like a coherent view of personality seems able to exist. We live in every concept of human motivation, and they are all at odds. Our minds are obliged to entertain everything from the structured hydraulics of the Freudians who tend to look at psychic disturbance as varieties of stopped-up plumbing, faulty pressure systems, and inoperative valves, to a hundred California-like conceptions of living it out—everything from Esalen to EST to Ram Dass—schools which see us as transmission belts for the universe: if my karma is taking a trip through you, yours may be off in premature exploration of the Bardol, be here now, man! The atomization is so complete that in compensation the world of legend descends to lower levels all the time. We have all the history to know better, but we still like our public personalities to be likeable. There is a passion finally to find the President of the United States as comprehensible as the high school principal next door or the professional golfer up the road. We do not wish to encounter the possibility that any man who has walked, leaped, and been transported over the long road to the Presidency can hardly still be simple. He has done too much damage to pure thought on his route. Therefore we allow legend to lap at the edges of our sentimentality. We content ourselves with the thought that Jerry Ford is basically a good guy. All the while we ignore the knowledge that any world leader who is so good and decent would crack up in three weeks out of his whole and total lack of relation to the questions he is having to decide every day. Nonetheless, we want our legend. In chaos, sugar us up.

So the authors who live best in legend offer personalities we can comprehend like movie stars. Hemingway and Fitzgerald impinge on our psyche with the clarity of Bogart or Cagney. We comprehend them at once. Faulkner bears the same privileged relation to a literary Southerner as Olivier to the London theatregoer. A grand and cultivated presence is enriching the marrow of your life. Nobody wishes to hear a bad story about Olivier or Faulkner.

Henry Miller, however, exists in the same relation to legend that anti-matter shows to matter. His life is antipathetic to the idea of legend itself. Where he is complex, he is too complex—we do not feel the resonance of slowly dissolving mystery but the madness of too many knots; where he is simple, he is not attractive—his air is harsh. If he had remained the protagonist by which he first presented himself in Tropic of Cancer—the man with iron in his phallus, acid in his mind, and some kind of incomparable relentless freedom in his heart, that paradox of tough misery and keen happiness, that connoisseur of the spectrum of odors between good sewers and bad sewers, that noble rat gnawing on existence and impossible to kill, then he could indeed have been a legend, a species of Parisian Bogart or American Belmondo. Everybody would have wanted to meet this poet-gangster, barbarian-genius. He would have been the American and heterosexual equivalent of Jean Genet.

In fact, he could never have been too near to the character he made of himself in Tropic of Cancer. One part never fits. It is obvious he must be more charming than he pretends—how else account for all the free dinners he is invited to, the people he lives on, the whores who love him? There has to be something splendid about him. He may even seem angelic to his friends, or, perish the word, vulnerable. Anaïs Nin when describing the apartment in Clichy that Miller kept with Alfred Perlès, made, we remember, the point that Miller was tidying the joint. "Henry keeps house like a Dutch housekeeper. He is very neat and clean. No dirty dishes about. It is all monastic, really, with no trimmings, no decoration."*

These few details are enough to suggest Tropic of Cancer is a fiction more than a fact. Which, of course, is not to take away a particle of its worth. Perhaps it becomes even more valuable. After all, we do not write to recapture an experience, we write to come as close to it as we can. Sometimes we are not very close, and yet, paradoxically, are nearer than if we had. Not nearer necessarily to the reality of what happened, but to the mysterious reality of what can happen on a page. Oil paints do not create clouds but the image of clouds; a page of manuscript can only evoke that special kind of reality which lives on the skin of the writing paper, a rainbow on a soap bubble. Miller is forever accused of caricature by people who knew his characters, and any good reader knows enough about personality to sense how much he must be leaving out of his people. Yet, what a cumulative reality they give us. His characters make up a Paris more real than its paving stones until a reluctant wonder bursts upon us—no French writer no matter how great, not Rabelais, nor Proust, not De Maupassant, Hugo, Huysmans, Zola, or even Balzac, not even Céline, has made Paris more vivid to us. Whenever before has a foreigner described a country better than its native writers? For in Tropic of Cancer Miller succeeded in performing one high literary act: he created a tone in prose which caught the tone of a period and a place. If that main character in Tropic of Cancer named Henry Miller

---

* *The Diary of Anaïs Nin* (*Vol. I*) (New York: The Swallow Press and Harcourt, Brace & World, Inc., 1966), p. 62.

never existed in life, it hardly matters—he is the voice of a spirit which existed at that time. The spirits of literature may be the nearest we come to historical truth.

For that matter, the great confessions of literature are apart from their authors. Augustine recollecting his sins is not the sinner but the pieties. Julien Sorel is not Stendhal, nor the Seducer a copy of Kierkegaard. On the Road is close to Jack Kerouac, yet he gives a happier Kerouac than the one who died too soon. Proust was not his own narrator, even as homosexuality is not heterosexuality but another land, and if we take The Sun Also Rises as the purest example of a book whose innovation in style became the precise air of a time and a place, then even there we come slowly to the realization that Hemingway at the time he wrote it was not the equal of Jake Barnes—he had created a consciousness wiser, drier, purer, more classic, more sophisticated, and more judicial than his own. He was still naïve in relation to his creation.

The difference between Hemingway and Miller is that Hemingway set out thereafter to grow into Jake Barnes and locked himself for better and worse, for enormous fame and eventual destruction, into that character who embodied the spirit of an age. Whereas Miller, eight years older than Hemingway but arriving at publication eight years later, and so sixteen years older in 1934 than Hemingway was in 1926, chose to go in the opposite direction. He proceeded to move away from the first Henry Miller he had created. He was not a character but a soul—he would be various.

He was. Not just a debrouillard, but a poet; not just a splenetic vision but a prophet; no mere caricaturist, rather a Daumier of the written line; and finally not just master of one style but the prodigy of a dozen. Miller had only to keep writing Tropic of Cancer over and over and refining his own personality to become less and less separate from his book, and he could have entered the American life of legend. There were obstacles in his way, of course, and the first was that he was not publishable in America—the growth of his legend would have taken longer. But he had something to offer which went beyond Hemingway.

The cruelest criticism ever delivered of Henry James is that he had a style so hermetic his pen would have been paralyzed if one of his characters had ever entered a town house, removed his hat, and found crap on his head (a matter, parenthetically, of small moment to Tolstoy let us say, or Dostoyevsky, or Stendhal). Hemingway would have been bothered more than he liked. Miller would have loved it. How did his host react to the shit? How did our host's wife? My God, the way she smacked her nostrils over the impact, you can be sure her thighs were in a lather.

In fact, Hemingway would have hated such a scene. He was trying to create a world where mood—which Hemingway saw as the staff of life—could be cultivated by the scrupulosity of the attention you paid to keeping mood aloft through the excellence of your gravity, courage, and diction.

The eye of every dream Hemingway ever had must have looked down the long vista of his future suicide—so he had a legitimate fear of chaos. He never wrote about the river—he contented himself, better, he created a quintessentially American aesthetic by writing about the camp he set up each night by the side of the river—that was the night we made camp at the foot of the cliffs just after the place where the rapids were bad.

Miller is the other half of literature. He is without fear of his end, a literary athlete at ease in earth, air or water. I am the river, he is always ready to say, I am the rapids and the placids, I'm the froth and the scum and twigs—what a roar as I go over the falls. Who gives a fart. Let others camp where they may. I am the river and there is nothing I can't join.

Hemingway's world was doomed to collapse so soon as the forces of the century pushed life into a technological tunnel; mood to Hemingway being a royal grace, could not survive grinding gears, surrealist manners—here's shit in your hat!—and electric machines which offered static, but Miller took off at the place where Hemingway ended. In Tropic of Cancer he was saying—and it is the force of the book—I am obliged to live in that place where mood is in the meat grinder, so I know more about it. I know all of the spectrum which runs from good mood to bad mood, and can tell you that a stinking mood is better than no mood. Life has also been designed to run in the stink.

Miller bounces in the stink. We read Tropic of Cancer, that book of horrors, and feel happy. It is because there is honor in the horror, and metaphor in the hideous. How, we cannot even begin to say. Maybe it is that mood is vastly more various, self-regenerative, hearty and sly than Hemingway ever guessed. Maybe mood is not a lavender lady, but a barmaid with full visions of heaven in the full corruption of her beer breath, and an old drunk's vomit is a clarion call to some mutants of the cosmos just now squeezing around the bend. It is as if without courage, or militancy, or the serious cultivation of strength, without stoicism or good taste, or even a nose for the nicety of good guts under terrible pressure, Miller is still living closer to death than Hemingway, certainly he is closer if the sewer is nearer to our end than the wound.

History proved to be on Miller's side. Twentieth-century life was leaving the world of individual effort, liquor, and tragic wounds, for the big-city garbage can of bruises, migraines, static, mood chemicals, amnesia, absurd relations and cancer. Down in the sewers of existence where the cancer was being cooked, Miller was cavorting. Look, he was forever saying, you do not have to die of this crud. You can breathe it, eat it, suck it, fuck it, and still bounce up for the next day.

There is something inestimable in us if we can stand the smell.

Considering where the world was going—right into the World-Wide Sewer of the Concentration Camps—Miller had a message which gave more life than Hemingway. "One reason why I have stressed so much the immoral, the wicked, the ugly, the cruel in my work is because I wanted others to know how valuable these are, how equally if not more important than the good things. . . . I was getting the poison out of my system. Curiously enough, this poison had a tonic effect for others. It was as if I had given them some kind of immunity."*

The legend, however, was never to develop. With his fingers and his nose and his toenails, he had gotten into the excrements of cancerland—he had to do no more than stay there, a dry sardonic demon, tough as nails, bright as radium. But he had had a life after all before this, tragic, twisted, near to atrophied in some of its vital parts, he was closer to the crud himself than he ever allowed. So he had to write himself out of his own dungeons and did in all the work which would follow Tropic of Cancer and some of the secrets of his unique, mysterious, and absolutely special personality are in his later work and we will yet live with him there, and try to comprehend him—a vital search. We would all know more if we could find him.

But for now let us take on the pleasure of Tropic of Cancer. Much of the first half is reprinted here.

---

* Jonathan Cott, "Reflections of a Cosmic Tourist," *Rolling Stone* (February 27, 1975), pp. 38–46, 57.

From **Tropic of Cancer**

I am living at the Villa Borghese. There is not a crumb of dirt anywhere, nor a chair misplaced. We are all alone here and we are dead.

Last night Boris discovered that he was lousy. I had to shave his armpits and even then the itching did not stop. How can one get lousy in a beautiful place like this? But no matter. We might never have known each other so intimately, Boris and I, had it not been for the lice.

Boris has just given me a summary of his views. He is a weather prophet. The weather will continue bad, he says. There will be more calamities, more death, more despair. Not the slightest indication of a change anywhere. The cancer of time is eating us away. Our heroes have killed themselves, or are killing themselves. The hero, then, is not Time, but Timelessness. We must get in step, a lock step, toward the prison of death. There is no escape. The weather will not change.

It is now the fall of my second year in Paris. I was sent here for a reason I have not yet been able to fathom.

I have no money, no resources, no hopes. I am the happiest man alive. A year ago, six months ago, I thought that I was an artist. I no longer think about it, I *am*. Everything that was literature has fallen from me. There are no more books to be written, thank God.

This then? This is not a book. This is libel, slander, defamation of character. This is not a book, in the ordinary sense of the word. No, this is a prolonged insult, a gob of spit in the face of Art, a kick in the pants to God, Man, Destiny, Time, Love, Beauty . . . what you will. I am going to sing for you, a little off key perhaps, but I will sing. I will sing while you croak, I will dance over your dirty corpse. . . .

To sing you must first open your mouth. You must have a pair of lungs, and a little knowledge of music. It is not necessary to have an accordion, or a guitar. The essential thing is to *want* to sing. This then is a song. I am singing.

It is to you, Tania, that I am singing. I wish that I could sing better, more melodiously, but then perhaps you would never have consented to listen to me. You have heard the others sing and they have left you cold. They sang too beautifully, or not beautifully enough.

It is the twenty-somethingth of October. I no longer keep track of the date. Would you say—my dream of the 14th November last? There are intervals, but they are between dreams, and there is no consciousness of them left. The world around me is dissolving, leaving here and there spots of time. The world is a cancer eating itself away. . . . I am thinking that when the great silence descends upon all and everywhere music will at last triumph. When into the womb of time everything is again withdrawn chaos will be restored and chaos is the score upon which reality is written. You, Tania, are my chaos. It is why I sing. It is not even I, it is the world dying, shedding the skin of time. I am still alive, kicking in your womb, a reality to write upon.

Dozing off. The physiology of love. The whale with his six-foot penis, in repose. The bat—*penis libre*. Animals with a bone in the penis. Hence, *a bone on*. . . . "Happily," says Gourmont, "the bony structure is lost in man." Happily? Yes, happily. Think of the human race walking around with a bone on. The kangaroo has a double penis—one for weekdays and one for holidays. Dozing. A letter from a female asking if I have found a title for my book. Title? To be sure: "Lovely Lesbians."

Your anecdotal life! A phrase of M. Borowski's. It is on Wednesdays that I have lunch with Borowski. His wife, who is a dried-up cow, officiates. She is studying English now—her favorite word is "filthy." You can see immediately what a pain in the ass the Borowskis are. But wait. . . .

Borowski wears corduroy suits and plays the accordion. An invincible combination, especially when you consider that he is not a bad artist. He puts on that he is a Pole, but he is not, of course. He is a Jew, Borowski, and his father was a philatelist. In fact, almost all Montparnasse is Jewish, or half-Jewish, which is worse. There's Carl and Paula, and Cronstadt and Boris, and Tania and Sylvester, and Moldorf and Lucille. All except Fillmore. Henry Jordan Oswald turned out to be a Jew also. Louis Nichols is a Jew. Even Van Norden and Chérie are Jewish. Frances Blake is a Jew, or a Jewess. Titus is a Jew. The Jews then are snowing me under. I am writing this for my friend Carl whose father is a Jew. All this is important to understand.

Of them all the loveliest Jew is Tania, and for her sake I too would become a Jew. Why not? I already speak like a Jew. And I am as ugly as a Jew. Besides, who hates the Jews more than the Jew?

Twilight hour. Indian blue, water of glass, trees glistening and liquescent. The rails fall away into the canal at Jaurès. The long caterpillar with lacquered sides dips like a roller coaster. It is not Paris. It is not Coney Island. It is a crepuscular melange of all the cities of Europe and Central America. The railroad yards below me, the tracks black, webby, not ordered by the engineer but cataclysmic in design, like those gaunt fissures in the polar ice which the camera registers in degrees of black.

Food is one of the things I enjoy tremendously. And in this beautiful Villa Borghese there is scarcely ever any evidence of food. It is positively appalling at times. I have asked Boris time and again to order bread for breakfast, but he always forgets. He goes out for breakfast, it seems. And when he comes back he is picking his teeth and there is a little egg hanging from his goatee. He eats in the restaurant out of consideration for me. He says it hurts to eat a big meal and have me watch him.

I like Van Norden but I do not share his opinion of himself. I do not agree, for instance, that he is a philosopher, or a thinker. He is cunt-struck, that's all. And he will never be a writer. Nor will Sylvester ever be a writer, though his name blaze in 50,000-candle-power red lights. The only writers about me for whom I have any respect, at present, are Carl and Boris. They are possessed. They glow inwardly with a white flame. They are mad and tone deaf. They are sufferers.

Moldorf, on the other hand, who suffers too in his peculiar way, is not mad. Moldorf is word drunk. He has no veins or blood vessels, no heart or kidneys. He is a portable trunk filled with innumerable drawers and in the drawers are labels written out in white ink, brown ink, red ink, blue ink, vermilion, saffron, mauve, sienna, apricot, turquoise, onyx, Anjou, herring, Corona, verdigris, gorgonzola. . . .

I have moved the typewriter into the next room where I can see myself in the mirror as I write.

Tania is like Irène. She expects fat letters. But there is another Tania, a Tania like a big seed, who scatters pollen everywhere—or, let us say, a little bit of Tolstoy, a stable scene in which the fetus is dug up. Tania is a fever, too—*les voies urinaires*, Café de la Liberté, Place des Vosges, bright neckties on the Boulevard Montparnasse, dark bathrooms, Porto Sec, Abdullah cigarettes, the adagio sonata *Pathétique,* aural amplificators, anecdotal seances, burnt sienna breasts, heavy garters, what time is it, golden pheasants stuffed with chestnuts, taffeta fingers, vaporish twilights turning to ilex, acromegaly, cancer and delirium, warm veils, poker chips, carpets of blood and soft thighs. Tania says so that every one may hear: "I love him!" And while Boris scalds himself with whisky she says: "Sit down here! O Boris . . . *Russia* . . . what'll I do? I'm bursting with it!"

At night when I look at Boris' goatee lying on the pillow I get hysterical. O Tania, where now is that warm cunt of yours, those fat, heavy garters, those soft, bulging thighs? There is a bone in my prick six inches long. I will ream out every wrinkle in your cunt, Tania, big with seed. I will send you home to your Sylvester with an ache in your belly and your womb turned inside out. Your Sylvester! Yes, he knows how to build a fire, but I know how to inflame a cunt. I shoot hot bolts into you, Tania, I make your ovaries incandescent. Your Sylvester is a little jealous now? He feels something, does he? He feels the remnants of my big prick. I have set the shores a little wider, I have ironed out the wrinkles. After me you can take on stallions, bulls, rams, drakes, St. Bernards. You can stuff toads, bats, lizards up your rectum. You can shit arpeggios if you like, or string a zither across your navel. I am fucking you, Tania, so that you'll stay fucked. And if you are afraid of being fucked publicly I will fuck you privately. I will tear off a few hairs from your cunt and paste them on Boris' chin. I will bite into your clitoris and spit out two franc pieces. . . .

Indigo sky swept clear of fleecy clouds, gaunt trees infinitely extended, their black boughs gesticulating like a sleepwalker. Somber, spectral trees, their trunks pale as cigar ash.

A silence supreme and altogether European. Shutters drawn, shops barred. A red glow here and there to mark a tryst. Brusque the façades, almost forbidding; immaculate except for the splotches of shadow cast by the trees. Passing by the Orangerie I am reminded of another Paris, the Paris of Maugham, of Gauguin, Paris of George Moore. I think of that terrible Spaniard who was then startling the world with his acrobatic leaps from style to style. I think of Spengler and of his terrible pronunciamentos, and I wonder if style, style in the grand manner, is done for. I say that my mind is occupied with these thoughts, but it is not true; it is only later, after I have crossed the Seine, after I have put behind me the carnival of lights, that I allow my mind to play with these ideas. For the moment I can think of nothing—except that I am a sentient being stabbed by the miracle of these waters that reflect a forgotten world. All along the banks the trees lean heavily over the tarnished mirror; when the wind rises and fills them with a rustling murmur they will shed a few tears and shiver as the water swirls by. I am suffocated by it. No one to whom I can communicate even a fraction of my feelings. . . .

The trouble with Irène is that she has a valise instead of a cunt. She wants fat letters to shove in her valise. Immense, *avec des choses inouïes*. Llona now, she had a cunt. I know because she sent us some hairs from down below. Llona—a wild ass snuffing pleasure out of the wind. On every high hill she played the harlot—and sometimes in telephone booths and toilets. She bought a bed for King Carol and a shaving mug with his initials on it. She lay in Tottenham Court Road with her dress pulled up and fingered herself. She used candles, Roman candles, and door knobs. Not a prick in the land big enough for her . . . *not one*. Men went inside her and curled up. She wanted extension pricks, self-exploding rockets, hot boiling oil made of wax and creosote. She would cut off your prick and keep it inside her forever, if you gave her permission. One cunt out of a million, Llona! A laboratory cunt and no litmus paper that could take her color. She was a liar, too, this Llona. She never bought a bed for her King Carol. She crowned him with a whisky bottle and her tongue was full of lice and tomorrows. Poor Carol, he could only curl up inside her and die. She drew a breath and he fell out—like a dead clam.

Enormous, fat letters, *avec des choses inouïes*. A valise without straps. A hole without a key. She had a German mouth, French ears, Russian ass. Cunt international. When the flag waved it was red all the way back to the throat. You entered on the Boulevard Jules-Ferry and came out at the Porte de la Villette. You dropped your sweetbreads into the tumbrils—red tumbrils with two wheels, naturally. At the confluence of the Ourcq and Marne, where the water sluices through the dikes and lies like glass under the bridges. Llona is lying there now and the canal is full of glass and splinters; the mimosas weep, and there is a wet, foggy fart on the windowpanes. One cunt out of a million Llona! All cunt and a glass ass in which you can read the history of the Middle Ages.

* * *

So fast and furiously am I compelled to live now that there is scarcely time to record even these fragmentary notes. After the telephone call, a gentleman and his wife arrived. I went upstairs to lie down during the transaction. Lay there wondering what my next move would be. Surely not to go back to the fairy's bed and toss about all night flicking bread crumbs with my toes. That puking little bastard! If there's anything worse than being a fairy it's being a miser. A timid, quaking little bugger who lived in constant fear of going broke some day—the 18th of March perhaps, or the 25th of May precisely. Coffee without milk or sugar. Bread without butter. Meat without gravy, or no meat at all. Without this and without that! That dirty little miser! Open the bureau drawer one day and find money hidden away in a sock. Over two thousand francs—and checks that he hadn't even cashed. Even that I wouldn't have minded so much if there weren't always coffee grounds in my beret and garbage on the floor, to say nothing of the cold cream jars and the greasy towels and the sink always stopped up. I tell you, the little bastard he smelled bad—except when he doused himself with cologne. His ears were dirty, his eyes were dirty, his ass was dirty. He was double-jointed, asthmatic, lousy, picayune, morbid. I could have forgiven him everything if only he had handed me a decent breakfast! But a man who has two thousand francs hidden away in a dirty sock and refuses to wear a clean shirt or smear a little butter over his bread, such a man is not just a fairy, nor even just a miser—he's an imbecile!

But that's neither here nor there, about the fairy. I'm keeping an ear open as to what's going on downstairs. It's a Mr. Wren and his wife who have called to look at the apartment. They're talking about taking it. Only *talking* about it, thank God. Mrs. Wren has a loose laugh—complications ahead. Now *Mister* Wren is talking. His voice is raucous, scraping, booming, a heavy blunt weapon that wedges its way through flesh and bone and cartilage.

Boris calls me down to be introduced. He is rubbing his hands, like a pawnbroker. They are talking about a story Mr. Wren wrote, a story about a spavined horse.

"But I thought Mr. Wren was a painter?"

"To be sure," says Boris, with a twinkle in his eye, "but in the wintertime he writes. And he writes well . . . remarkably well."

I try to induce Mr. Wren to talk, to say something, anything, to talk about the spavined horse, if necessary. But Mr.

Wren is almost inarticulate. When he essays to speak of those dreary months with the pen he becomes unintelligible. Months and months he spends before setting a word to paper. (And there are only three months of winter!) What does he cogitate all those months and months of winter? So help me God, I can't see this guy as a writer. Yet Mrs. Wren says that when he sits down to it the stuff *just pours out.*

The talk drifts. It is difficult to follow Mr. Wren's mind because he says nothing. *He thinks as he goes along*—so Mrs. Wren puts it. Mrs. Wren puts everything about Mr. Wren in the loveliest light. "He thinks as he goes along"—very charming, charming indeed, as Borowski would say, but really very painful, particularly when the thinker is nothing but a spavined horse.

Boris hands me money to buy liquor. Going for the liquor I am already intoxicated. I know just how I'll begin when I get back to the house. Walking down the street it commences, the grand speech inside me that's gurgling like Mrs. Wren's loose laugh. Seems to me she had a slight edge on already. Listens beautifully when she's tight. Coming out of the wine shop I hear the urinal gurgling. Everything is loose and splashy. I want Mrs. Wren to listen. . . .

Boris is rubbing his hands again. Mr. Wren is still stuttering and spluttering. I have a bottle between my legs and I'm shoving the corkscrew in. Mrs. Wren has her mouth parted expectantly. The wine is splashing between my legs, the sun is splashing through the bay window, and inside my veins there is a bubble and splash of a thousand crazy things that commence to gush out of me now pell-mell. I'm telling them everything that comes to mind, everything that was bottled up inside me and which Mrs. Wren's loose laugh has somehow released. With that bottle between my legs and the sun splashing through the window I experience once again the splendor of those miserable days when I first arrived in Paris, a bewildered, poverty-stricken individual who haunted the streets like a ghost at a banquet. Everything comes back to me in a rush—the toilets that wouldn't work, the prince who shined my shoes, the Cinema Splendide where I slept on the patron's overcoat, the bars in the window, the feeling of suffocation, the fat cockroaches, the drinking and carousing that went on between times, Rose Cannaque and Naples dying in the sunlight. Dancing the streets on an empty belly and now and then calling on strange people—Madame Delorme, for instance. How I ever got to Madame Delorme's, I can't imagine any more. But I got there, got inside somehow, past the butler, past the maid with her little white apron, got right inside the palace with my corduroy trousers and my hunting jacket—and not a button on my fly. Even now I can taste again the golden ambience of that room where Madame Delorme sat upon a throne in her mannish rig, the goldfish in the bowls, the maps of the ancient world, the beautifully bound books; I can feel again her heavy hand resting upon my shoulder, frightening me a little with her heavy Lesbian air. More comfortable down below in that thick stew pouring into the Gare St. Lazare, the whores in the doorways, seltzer bottles on every table; a thick tide of semen flooding the gutters. Nothing better between five and seven than to be pushed around in that throng, to follow a leg or a beautiful bust, to move along with the tide and everything whirling in your brain. A weird sort of contentment in those days. No appointments, no invitations for dinner, no program, no dough. The golden period, when I had not a single friend. Each morning the dreary walk to the American Express, and each morning the inevitable answer from the clerk. Dashing here and there like a bedbug, gathering butts now and then, sometimes furtively, sometimes brazenly; sitting down on a bench and squeezing my guts to stop the gnawing, or walking through the Jardin des Tuileries and getting an erection looking at the dumb statues. Or wandering along the Seine at night, wandering and wandering, and going mad with the beauty of it, the trees leaning to, the broken images in the water, the rush of the current under the bloody lights of the bridges, the women sleeping in doorways, sleeping on newspapers, sleeping in the rain; everywhere the musty porches of the cathedrals and beggars and lice and old hags full of St. Vitus' dance; pushcarts stacked up like wine barrels in the side streets, the smell of berries in the market place and the old church surrounded with vegetables and blue arc lights, the gutters slippery with garbage and women in satin pumps staggering through the filth and vermin at the end of an all-night souse. The Place St. Sulpice, so quiet and deserted, where toward midnight there came every night the woman with the busted umbrella and the crazy veil; every night she slept there on a bench under her torn umbrella, the ribs hanging down, her dress turning green, her bony fingers and the odor of decay oozing from her body; and in the morning I'd be sitting there myself, taking a quiet snooze in the sunshine, cursing the goddamned pigeons gathering up the crumbs everywhere. St. Sulpice! The fat belfries, the garish posters over the door, the candles flaming inside. The Square so beloved of Anatole France, with that drone and buzz from the altar, the splash of the fountain, the pigeons cooing, the crumbs disappearing like magic and only a dull rumbling in the hollow of the guts. Here I would sit day after day thinking of Germaine and that dirty little street near the Bastille where she lived, and that buzz-buzz going on behind the altar, the buses whizzing by, the sun beating down into the asphalt and the asphalt working into me and Germaine, into the asphalt and all Paris in the big fat belfries.

And it was down the Rue Bonaparte that only a year before Mona and I used to walk every night, after we had taken leave of Borowski. St. Sulpice not meaning much to me then, nor anything in Paris. Washed out with talk. Sick of faces. Fed up with cathedrals and squares and menageries and what not. Picking up a book in the red bedroom and the cane chair uncomfortable; tired of sitting on my ass all day long, tired of red wallpaper, tired of seeing so many people jabbering away about nothing. The red bedroom and the trunk always open; her gowns lying about in a delirium of disorder. The red bedroom with my galoshes and canes, the notebooks I never touched, the manuscripts lying cold and dead. Paris! Meaning the Café Select, the Dôme, the Flea Market, the American Express. Paris! Meaning Borowski's canes, Borowski's hats, Borowski's *gouaches*, Borowski's prehistoric fish—and prehistoric jokes. In that Paris of '28 only one night stands out in my memory—the night before sailing for America. A rare night, with Borowski slightly pickled and a little disgusted with me because I'm dancing with every slut in the place. But we're leaving in the morning! That's what I tell every cunt I grab hold of—*leaving in the morning!* That's what I'm telling the blonde with agate-colored eyes. And while I'm telling her she takes my hand and squeezes it between her legs. In the lavatory I stand before the bowl with a tremendous erection; it seems light and heavy at the same time, like a piece of lead with wings on it. And while I'm standing there like that two cunts sail in—Americans. I greet them cordially, prick in hand. They give me a wink and pass on. In the vestibule, as I'm buttoning my fly, I notice one of them waiting for her friend to come out of the can. The music is still playing and maybe Mona'll be coming to fetch me, or Borowski with his gold-knobbed cane, but I'm in her arms now and she has hold of me and I don't care who comes or what happens. We wriggle into the cabinet and there I stand her up, slap up against the wall, and I try to get it into her but it won't work and so we sit down on the seat and try it that way but it won't work either. No matter how we try it it won't work. And all the while she's got hold of my prick, she's clutching it like a lifesaver, but it's no use, we're too hot, too eager. The music is still playing and so we waltz out of the cabinet into the vestibule again and as we're dancing there in the shithouse I come all over her beautiful gown and she's sore as hell about it. I stumble back to the table and there's Borowski with his ruddy face and Mona with her disapproving eye. And Borowski says "Let's all go to Brussels tomorrow," and we agree, and when we get back to the hotel I vomit all over the place, in the bed, in the washbowl, over the suits and gowns and the galoshes and canes and notebooks I never touched and the manuscripts cold and dead.

A few months later. The same hotel, the same room. We look out on the courtyard where the bicycles are parked, and there is the little room up above, under the attic, where some smart young Alec played the phonograph all day long and repeated clever little things at the top of his voice. I say "we" but I'm getting ahead of myself, because Mona has been away a long time and it's just today that I'm meeting her at the Gare St. Lazare. Toward evening I'm standing there with my face squeezed between the bars, but there's no Mona, and I read the cable over again but it doesn't help any. I go back to the Quarter and just the same I put away a hearty meal. Strolling past the Dôme a little later suddenly I see a pale, heavy face and burning eyes—and the little velvet suit that I always adore because under the soft velvet there were always her warm breasts, the marble legs, cool, firm, muscular. She rises up out of a sea of faces and embraces me, embraces me passionately—a thousand eyes, noses, fingers, legs, bottles, windows, purses, saucers all glaring at us and we in each other's arms oblivious. I sit down beside her and she talks—a flood of talk. Wild consumptive notes of hysteria, perversion, leprosy. I hear not a word because she is beautiful and I love her and now I am happy and willing to die.

We walk down the Rue du Château, looking for Eugene. Walk over the railroad bridge where I used to watch the trains pulling out and feel all sick inside wondering where the hell she could be. Everything soft and enchanting as we walk over the bridge. Smoke coming up between our legs, the tracks creaking, semaphores in our blood. I feel her body close to mine—all mine now—and I stop to rub my hands over the warm velvet. Everything around us is crumbling, crumbling and the warm body under the warm velvet is aching for me. . . .

Back in the very same room and fifty francs to the good, thanks to Eugene. I look out on the court but the phonograph is silent. The trunk is open and her things are lying around everywhere just as before. She lies down on the bed with her clothes on. Once, twice, three times, four times . . . I'm afraid she'll go mad . . . in bed, under the blankets, how good to feel her body again! But for how long? Will it last this time? Already I have a presentiment that it won't.

She talks to me so feverishly—as if there will be no tomorrow. "Be quiet, Mona! Just look at me . . . *don't talk!*" Finally she drops off and I pull my arm from under her. My eyes close. Her body is there beside me . . . it will be there till morning surely. . . . It was in February I pulled out of the harbor in a blinding snowstorm. The last glimpse I had of her was in the window waving good-bye to me. A man standing on the other side of the street, at the corner, his hat pulled down over his eyes, his jowls resting on his lapels. A fetus watching me. A fetus with a cigar in his mouth. Mona at the window waving good-bye. White heavy face, hair streaming wild. And now it is a heavy bedroom, breathing regularly through the gills, sap still oozing from between her legs, a warm feline odor and her hair in my mouth. My eyes are closed. We breathe warmly into each other's mouth. Close together, America three thousand miles away. I never want to see it again. To have her here in bed with me, breathing on me, her hair in my mouth—I count that something of a miracle. Nothing can happen now till morning. . . .

I wake from a deep slumber to look at her. A pale light is trickling in. I look at her beautiful wild hair. I feel something crawling down my neck. I look at her again, closely. Her hair is alive. I pull back the sheet—more of them. They are swarming over the pillow.

It is a little after daybreak. We pack hurriedly and sneak out of the hotel. The cafés are still closed. We walk, and as we walk we scratch ourselves. The day opens in milky whiteness, streaks of salmon-pink sky, snails leaving their shells. Paris. Paris. Everything happens here. Old, crumbling walls and the pleasant sound of water running in the urinals. Men licking their mustaches at the bar. Shutters going up with a bang and little streams purling in the gutters. *Amer Picon* in huge scarlet letters. *Zigzag*. Which way will we go and why or where or what?

Mona is hungry, her dress is thin. Nothing but evening wraps, bottles of perfume, barbaric earrings, bracelets, depilatories. We sit down in a billiard parlor on the Avenue du Maine and order hot coffee. The toilet is out of order. We shall have to sit some time before we can go to another hotel. Meanwhile we pick bedbugs out of each other's hair. Nervous. Mona is losing her temper. Must have a bath. Must have this. Must have that. Must, must, must. . . .

"How much money have you left?"

Money! Forgot all about that.

Hôtel des Etats-Unis. An *ascenseur*. We go to bed in broad daylight. When we get up it is dark and the first thing to do is to raise enough dough to send a cable to America. A cable to the fetus with the long juicy cigar in his mouth. Meanwhile there is the Spanish woman on the Boulevard Raspail—she's always good for a warm meal. By morning something will happen. At least we're going to bed together. No more bedbugs now. The rainy season has commenced. The sheets are immaculate. . . .

* * *

How a man can wander about all day on an empty belly, and even get an erection once in a while, is one of those mysteries which are too easily explained by the "anatomists of the soul." On a Sunday afternoon, when the shutters are down and the proletariat possesses the street in a kind of dumb torpor, there are certain thoroughfares which remind one of nothing less than a big chancrous cock laid open longitudinally. And it is just these highways, the Rue St. Denis, for instance, or the Faubourg du Temple—which attract one irresistibly, much as in the old days, around Union Square or the upper reaches of the Bowery, one was drawn to the dime museums where in the show windows there were displayed wax reproductions of various organs of the body eaten away by syphilis and other venereal diseases. The city sprouts out like a huge organism diseased in every part, the beautiful thoroughfares only a little less repulsive because they have been drained of their pus.

At the Cité Nortier, somewhere near the Place du Combat, I pause a few minutes to drink in the full squalor of the scene. It is a rectangular court like many another which one glimpses through the low passageways that flank the old arteries of Paris. In the middle of the court is a clump of decrepit buildings which have so rotted away that they have collapsed on one another and formed a sort of intestinal embrace. The ground is uneven, the flagging slippery with slime. A sort of human dump heap which has been filled in with cinders and dry garbage. The sun is setting fast. The colors die. They shift from purple to dried blood, from nacre to blister, from cool dead grays to pigeon shit. Here and there a lopsided monster stands in the window blinking like an owl. There is the shrill squawk of children with pale faces and bony limbs, rickety little urchins marked with the forceps. A fetid odor seeps from the walls, the odor of a mildewed mattress. Europe—medieval, grotesque, monstrous: a symphony in B-mol. Directly across the street the Ciné Combat offers its distinguished clientele *Metropolis*.

Coming away my mind reverts to a book that I was reading only the other day. "The town was a shambles; corpses, mangled by butchers and stripped by plunderers, lay thick in the streets; wolves sneaked from the suburbs to eat them; the black death and other plagues crept in to keep them company, and the English came marching on; the while the *danse macabre* whirled about the tombs in the cemeteries. . . ." Paris during the days of Charles the Silly! A lovely book! Refreshing, appetizing. I'm still enchanted by it. About the patrons and prodromes of the Renaissance I know little, but Madam Pimpernel, *la belle boulangère*, and Maître Jehan Crapotte, *l'orfèvre*, these occupy my spare thoughts still. Not forgetting Rodin, the evil genius of *The Wandering Jew*, who practiced his nefarious ways "until the day when he was enflamed and outwitted by the octoroon Cecily." Sitting in the Square du Temple, musing over the doings of the horse knackers led by Jean Caboche, I have thought long and ruefully over the sad fate of Charles the Silly. A halfwit, who prowled about the halls of his Hôtel St. Paul, garbed in the filthiest rags, eaten away by ulcers and vermin, gnawing a bone, when they flung him one, like a mangy dog. At the Rue des Lions I looked for the stones of the old menagerie where he once fed his pets. His only diversion, poor dolt, aside from those card games with his "low-born companion," Odette de Champdivers.

It was a Sunday afternoon, much like this, when I first met Germaine. I was strolling along the Boulevard Beaumarchais, rich by a hundred francs or so which my wife had frantically cabled from America. There was a touch of spring in the air, a poisonous, malefic spring that seemed to burst from the manholes. Night after night I had been coming back to this quarter, attracted by certain leprous streets which only revealed their sinister splendor when the light of day had oozed away and the whores commenced to take up their posts. The Rue du Pasteur-Wagner is one I recall in particular, corner of the Rue Amelot which hides behind the boulevard like a slumbering lizard. Here, at the neck of the bottle, so to speak, there was always a cluster of vultures who croaked and flapped their dirty wings, who reached out with sharp talons and plucked you into a doorway. Jolly, rapacious devils who didn't even give you time to button your pants when it was over. Led you into a little room off the street, a room without a window usually, and, sitting on the edge of the bed with skirts tucked up gave you a quick inspection, spat on your cock, and placed it for you. While you washed yourself another one stood at the door, holding her victim by the hand, watched nonchalantly as you gave the finishing touches to your toilet.

Germaine was different. There was nothing to tell me so from her appearance. Nothing to distinguish her from the other trollops who met each afternoon and evening at the Café de l'Eléphant. As I say, it was a spring day and the few francs my wife had scraped up to cable me were jingling in my pocket. I had a sort of vague premonition that I would not reach the Bastille without being taken in tow by one of these buzzards. Sauntering along the boulevard I had noticed her verging toward me with that curious trot-about air of a whore and the run-down heels and cheap jewelry and the pasty look of their kind which the rouge only accentuates. It was not difficult to come to terms with her. We sat in the back of the little *tabac* called L'Eléphant and talked it over quickly. In a few minutes we were in a five franc room on the Rue Amelot, the curtains drawn and the covers thrown back. She didn't rush things, Germaine. She sat on the *bidet* soaping herself and talked to me pleasantly about this and that; she liked the knickerbockers I was wearing. *Très chic!* she thought. They were once, but I had worn the seat out of them; fortunately the jacket covered my ass. As she stood up to dry herself, still talking to me pleasantly, suddenly she dropped the towel and, advancing toward me leisurely, she commenced rubbing her pussy affectionately, stroking it with her two hands, caressing it, patting it, patting it. There was something about her eloquence at that moment and the way she thrust that rosebush under my nose which remains unforgettable; she spoke of it as if it were some extraneous object which she had acquired at great cost, an object whose value had increased with time and which now she prized above everything in the world. Her words imbued it with a peculiar fragrance; it was no longer just her private organ, but a treasure, a magic, potent treasure, a God-given thing—and none the less so because she traded it day in and day out for a few pieces of silver. As she flung herself on the bed, with legs spread wide apart, she cupped it with her hands and stroked it some more, murmuring all the while in that hoarse, cracked voice of hers that it was good, beautiful, a treasure, a little treasure. And it *was* good, that little pussy of hers! That Sunday afternoon, with its poisonous breath of spring in the air, everything clicked again. As we stepped out of the hotel I looked her over again in the harsh light of day and I saw clearly what a whore she was—the gold teeth, the geranium in her hat, the run-down heels, etc., etc. Even the fact that she had wormed a dinner out of me and cigarettes and taxi hadn't the least disturbing effect upon me. I encouraged it, in fact. I liked her so well that after dinner we went back to the hotel again and took another shot at it. "For love," this time. And again that big, bushy thing of hers worked its bloom and magic. It began to have an independent existence—for me too. There was Germaine and there was that rosebush of hers. I liked them separately and I liked them together.

As I say, she was different, Germaine. Later, when she discovered my true circumstances, she treated me nobly—blew me to drinks, gave me credit, pawned my things, introduced me to her friends, and so on. She even apologized for not lending me money, which I understood quite well after her *maquereau* had been pointed out to me. Night after night I walked down the Boulevard Beaumarchais to the little *tabac* where they all congregated and I waited for her to stroll in and give me a few minutes of her precious time.

When some time later I came to write about Claude, it was not Claude that I was thinking of but Germaine. . . . "All the men she's been with and now you, just you, and barges going by, masts and hulls, the whole damned current of life flowing through you, through her, through all the guys behind you and after you, the flowers and the birds and the sun streaming in and the fragrance of it choking you, annihilating you." That was for Germaine! Claude was not the same, though I admired her tremendously—I even thought for a while that I loved her. Claude had a soul and a conscience; she had refinement, too, which is bad—in a whore. Claude always imparted a feeling of sadness; she left the impression, unwittingly, of course, that you were just one more added to the stream which fate had ordained to destroy her. *Unwittingly,* I say, because Claude was the last person in the world who would consciously create such an image in one's mind. She was too delicate, too sensitive for that. At bottom, Claude was just a good French girl of average breed and intelligence whom life had tricked somehow; something in her there was which was not tough enough to withstand the shock of daily experience. For her were meant those terrible words of Louis-Philippe, "and a night comes when all is over, when so many jaws have closed upon us that we no longer have the strength to stand, and our meat hangs upon our bodies, as though it had been masticated by every mouth." Germaine, on the other hand, was a whore from the cradle; she was thoroughly satisfied with her role, enjoyed it in fact, except when her stomach pinched or her shoes gave out, little surface things of no account, nothing that ate into her soul, nothing that created torment. *Ennui!* That was the worst she ever felt. Days there were, no doubt, when she had a bellyful, as we say—but no more than that! Most of the time she enjoyed it—or gave the illusion of enjoying it. It made a difference of course, whom she went with—or *came* with. But the principal thing was *a man*. A man! That was what she craved. A man with something between his legs that could tickle her, that could make her writhe in ecstasy, make her grab that bushy twat of hers with both hands and rub it joyfully, boastfully, proudly, with a sense of connection, a sense of life. That was the only place where she experienced any life—down there where she clutched herself with both hands.

Germaine was a whore all the way through, even down to her good heart, her whore's heart which is not really a good heart but a lazy one, an indifferent, flaccid heart that can be touched for a moment, a heart without reference to any fixed point within, a big, flaccid whore's heart that can detach itself for a moment from its true center. However vile and circumscribed was that world which she had created for herself, nevertheless she functioned in it superbly. And that in itself is a tonic thing. When, after we had become well acquainted, her companions would twit me, saying that I was in love with Germaine (a situation almost inconceivable to them), I would say: "Sure! Sure, I'm in love with her! And what's more, I'm going to be faithful to her!" A lie, of course, because I could no more think of loving Germaine than I could think of loving a spider; and if I *was* faithful, it was not to Germaine but to that bushy thing she carried between her legs. Whenever I looked at another woman I thought immediately of Germaine, of that flaming bush which she had left in my mind and which seemed imperishable. It gave me pleasure to sit on the *terrasse* of the little *tabac* and observe her as she plied her trade, observe her as she resorted to the same grimaces, the same tricks, with others as she had with me. "She's doing her job!"—that's how I felt about it, and it was with approbation that I regarded her transactions. Later, when I had taken up with Claude, and I saw her night after night sitting in her accustomed place, her round little buttocks chubbily ensconced in the plush settee, I felt sort of inexpressible rebellion toward her; a whore, it seemed to me, had no right to be sitting there like a lady, waiting timidly for someone to approach and all the while abstemiously sipping her *chocolat*. Germaine was a hustler. She didn't wait for you to come to her—she went out and grabbed you. I remember so well the holes in her stockings, and the torn ragged shoes; I remember too how she stood at the bar and with blind, courageous defiance threw a strong drink down her stomach and marched out again. A hustler! Perhaps it wasn't so pleasant to smell that boozy breath of hers, that breath compounded of weak coffee, cognac, *apéritifs*, Pernods and all the other stuff she guzzled between times, what to warm herself and what to summon up strength and courage, but the fire of it penetrated her, it glowed down there between her legs where women ought to glow, and there was established that circuit which makes one feel the earth under his legs again. When she lay there with her legs apart and moaning, even if she did moan that way for any and everybody, it was good, it was a proper show of feeling. She didn't stare up at the ceiling with a vacant look or count the bedbugs on the wallpaper; she kept her mind on her business, she talked about the things a man wants to hear when he's climbing over a woman. Whereas Claude—well, with Claude there was always a certain delicacy, even when she got under the sheets with you. And her delicacy offended. Who wants a *delicate* whore! Claude would even ask you to turn your face away when she squatted over the *bidet*. All wrong! A man, when he's burning up with passion, wants to see things; he wants to see *everything*, even how they make water. And while it's all very nice to know that a woman has a mind, literature coming from the cold corpse of a whore is the last thing to be served in bed. Germaine had the right idea: she was ignorant and lusty, she put her heart and soul into her work. She was a whore all the way through—and that was her virtue!

* * *

"Life," said Emerson, "consists in what a man is thinking all day." If that be so, then my life is nothing but a big intestine. I not only think about food all day, but I dream about it at night.

But I don't ask to go back to America, to be put in double harness again, to work the treadmill. No, I prefer to be a poor man of Europe. God knows, I am poor enough; it only remains to be a man. Last week I thought the problem of living was about to be solved, thought I was on the way to becoming self-supporting. It happened that I ran across another Russian—Serge is his name. He lives in Suresnes where there is a little colony of *émigrés* and run-down artists. Before the revolution Serge was a captain in the Imperial Guard; he stands six foot three in his stockinged feet and drinks vodka like a fish. His father was an admiral, or something like that, on the battleship "Potemkin."

I met Serge under rather peculiar circumstances. Sniffing about for food I found myself toward noon the other day in the neighborhood of the Folies-Bergère—the back entrance, that is to say, in the narrow little lane with an iron gate at one end. I was dawdling about the stage entrance, hoping vaguely for a casual brush with one of the butterflies, when an open truck pulls up to the sidewalk. Seeing me standing there with my hands in my pockets the driver, who was Serge, asks me if I would give him a hand unloading the iron barrels. When he learns that I am an American and that I'm broke he almost weeps with joy. He has been looking high and low for an English teacher, it seems. I help him roll the barrels of insecticide inside and I look my fill at the butterflies fluttering about the wings. The incident takes on strange proportions to me—the empty house, the sawdust dolls bouncing in the wings, the barrels of germicide, the battleship "Potemkin"—above all, Serge's gentleness. He is big and tender, a man every inch of him, but with a woman's heart.

In the café nearby—Café des Artistes—he proposes immediately to put me up; says he will put a mattress on the floor in the hallway. For the lessons he says he will give me a meal every day, a big Russian meal, or if for any reason the meal is lacking then five francs. It sounds wonderful to me—*wonderful*. The only question is, how will I get from Suresnes to the American Express every day?

Serge insists that we begin at once—he gives me the carfare to get out to Suresnes in the evening. I arrive a little before dinner, with my knapsack, in order to give Serge a lesson. There are some guests on hand already—seems as though they always eat in a crowd, everybody chipping in.

There are eight of us at the table—and three dogs. The dogs eat first. They eat oatmeal. Then we commence. We eat oatmeal too—as an hors d'œuvre. "*Chez nous,*" says Serge, with a twinkle in his eye, "*c'est pour les chiens, les Quaker Oats. Ici pour le gentleman. Ça va.*" After the oatmeal, mushroom soup and vegetables; after that bacon omelet, fruit, red wine, vodka, coffee, cigarettes. Not bad, the Russian meal. Everyone talks with his mouth full. Toward the end of the meal Serge's wife, who is a lazy slut of an Armenian, flops on the couch and begins to nibble bonbons. She fishes around in the box with her fat fingers, nibbles a tiny piece to see if there is any juice inside, and then throws it on the floor for the dogs.

The meal over, the guests rush away. They rush away precipitously, as if they feared a plague. Serge and I are left with the dogs—his wife has fallen asleep on the couch. Serge moves about unconcernedly, scraping the garbage for the dogs. "Dogs like very much," he says. "Very good for dogs. Little dog he has worms . . . he is too young yet." He bends down to examine some white worms lying on the carpet between the dog's paws. Tries to explain about the worms in English, but his vocabulary is lacking. Finally he consults the dictionary. "Ah," he says, looking at me exultantly, "*tapeworms!*" My response is evidently not very intelligent. Serge is confused. He gets down on his hands and knees to examine them better. He picks one up and lays it on the table beside the fruit. "Huh, him not very beeg," he grunts. "Next lesson you learn me worms, no? You are gude teacher. I make progress with you. . . ."

Lying on the mattress in the hallway the odor of the germicide stifles me. A pungent, acrid odor that seems to invade every pore of my body. The food begins to repeat on me—the Quaker Oats, the mushrooms, the bacon, the fried apples. I see the little tapeworm lying beside the fruit and all the varieties of worms that Serge drew on the tablecloth to explain what was the matter with the dog. I see the empty pit of the Folies-Bergère and in every crevice there are cockroaches and lice and bedbugs; I see people scratching themselves frantically, scratching and scratching until the blood comes. I see the worms crawling over the scenery like an army of red ants, devouring everything in sight. I see the chorus girls throwing away their gauze tunics and running through the aisles naked; I see the spectators in the pit throwing off their clothes also and scratching each other like monkeys.

I try to quiet myself. After all, this is a home I've found, and there's a meal waiting for me every day. And Serge is a brick, there's no doubt about that. But I can't sleep. It's like going to sleep in a morgue. The mattress is saturated with embalming fluid. It's a morgue for lice, bedbugs, cockroaches, tapeworms. I can't stand it. I *won't* stand it! After all I'm a man, not a louse.

In the morning I wait for Serge to load the truck. I ask him to take me in to Paris. I haven't the heart to tell him I'm leaving. I leave the knapsack behind, with the few things that were left me. When we get to the Place Péreire I jump out. No particular reason for getting off here. No particular reason for anything. *I'm free*—that's the main thing. . . .

Light as a bird I flit about from one quarter to another. It's as though I had been released from prison. I look at the world with new eyes. Everything interests me profoundly. Even trifles. On the Rue du Faubourg Poissonnière I stop before the window of a physical culture establishment. There are photographs showing specimens of manhood "before and after." All frogs. Some of them are nude, except for a pince-nez or a beard. Can't understand how these birds fall for parallel bars and dumbbells. A frog should have just a wee bit of a paunch, like the Baron de Charlus. He should wear a beard and a pince-nez, but he should never be photographed in the nude. He should wear twinkling patent-leather boots and in the breast pocket of his sack coat there should be a white handkerchief protruding about three-quarters of an inch above the vent. If possible, he should have a red ribbon in his lapel, through the buttonhole. He should wear pajamas on going to bed.

Approaching the Place Clichy toward evening I pass the little whore with the wooden stump who stands opposite the Gaumont Palace day in and day out. She doesn't look a day over eighteen. Has her regular customers, I suppose. After midnight she stands there in her black rig rooted to the spot. Back of her is the little alleyway that blazes like an inferno. Passing her now with a light heart she reminds me somehow of a goose tied to a stake, a goose with a diseased liver, so that the world may have its *pâté de foie gras*. Must be strange taking that wooden stump to bed with you. One imagines all sorts of things—splinters, etc. However, every man to his taste!

Going down the Rue des Dames I bump into Peckover, another poor devil who works on the paper. He complains of getting only three or four hours' sleep a night—has to get up at eight in the morning to work at a dentist's office. It isn't for the money he's doing it, so he explains—it's for to buy himself a set of false teeth. "It's hard to read proof when you're dropping with sleep," he says. "The wife, she thinks I've got a cinch of it. What would we do if you lost your job? she says." But Peckover doesn't give a damn about the job; it doesn't even allow him spending money. He has to save his cigarette butts and use them for pipe tobacco. His coat is held together with pins. He has halitosis and his hands sweat. And only three hours' sleep a night. "It's no way to treat a man," he says. "And that boss of mine, he bawls the piss out of me if I miss a semicolon." Speaking of his wife he adds: "That woman of mine, she's got no fucking gratitude, I tell you!"

In parting I manage to worm a franc fifty out of him. I try to squeeze another fifty centimes out of him but it's impossible. Anyway I've got enough for a coffee and *croissants*. Near the Gare St. Lazare there's a bar with reduced prices.

As luck would have it I find a ticket in the *lavabo* for a concert. Light as a feather now I go there to the Salle Gaveau. The usher looks ravaged because I overlook giving him his little tip. Every time he passes me he looks at me inquiringly, as if perhaps I will suddenly remember.

It's so long since I've sat in the company of well-dressed people that I feel a bit panic-stricken. I can still smell the formaldehyde. Perhaps Serge makes deliveries here too. But nobody is scratching himself, thank God. A faint odor of perfume . . . very faint. Even before the music begins there is that bored look on people's faces. A polite form of self-imposed torture, the concert. For a moment, when the conductor raps with his little wand, there is a tense spasm of concentration followed almost immediately by a general slump, a quiet vegetable sort of repose induced by the steady, uninterrupted drizzle from the orchestra. My mind is curiously alert; it's as though my skull had a thousand mirrors inside it. My nerves are taut, vibrant! the notes are like glass balls dancing on a million jets of water. I've never been to a concert before on such an empty belly. Nothing escapes me, not even the tiniest pin falling. It's as though I had no clothes on and every pore of my body was a window and all the windows open and the light flooding my gizzards. I can feel the light curving under the vault of my ribs and my ribs hang there over a hollow nave trembling with reverberations. How long this lasts I have no idea; I have lost all sense of time and place. After what seems like an eternity there follows an interval of semiconsciousness balanced by such a calm that I feel a great lake inside me, a lake of iridescent sheen, cool as jelly; and over this lake, rising in great swooping spirals, there emerge flocks of birds of passage with long slim legs and brilliant plumage. Flock after flock surge up from the cool, still surface of the lake and, passing under my clavicles, lose themselves in the white sea of space. And then slowly, very slowly, as if an old woman in a white cap were going the rounds of my body, slowly the windows are closed and my organs drop back into place. Suddenly the lights flare up and the man in the white box whom I had taken for a Turkish officer turns out to be a woman with a flowerpot on her head.

* * *

Afternoons there are always a few cronies from the pearl market dropping in to pay him a visit. They're all very suave, butter-tongued bastards with soft, doelike eyes; they sit around the table drinking the perfumed tea with a loud hissing noise while Nanantatee jumps up and down like a jack-in-the-box or points to a crumb on the floor and says in his smooth slippery voice—"Will you please to pick that up, Endree." When the guests arrive he goes unctuously to the cupboard and gets out the dry crusts of bread which he toasted maybe a week ago and which taste strongly now of the moldy wood. Not a crumb is thrown away. If the bread gets too sour he takes it downstairs to the concierge who, so he says, has been very kind to him. According to him, the concierge is delighted to get the stale bread—she makes bread pudding with it.

One day my friend Anatole came to see me. Nanantatee was delighted. Insisted that Anatole stay for tea. Insisted that he try little grease cakes and the stale bread. "You must come every day," he says, "and teach me Russian. Fine language, Russian . . . I want to speak it. How do you say that again, Endree—*borsht?* You will write that down for me, please, Endree. . . ." And I must write it on the typewriter, no less, so that he can observe my technique. He bought the typewriter, after he had collected on the bad arm, because the doctor recommended it as a good exercise. But he got tired of the typewriter shortly—it was an *English* typewriter.

When he learned that Anatole played the mandolin he said: "Very good! You must come every day and teach me the music. I will buy a mandolin as soon as business is better. It is good for my arm." The next day he borrows a phonograph from the concierge. "You will please teach me to dance, Endree. My stomach is too big." I am hoping that he will buy a porterhouse steak some day so that I can say to him: "You will please bite it for me, *Mister* Nonentity. My teeth are not strong!"

As I said a moment ago, ever since my arrival he has become extraordinarily meticulous. "Yesterday," he says, "you made three mistakes, Endree. First, you forgot to close the toilet door and so all night it makes boom-boom; second, you left the kitchen window open and so the window is cracked this morning. And you forgot to put out the milk bottle! Always you will put out the milk bottle please, before you go to bed, and in the morning you will please bring in the bread."

Every day his friend Kepi drops in to see if any visitors have arrived from India. He waits for Nanantatee to go out and then he scurries to the cupboard and devours the sticks of bread that are hidden away in a glass jar. The food is no good, he insists, but he puts it away like a rat. Kepi is a scrounger, a sort of human tick who fastens himself to the hide of even the poorest compatriot. From Kepi's standpoint they are all nabobs. For a Manila cheroot and the price of a drink he will suck any Hindu's ass. A Hindu's, mind you, but not an Englishman's. He has the address of every whorehouse in Paris, and the rates. Even from the ten franc joints he gets his little commission. And he knows the shortest way to any place you want to go. He will ask you first if you want to go by taxi; if you say no, he will suggest the bus, and if that is too high then the streetcar or the metro. Or he will offer to walk you there and save a franc or two, knowing very well that it will be necessary to pass a *tabac* on the way and that you will please be so good as to buy me a little cheroot.

Kepi is interesting, in a way, because he has absolutely no ambition except to get a fuck every night. Every penny he makes, and they are damned few, he squanders in the dance halls. He has a wife and eight children in Bombay, but that does not prevent him from proposing marriage to any little *femme de chambre* who is stupid and credulous enough to be taken in by him. He has a little room on the Rue Condorcet for which he pays sixty francs a month. He papered it all himself. Very proud of it, too. He uses violet-colored ink in his fountain pen because it lasts longer. He shines his own shoes, presses his own pants, does his own laundry. For a little cigar, a cheroot, if you please, he will escort you all over Paris. If you stop to look at a shirt or a collar button his eyes flash. "Don't buy it here," he will say. "They ask too much. I will show you a cheaper place." And before you have time to think about it he will whisk you away and deposit you before another show window where there are the same ties and shirts and collar buttons—maybe it's the very same store! but you don't know the difference. When Kepi hears that you want to buy something his soul becomes animated. He will ask you so many questions and drag you to so many places that you are bound to get thirsty and ask him to have a drink, whereupon you will discover to your amazement that you are again standing in a *tabac*—maybe the same *tabac!*—and Kepi is saying again in that small unctuous voice: "Will you please be so good as to buy me a little cheroot?" No matter what you propose doing, even if it's only to walk around the corner, Kepi will economize for you. Kepi will show you the shortest way, the cheapest place, the biggest dish, because whatever you have to do you *must* pass a *tabac*, and whether there is a revolution or a lockout or a quarantine Kepi must be at the Moulin

Rouge or the Olympia or the Ange Rouge when the music strikes up.

The other day he brought a book for me to read. It was about a famous suit between a holy man and the editor of an Indian paper. The editor, it seems, had openly accused the holy man of leading a scandalous life; he went further, and accused the holy man of being diseased. Kepi says it must have been the great French pox, but Nanantatee avers that it was the Japanese clap. For Nanantatee everything has to be a little exaggerated. At any rate, says Nanantatee cheerily: "You will please tell me what it says, Endree. I can't read the book—it hurts my arm." Then, by way of encouraging me—"it is a fine book about the fucking, Endree. Kepi has brought it for you. He thinks about nothing but the girls. So many girls he fucks—just like Krishna. We don't believe in that business, Endree. . . ."

A little later he takes me upstairs to the attic which is loaded down with tin cans and crap from India wrapped in burlap and firecracker paper. "Here is where I bring the girls," he says. And then rather wistfully: "I am not a very good fucker, Endree. I don't screw the girls any more. I hold them in my arms and I say the words. I like only to say the words now." It isn't necessary to listen any further: I know that he is going to tell me about his arm. I can see him lying there with that broken hinge dangling from the side of the bed. But to my surprise he adds: "I am no good for the fucking, Endree. I never was a very good fucker. My brother, he is good! Three times a day, every day! And Kepi, he is good—just like Krishna."

His mind is fixed now on the "fucking business." Downstairs, in the little room where he kneels before the open cabinet, he explains to me how it was when he was rich and his wife and the children were here. On holidays he would take his wife to the House of All Nations and hire a room for the night. Every room was appointed in a different style. His wife liked it there very much. "A wonderful place for the fucking, Endree. I know all the rooms. . . ."

The walls of the little room in which we are sitting are crammed with photographs. Every branch of the family is represented, it is like a cross section of the Indian empire. For the most part the members of this genealogical tree look like withered leaves: the women are frail and they have a startled, frightened look in their eyes: the men have a keen, intelligent look, like educated chimpanzees. They are all there, about ninety of them, with their white bullocks, their dung cakes, their skinny legs, their old-fashioned spectacles; in the background, now and then, one catches a glimpse of the parched soil, of a crumbling pediment, of an idol with crooked arms, a sort of human centipede. There is something so fantastic, so incongruous about this gallery that one is reminded inevitably of the great spawn of temples which stretch from the Himalayas to the tip of Ceylon, a vast jumble of architecture, staggering in beauty and at the same time monstrous, hideously monstrous because the fecundity which seethes and ferments in the myriad ramifications of design seems to have exhausted the very soil of India itself. Looking at the seething hive of figures which swarm the façades of the temples one is overwhelmed by the potency of these dark, handsome peoples who mingled their mysterious streams in a sexual embrace that has lasted thirty centuries or more. These frail men and women with piercing eyes who stare out of the photographs seem like the emaciated shadows of those virile, massive figures who incarnated themselves in stone and fresco from one end of India to the other in order that the heroic myths of the races who here intermingled should remain forever entwined in the hearts of their countrymen. When I look at only a fragment of these spacious dreams of stone, these toppling, sluggish edifices studded with gems, coagulated with human sperm, I am overwhelmed by the dazzling splendor of those imaginative flights which enabled half a billion people of diverse origins to thus incarnate the most fugitive expressions of their longing.

It is a strange, inexplicable medley of feelings which assails me now as Nanantatee prattles on about the sister who died in childbirth. There she is on the wall, a frail, timid thing of twelve or thirteen clinging to the arm of a dotard. At ten years of age she was given in wedlock to this old roué who had already buried five wives. She had seven children, only one of whom survived her. She was given to the aged gorilla in order to keep the pearls in the family. As she was passing away, so Nanantatee puts it, she whispered to the doctor: "I am tired of this fucking. . . . I don't want to fuck any more, doctor." As he relates this to me he scratches his head solemnly with his withered arm. "The fucking business is bad, Endree," he says. "But I will give you a word that will always make you lucky; you must say it every day, over and over, a million times you must say it. It is the best word there is, Endree . . . say it now . . . OOMAHARUMOOMA!"

"OOMARABOO. . . ."

"No, Endree . . . like this . . . OOMAHARUMOOMA!"

"OOMAMABOOMBA. . . ."

"No, Endree . . . like this. . . ."

. . . But what with the murky light, the botchy print, the tattered cover, the jigjagged page, the fumbling fingers, the fox-trotting fleas, the lie-a-bed lice, the scum on his tongue, the drop in his eye, the lump in his throat, the drink in his pottle, the itch in his palm, the wail of his wind, the grief from his breath, the fog of his brainfag, the tic of his conscience, the height of his rage, the gush of his fundament, the fire in his gorge, the tickle of his tail, the rats in his garret, the hullabaloo and the dust in his ears, since it took him a month to steal a march, he was hard-set to memorize more than a word a week.

I suppose I would never have gotten out of Nanantatee's clutches if fate hadn't intervened. One night, as luck would have it, Kepi asked me if I wouldn't take one of his clients to a whorehouse nearby. The young man had just come from India and he had not very much money to spend. He was one of Gandhi's men, one of that little band who made the historic march to the sea during the salt trouble. A very gay disciple of Gandhi's I must say, despite the vows of abstinence he had taken. Evidently he hadn't looked at a woman for ages. It was all I could do to get him as far as the Rue Laferrière; he was like a dog with his tongue hanging out. And a pompous, vain little devil to boot! He had decked himself out in a corduroy suit, a beret, a cane, a Windsor tie; he had bought himself two fountain pens, a kodak, and some fancy underwear. The money he was spending was a gift from the merchants of Bombay; they were sending him to England to spread the gospel of Gandhi.

Once inside Miss Hamilton's joint he began to lose his *sang-froid*. When suddenly he found himself surrounded by a bevy of naked women he looked at me in consternation. "Pick one out," I said. "You can have your choice." He had become so rattled that he could scarcely look at them. "You do it for me," he murmured, blushing violently. I looked them over coolly and picked out a plump young wench who seemed full of feathers. We sat down in the reception room and waited for the drinks. The madam wanted to know why I didn't take a girl also. "Yes, you take one too," said the young Hindu. "I don't want to be alone with her." So the girls were brought in again and I chose one for myself, a rather tall, thin one with melancholy eyes. We were left alone, the four of us, in the reception room. After a few moments my young Gandhi leans over and whispers something in my ear. "Sure, if you like her better, take her," I said, and so, rather awkwardly and considerably embarrassed, I explained to the girls that we would like to switch. I saw at once that we had made a *faux pas*, but by now my young friend had became gay and lecherous and nothing would do but to get upstairs quickly and have it over with.

We took adjoining rooms with a connecting door between. I think my companion had in mind to make another switch once he had satisfied his sharp, gnawing hunger. At any rate, no sooner had the girls left the room to prepare themselves than I hear him knocking on the door. "Where is the toilet, please?" he asks. Not thinking that it was anything serious I urge him to do in the *bidet*. The girls return with towels in their hands. I hear him giggling in the next room.

As I'm putting on my pants suddenly I hear a commotion in the next room. The girl is bawling him out, calling him a pig, a dirty little pig. I can't imagine what he has done to warrant such an outburst. I'm standing there with one foot in my trousers listening attentively. He's trying to explain to her in English, raising his voice louder and louder until it becomes a shriek.

I hear a door slam and in another moment the madam bursts into my room, her face as red as a beet, her arms gesticulating wildly. "You ought to be ashamed of yourself," she screams, "bringing a man like that to my place! He's a barbarian . . . he's a pig . . . he's a . . . !" My companion is standing behind her, in the doorway, a look of utmost discomfiture on his face "What did you do?" I ask.

"What did he do?" yells the madam. "I'll show you. . . . Come here!" And grabbing me by the arm she drags me into the next room. "There! There!" she screams, pointing to the *bidet*.

"Come on, let's get out," says the Hindu boy.

"Wait a minute, you can't get out as easily as all that."

The madam is standing by the *bidet*, fuming and spitting. The girls are standing there too, with towels in their hands. The five of us are standing there looking at the *bidet*. There are two enormous turds floating in the water. The madam bends down and puts a towel over it. "Frightful! Frightful!" she wails. "Never have I seen anything like this! A pig! A dirty little pig!"

The Hindu boy looks at me reproachfully. "You should have told me" he says. "I didn't know it wouldn't go down. I asked you where to go and you told me to use that." He is almost in tears.

Finally the madam takes me to one side. She has become a little more reasonable now. After all, it was a mistake. Perhaps the gentlemen would like to come downstairs and order another drink—for the girls. It was a great shock to the girls. They are not used to such things. And if the good gentlemen will be so kind as to remember the *femme de chambre*. . . . It is not so pretty for the *femme de chambre*—that mess, that ugly mess. She shrugs her shoulders and winks her eye. A lamentable incident. But an accident. If the gentlemen will wait here a few moments the maid will bring the drinks. Would the gentlemen like to have some champagne? Yes?

"I'd like to get out of here," says the Hindu boy weakly.

"Don't feel so badly about it," says the madam. "It is all over now. Mistakes will happen sometimes. Next time you will ask for the toilet." She goes on about the toilet—one on every floor, it seems. And a bathroom too. "I have lots of English clients," she says. "They are all gentlemen. The gentleman is a Hindu? Charming people, the Hindus. So intelligent. So handsome."

When we get into the street the charming young gentleman is almost weeping. He is sorry now that he bought a corduroy suit and the cane and the fountain pens. He talks about the eight vows that he took, the control of the palate, etc. On the march to Dandi even a plate of ice cream it was forbidden to take. He tells me about the spinning wheel—how the little band of Satyagrahists imitated the devotion of their master. He relates with pride how he walked beside the master and conversed with him. I have the illusion of being in the presence of one of the twelve disciples.

* * *

The following day, at one-thirty, I call on Van Norden. It's his day off, or rather his night off. He has left word with Carl that I am to help him move today.

I find him in a state of unusual depression. He hasn't slept a wink all night, he tells me. There's something on his mind, something that's eating him up. It isn't long before I discover what it is; he's been waiting impatiently for me to arrive in order to spill it.

"That guy," he begins, meaning Carl, "that guy's an artist. He described every detail minutely. He told it to me with such accuracy that I know it's all a goddamned lie . . . but I can't dismiss it from my mind. You know how my mind works!"

He interrupts himself to inquire if Carl has told me the whole story. There isn't the least suspicion in his mind that Carl may have told me one thing and him another. He seems to think that the story was invented expressly to torture him. He doesn't seem to mind so much that it's a fabrication. It's the "images" as he says, which Carl left in his mind, that get him. The images are real, even if the whole story is false. And besides, the fact that there actually is a rich cunt on the scene and that Carl actually paid her a visit, that's undeniable. What actually happened is secondary; he takes it for granted that Carl put the boots to her. But what drives him desperate is the thought that what Carl has described to him might have been *possible*.

"It's just like that guy," he says, "to tell me he put it to her six or seven times. I know that's a lot of shit and I don't mind that so much, but when he tells me that she hired a carriage and drove him out to the Bois and that they used the husband's fur coat for a blanket, that's too much. I suppose he told you about the chauffeur waiting respectfully . . . and listen, did he tell you how the engine purred all the time? Jesus, he built that up wonderfully. It's just like him to think of a detail like that . . . it's one of those little details which makes a thing psychologically real . . . you can't get in out of your head afterward. And he tells it to me so smoothly, so naturally. . . . I wonder, did he think it up in advance or did it just pop out of his head like that, spontaneously? He's such a cute little liar you can't walk away from him . . . it's like he's writing you a letter, one of those flowerpots that he makes overnight. I don't understand how a guy can write such letters . . . I don't get the mentality behind it . . . it's a form of masturbation . . . what do you think?"

But before I have an opportunity to venture an opinion, or even to laugh in his face, Van Norden goes on with his monologue.

"Listen, I suppose he told you everything . . . did he tell you how he stood on the balcony in the moonlight and kissed her? That sounds banal when you repeat it, but the way that guy describes it . . . I can just see the little prick standing there with the woman in his arms and already he's writing another letter to her, another flowerpot above the roof tops and all that crap he steals from his French authors. That guy never says a thing that's original, I found that out. You have to get a clue like . . . find out whom he's been reading lately . . . and it's hard to do that because he's so damned secretive. Listen, if I didn't know that you went there with him, I wouldn't believe that the woman existed. A guy like that could write letters to himself. And yet he's lucky . . . he's so damned tiny, so frail, so romantic looking, that women fall for him now and then . . . they sort of adopt him . . . they feel sorry for him, I guess. And some cunts like to receive flowerpots . . . it makes them feel important. . . . But this woman's an intelligent woman, so he says. You ought to know . . . you've seen her letters. What do you suppose a woman like that saw in him? I can understand her falling for the letters . . . but how do you suppose she felt when she *saw* him?

"But listen, all that's beside the point. What I'm getting at is the way he tells it to me. You know how he embroiders things . . . well, after that scene on the balcony—he gives me that like an hors d'oeuvre, you know—after that, so he says, they went inside and he unbuttoned her pajamas. What are you smiling for? Was he shitting me about that?"

"No, no! You're giving it to me exactly as he told me. Go ahead . . ."

"After that"—here Van Norden has to smile himself—"after that, mind you, he tells me how she sat in the chair with her legs up . . . not a stitch on . . . and he's sitting on the floor looking up at her, telling her how beautiful she looks . . . did he tell you that she looked like a Matisse? . . . Wait a minute . . . I'd like to remember exactly what he said. He had some cute little phrase there about an odalisque . . . what the hell's an odalisque anyway? He said it in French, that's why it's hard to remember the fucking thing . . . but it sounded good. It sounded just like the sort of thing he might say. And she probably thought it was original with him . . . I suppose she thinks he's a poet or something. But listen, all this is nothing . . . I make allowance for his imagination. It's what happened after that that drives me crazy. All night long I've been tossing about, playing with these images he left in my mind. I can't get it out of my head. It sounds so real to me that if it didn't happen I could strangle the bastard. A guy has no right to invent things like that. Or else he's diseased. . . .

"What I'm getting at is that moment when, he says, he got down on his knees and with those two skinny fingers of his he spread her cunt open. You remember that? He says she was sitting there with her legs dangling over the arms of the chair and suddenly, he says, he got an inspiration. This was after he had given her a couple of lays already . . . after he had made that little spiel about Matisse. He gets down on his knees—*get this!*—and with his two fingers . . . just the tips of them, mind you . . . he opens the little petals . . . *squish-squish* . . . just like that. A sticky little sound . . . almost inaudible. *Squish-squish!* Jesus, I've been hearing it all night long! And then he says—as if that weren't enough for me—then he tells me he buried his head in her muff. And when he did that, so help me Christ, if she didn't swing her legs around his neck and lock him there. *That finished me!* Imagine it! Imagine a fine, sensitive woman like that swinging her legs around *his neck!* There's something poisonous about it. It's so fantastic that it sounds convincing. If he had only told me about the champagne and the ride in the Bois and even that scene on the balcony I could have dismissed it. But this thing is so incredible that it doesn't sound like a lie any more. I can't believe that he ever read anything like that anywhere, and I can't see what could have put the idea into his head unless there was some truth in it. With a little prick like that, you know, anything can happen. He may not have fucked her at all, but she may have let him diddle her . . . you never know with these rich cunts what they might expect you to do. . . ."

When he finally pulls himself out of bed and starts to

shave the afternoon is already well advanced. I've finally succeeded in switching his mind to other things, to the moving principally. The maid comes in to see if he's ready—he's supposed to have vacated the room by noon. He's just in the act of slipping into his trousers. I'm a little surprised that he doesn't excuse himself, on turn away. Seeing him standing there nonchalantly buttoning his fly as he gives her orders I begin to titter. "Don't mind her," he says, throwing her a look of supreme contempt, "she's just a big sow. Give her a pinch in the ass, if you like. She won't say anything." And then addressing her, in English, he says, "Come here, you bitch, put your hand on this!" At this I can't restrain myself any longer. I burst out laughing, a fit of hysterical laughter which infects the maid also, though she doesn't know what it's all about. The maid commences to take down the pictures and the photographs, mostly of himself, which line the walls. "*You*," he says, jerking his thumb, "come here! Here's something to remember me by"—ripping a photograph off the wall—"when I go you can wipe your ass with it. See," he says, turning to me, "she's a dumb bitch. She wouldn't look any more intelligent if I said it in French." The maid stands there with her mouth open; she is evidently convinced that he is cracked. "Hey!" he yells at her as if she were hard of hearing. "Hey, *you!* Yes, *you!* Like this . . . !" and he takes the photograph, his own photograph, and wipes his ass with it. "*Comme ça!* Savvy? You've got to draw pictures for her," he says, thrusting his lower lip forward in absolute disgust.

He watches her helplessly as she throws his things into the big valises. "Here, put these in too," he says, handing her a toothbrush and the douche bag. Half of his belongings are lying on the floor. The valises are crammed full and there is nowhere to put the paintings and the books and the bottles that are half empty. "Sit down a minute," he says. "We've got plenty of time. We've got to think this thing out. If you hadn't come around I'd never have gotten out of here. You see how helpless I am. Don't let me forget to take the bulbs out . . . they belong to me. That wastebasket belongs to me too. They expect you to live like pigs, these bastards." The maid has gone downstairs to get some twine. . . . "Wait till you see . . . she'll charge me for the twine even if it's only three sous. They wouldn't sew a button on your pants here without charging for it. The lousy, dirty scroungers!" He takes a bottle of Calvados from the mantelpiece and nods to me to grab the other. "No use carrying these to the new place. Let's finish them off now. But don't give *her* a drink! That bastard, I wouldn't leave her a piece of toilet paper. I'd like to ruin the joint before I go. Listen . . . piss on the floor, if you like. I wish I could take a crap in the bureau drawer." He feels so utterly disgusted with himself and everything else that he doesn't know what to do by way of venting his feelings. He walks over to the bed with the bottle in his hand and pulling back the covers he sprinkles Calvados over the mattress. Not content with that he digs his heel into the mattress. Unfortunately there's no mud on his heels. Finally he takes the sheet and cleans his shoes with it. "That'll give them something to do," he mutters vengefully. Then, taking a good swig, he throws his head back and gargles his throat, and after he's gargled it good and proper he spits it out on the mirror. "There, you cheap bastards! Wipe that off when I go!" He walks back and forth mumbling to himself. Seeing his torn socks lying on the floor he picks them up and tears them to bits. The paintings enrage him too. He picks one up —a portrait of himself done by some Lesbian he knew and he puts his foot through it. "That bitch! You know what she had the nerve to ask me? She asked me to turn over my cunts to her after I was through with them. She never gave you a sou for writing her up. She thought I honestly admired her work.

I wouldn't have gotten that painting out of her if I hadn't promised to fix her up with that cunt from Minnesota. She was nuts about her . . . used to follow us around like a dog in heat . . . we couldn't get rid of the bitch! She bothered the life out of me. I got so that I was almost afraid to bring a cunt up here for fear that she'd bust in on me. I used to creep up here like a burglar and lock the door behind me as soon as I got inside. . . . She and that Georgia cunt—they drive me nuts. The one is always in heat and the other is always hungry. I hate fucking a woman who's hungry. It's like you push a feed inside her and then you push it out again. . . . Jesus, that reminds me of something . . . where did I put that blue ointment? That's important. Did you ever have those things? It's worse than having a dose. And I don't know where I got them from either. I've had so many women up here in the last week or so I've lost track of them. Funny too, because they all smelled so fresh. But you know how it is. . . ."

The maid has piled his things up on the sidewalk. The *patron* looks on with a surly air. When everything has been loaded into the taxi there is only room for one of us inside. As soon as we commence to roll Van Norden gets out a newspaper and starts bundling up his pots and pans; in the new place all cooking is strictly forbidden. By the time we reach our destination all his luggage has come undone; it wouldn't be quite so embarrassing if the madam had not stuck her head out of the doorway just as we rolled up. "My God!" she exclaims, "what in the devil is all this? What does it mean?" Van Norden is so intimidated that he can think of nothing more to say than "*C'est moi . . . c'est moi, madame!*" And turning to me he mumbles savagely: "That cluck! did you notice her face? She's going to make it hard for me."

The hotel lies back of a dingy passage and forms a rectangle very much on the order of a modern penitentiary. The *bureau* is large and gloomy, despite the brilliant reflections from the tile walls. There are bird cages hanging in the windows and little enamel signs everywhere begging the guests in an obsolete language not to do this and not to forget that. It is almost immaculately clean but absolutely poverty-stricken, threadbare, woebegone. The upholstered chairs are held together with wired thongs; they remind one unpleasantly of the electric chair. The room he is going to occupy is on the fifth floor. As we climb the stairs Van Norden informs me that Maupassant once lived here. And in the same breath remarks that there is a peculiar odor in the hall. On the fifth floor a few windowpanes are missing; we stand a moment gazing at the tenants across the court. It is getting toward dinner time and people are straggling back to their rooms with that weary, dejected air which comes from earning a living honestly. Most of the windows are wide open: the dingy rooms have the appearance of so many yawning mouths. The occupants of the rooms are yawning too, or else scratching themselves. They move about listlessly and apparently without much purpose; they might just as well be lunatics.

As we turn down the corridor toward room 57, a door suddenly opens in front of us and an old hag with matted hair and the eyes of a maniac peers out. She startles us so that we stand transfixed. For a full minute the three of us stand there powerless to move or even to make an intelligent gesture. Back of the old hag I can see a kitchen table and on it lies a baby all undressed, a puny little brat no bigger than a plucked chicken. Finally the old one picks up a slop pail by her side and makes a move forward. We stand aside to let her pass and as the door closes behind her the baby lets out a piercing scream. It is room 56, and between 56 and 57 is the toilet where the old hag is emptying her slops.

Ever since we have mounted the stairs Van Norden has kept silence. But his looks are eloquent. When he opens the door of 57 I have for a fleeting moment the sensation of going mad. A huge mirror covered with green gauze and tipped at an angle of 45 degrees hangs directly opposite the entrance over a baby carriage which is filled with books. Van Norden doesn't even crack a smile; instead he walks nonchalantly over to the baby carriage and picking up a book begins to skim it through, much as a man would enter the public library and go unthinkingly to the rack nearest to hand. And perhaps this would not seem so ludicrous to me if I had not espied at the same time a pair of handle bars resting in the corner. They look so absolutely peaceful and contented, as if they had been dozing there for years, that suddenly it seems to me as if we had been standing in this room, in exactly this position, for an incalculably long time, that it was a pose we had struck in a dream from which we never emerged, a dream which the least gesture, the wink of an eye even, will shatter. But more remarkable still is the remembrance that suddenly floats up of an actual dream which occurred only the other night, a dream in which I saw Van Norden in just such a corner as is occupied now by the handle bars, only instead of the handle bars there was a woman crouching with her legs drawn up. I see him standing over the woman with that alert, eager look in his eye which comes when he wants something badly. The street in which this is going on is blurred—only the angle made by the two walls is clear, and the cowering figure of the woman. I can see him going at her in that quick, animal way of his, reckless of what's going on about him, determined only to have his way. And a look in his eyes as though to say—"you can kill me afterwards, but just let me get it in . . . I've got to get it in!" And there he is, bent over her, their heads knocking against the wall, he has such a tremendous erection that it's simply impossible to get it in her. Suddenly, with that disgusted air which he knows so well how to summon, he picks himself up and adjusts his clothes. He is about to walk away when suddenly he notices that his penis is lying on the sidewalk. It is about the size of a sawed-off broomstick. He picks it up nonchalantly and slings it under his arm. As he walks off I notice two huge bulbs, like tulip bulbs, dangling from the end of the broomstick, and I can hear him muttering to himself "flowerpots . . . flowerpots."

The *garçon* arrives panting and sweating. Van Norden looks at him uncomprehendingly. The madam now marches in and, walking straight up to Van Norden, she takes the book out of his hand, thrusts it in the baby carriage, and, without saying a word, wheels the baby carriage into the hallway.

"This is a bughouse," says Van Norden, smiling distressedly. It is such a faint, indescribable smile that for a moment the dream feeling comes back and it seems to me that we are standing at the end of a long corridor at the end of which is a corrugated mirror. And down this corridor, swinging his distress like a dingy lantern, Van Norden staggers, staggers in and out as here and there a door opens and a hand yanks him in or a hoof pushes him out. And the further off he wanders the more lugubrious is his distress; he wears it like a lantern which the cyclists hold between their teeth on a night when the pavement is wet and slippery. In and out of the dingy rooms he wanders, and when he sits down the chair collapses, when he opens his valise there is only a toothbrush inside. In every room there is a mirror before which he stands attentively and chews his rage, and from the constant chewing, from the grumbling and mumbling and the muttering and cursing his jaws have gotten unhinged and they sag badly and, when he rubs his beard, pieces of his jaw crumble away and he's so disgusted with himself that he stamps on his own jaw, grinds it to bits with his big heels.

Meanwhile the luggage is being hauled in. And things begin to look crazier even than before—particularly when he attaches his exerciser to the bedstead and begins his Sandow exercises. "I like this place," he says, smiling at the *garçon*. He takes his coat and vest off. The *garçon* is watching him with a puzzled air; he has a valise in one hand and the douche bag in the other. I'm standing apart in the antechamber holding the mirror with the green gauze. Not a single object seems to possess a practical use. The antechamber itself seems useless, a sort of vestibule to a barn. It is exactly the same sort of sensation which I get when I enter the Comédie-Française or the Palais-Royal Theatre; it is a world of bric-a-brac, of trap doors, of arms and busts and waxed floors, of candelabras and men in armor, of statues without eyes and love letters lying in glass cases. Something is going on, but it makes no sense; it's like finishing the half-empty bottle of Calvados because there's no room in the valise.

Climbing up the stairs, as I said a moment ago, he had mentioned the fact that Maupassant used to live here. The coincidence seems to have made an impression upon him. He would like to believe that it was in this very room that Maupassant gave birth to some of those gruesome tales on which his reputation rests. "They lived like pigs, those poor bastards," he says. We are sitting at the round table in a pair of comfortable old armchairs that have been trussed up with thongs and braces; the bed is right beside us, so close indeed that we can put our feet on it. The *armoire* stands in a corner behind us, also conveniently within reach. Van Norden has emptied his dirty wash on the table; we sit there with our feet buried in his dirty socks and shirts and smoke contentedly. The sordidness of the place seems to have worked a spell on him: he is content here. When I get up to switch on the light he suggests that we play a game of cards before going out to eat. And so we sit there by the window, with the dirty wash strewn over the floor and the Sandow exerciser hanging from the chandelier, and we play a few rounds of two-handed pinochle. Van Norden has put away his pipe and packed a wad of snuff on the underside of his lower lip. Now and then he spits out of the window, big healthy gobs of brown juice which resound with a smack on the pavement below. He seems content now.

"In America," he says, "you wouldn't dream of living in a joint like this. Even when I was on the bum I slept in better rooms than this. But here it seems natural—it's like the books you read. If I ever go back there I'll forget all about this life, just like you forget a bad dream. I'll probably take up the old life again just where I left off . . . if I ever get back. Sometimes I lie in bed dreaming about the past and it's so vivid to me that I have to shake myself in order to realize where I am. Especially when I have a woman beside me; a woman can set me off better than anything. That's all I want of them—to forget myself. Sometimes I get so lost in my reveries that I can't remember the name of the cunt or where I picked her up. That's funny, eh? It's good to have a fresh warm body beside you when you wake up in the morning. It gives you a clean feeling. You get spiritual like . . . until they start pulling that mushy crap about love et cetera. Why do all these cunts talk about love so much, can you tell me that? A good lay isn't enough for them apparently . . . they want your soul too. . . ."

Now this word soul, which pops up frequently in Van Norden's soliloquies, used to have a droll effect upon me at first. Whenever I heard the word soul from his lips I would get hysterical; somehow it seemed like a false coin, more particularly because it was usually accompanied by a gob of brown juice which left a trickle down the corner of his mouth. And as I never hesitated to laugh in his face it happened invariably that when this little word bobbed up Van Norden would pause just long enough for me to burst into a cackle and then, as if nothing had happened, he would resume his monologue, repeating the word more and more frequently and each time with a more caressing emphasis. It was the soul of him that women were trying to possess—that he made clear to me. He has explained it over and over again, but he comes back to it afresh each time like a paranoiac to his obsession. In a sense Van Norden is mad, of that I'm convinced. His one fear is to be left alone, and this fear is so deep and so persistent that even when he is on top of a woman, even when he has welded himself to her, he cannot escape the prison which he has created for himself. "I try all sorts of things," he explains to me. "I even count sometimes, or I begin to think of a problem in philosophy, but it doesn't work. It's like I'm two people, and one of them is watching me all the time. I get so goddamned mad at myself that I could kill myself . . . and in a way, that's what I do every time I have an orgasm. For one second like I obliterate myself. There's not even one me then . . . there's nothing . . . not even the cunt. It's like receiving communion. Honest, I mean that. For a few seconds afterward I have a fine spiritual glow . . . and maybe it would continue that way indefinitely—how can you tell?—if it weren't for the fact that there's a woman beside you and then the douche bag and the water running . . . all those little details that make you desperately self-conscious, desperately lonely. And for that one moment of freedom you have to listen to all that love crap . . . it drives me nuts sometimes . . . I want to kick them out immediately . . . I do now and then. But that doesn't keep them away. They like it, in fact. The less you notice them the more they chase after you. There's something perverse about women . . . they're all masochists at heart."

"But what is it you want of a woman, then?" I demand.

He begins to mold his hands; his lower lip droops. He looks completely frustrated. When eventually he succeeds in stammering out a few broken phrases it's with the conviction that behind his words lies an overwhelming futility. "I want to be able to surrender myself to a woman," he blurts out. "I want her to take me out of myself. But to do that, she's got to be better than I am; she's got to have a mind, not just a cunt. She's got to make me believe that I need her, that I can't live without her. Find me a cunt like that, will you? If you could do that I'd give you my job. I wouldn't care then what happened to me: I wouldn't need a job or friends or books or anything. If she could only make me believe that there was something more important on earth than myself. Jesus, I hate myself! But I hate these bastardly cunts even more—because they're none of them any good.

"You think I like myself," he continues. "That shows how little you know about me. I know I'm a great guy. . . . I wouldn't have these problems if there weren't something to me. But what eats me up is that I can't express myself. People think I'm a cunt-chaser. That's how shallow they are, these high brows who sit on the *terrasse* all day chewing the psychologic cud. . . . That's not so bad, eh—psychologic cud? Write it down for me. I'll use it in my column next week. . . . By the way, did you ever read Stekel? Is he any good? It looks like nothing but case histories to me. I wish to Christ I could get up enough nerve to visit an analyst . . . a good one, I mean. I don't want to see these little shysters with goatees and frock coats, like your friend Boris. How do you manage to tolerate those guys? Don't they bore you stiff? You talk to anybody, I notice. You don't give a goddamn. Maybe you're right. I wish I weren't so damned critical. But these dirty little Jews who hang around the Dôme, Jesus, they give me the creeps. They sound just like textbooks. If I could talk to you every day maybe I could get things off my chest. You're a good listener. I know you don't give a damn about me, but you're patient. And you don't have any theories to exploit. I suppose you put it all down afterward in that notebook of yours. Listen, I don't mind what you say about me, but don't make me out to be a cunt-chaser—it's too simple. Some day I'll write a book about myself, about my thoughts. I don't mean just a piece of introspective analysis . . . I mean that I'll lay myself down on the operating table and I'll expose my whole guts . . . every goddamned thing. Has anybody ever done that before?—What the hell are you smiling at? Does it sound naïf?"

I'm smiling because whenever we touch on the subject of this book which he is going to write some day things assume an incongruous aspect. He has only to say "my book" and immediately the world shrinks to the private dimensions of Van Norden and Co. The book must be absolutely original, absolutely perfect. That is why, among other things, it is impossible for him to get started on it. As soon as he gets an idea he begins to question it. He remembers that Dostoevski used it, or Hamsun, or somebody else. "I'm not saying that I want to be better than them, but I want to be different," he explains. And so, instead of tackling his book, he reads one author after another in order to make absolutely certain that he is not going to tread on their private property. And the more he reads the more disdainful he becomes. None of them are satisfying; none of them arrive at that degree of perfection which he has imposed on himself. And forgetting completely that he has not written as much as a chapter he talks about them condescendingly, quite as though there existed a shelf of books bearing his name, books which everyone is familiar with and the titles of which it is therefore superfluous to mention. Though he has never overtly lied about this fact, nevertheless it is obvious that the people whom he buttonholes in order to air his private philosophy, his criticism, and his grievances, take it for granted that behind his loose remarks there stands a solid body of work. Especially the young and foolish virgins whom he lures to his room on the pretext of reading to them his poems, or on the still better pretext of asking their advice.

Without the least feeling of guilt or self-consciousness he will hand them a piece of soiled paper on which he has scribbled a few lines—the basis of a new poem, as he puts it—and with absolute seriousness demand of them an honest expression of opinion. As they usually have nothing to give by way of comment, wholly bewildered as they are by the utter senselessness of the lines, Van Norden seizes the occasion to expound to them his view of art, a view, needless to say, which is spontaneously created to suit the event. So expert has he become in this role that the transition from Ezra Pound's cantos to the bed is made as simply and naturally as a modulation from one key to another; in fact, if it were not made there would be discord, which is what happens now and then when he makes a mistake as regards those nitwits whom he refers to as "push-overs." Naturally, constituted as he is, it is with reluctance that he refers to these fatal errors of judgment. But when he does bring himself to confess to an error of this kind it is with absolute frankness; in fact, he seems to derive a perverse pleasure in dwelling upon his inaptitude. There is one woman, for example, whom he has been trying to make for almost ten years now—first in America, and finally here in Paris. It is the only person of the opposite sex with whom he has a cordial, friendly relationship. They seem not only to like each other, but to understand each other. At first it seemed to me that if he could really make this creature his problem might be solved. All the elements for a successful union were there—except the fundamental one. Bessie was almost as unusual in her way as himself. She had as little concern about giving herself to a man as she has about the dessert which follows the meal. Usually she singled out the object of her choice and made the proposition herself. She was not bad-looking, nor could one say that she was good-looking either. She had a fine body, that was the chief thing—and she liked it, as they say.

They were so chummy, these two, that sometimes, in order to gratify her curiosity (and also in the vain hope of inspiring her by his prowess), Van Norden would arrange to hide her in his closet during one of his seances. After it was over Bessie would emerge from her hiding place and they would discuss the matter casually, that is to say, with an almost total indifference to everything except "technique." Technique was one of her favorite terms, at least in those discussions which I was privileged to enjoy. "What's wrong with my technique?" he would say. And Bessie would answer: "You're too crude. If you ever expect to make me you've got to become more subtle."

There was such a perfect understanding between them, as I say, that often when I called for Van Norden at one-thirty, I would find Bessie sitting on the bed, the covers thrown back and Van Norden inviting her to stroke his penis . . . "just a few silken strokes," he would say, "so as I'll have the courage to get up." Or else he would urge her to blow on it, or failing that, he would grab hold of himself and shake it like a dinner bell, the two of them laughing fit to die. "I'll never make this bitch," he would say. "She has no respect for me. That's what I get for taking her into my confidence." And then abruptly he might add: "What do you make of that blonde I showed you yesterday?" Talking to Bessie, of course. And Bessie would jeer at him, telling him he had no taste. "Aw, don't give me that line," he would say. And then playfully, perhaps for the thousandth time, because by now it had become a standing joke between them—"Listen, Bessie, what about a quick lay? Just one little lay . . . no." And when this had passed off in the usual manner he would add, in the same tone: "Well, what about *him?* Why don't you give *him* a lay?"

The whole point about Bessie was that she couldn't, or just wouldn't, regard herself as a lay. She talked about passion, as if it were a brand new word. She was passionate about things, even a little thing like a lay. She had to put her soul into it.

"I get passionate too sometimes," Van Norden would say.

"Oh, *you*," says Bessie. "You're just a worn-out satyr. You don't know the meaning of passion. When you get an erection you think you're passionate."

"All right, maybe it's not passion . . . but you can't get passionate without having an erection, that's true isn't it?"

All this about Bessie, and the other women whom he drags to his room day in and out, occupies my thoughts as we walk to the restaurant. I have adjusted myself so well to his monologues that without interrupting my own reveries I make whatever comment is required automatically, the moment I hear his voice die out. It is a duet, and like most duets moreover in that one listens attentively only for the signal which announces the advent of one's own voice. As it is his night off, and as I have promised to keep him company, I have already dulled myself to his queries. I know that before the evening is over I shall be thoroughly exhausted; if I am lucky, that is, if I can worm a few francs out of him on some pretext or other, I will duck him the moment he goes to the toilet. But he knows my propensity for slipping away, and, instead of being insulted, he simply provides against the possibility by guarding his sous. If I ask him for money to buy cigarettes he insists on going with me to purchase them. He will not be left alone, not for a second. Even when he has succeeded in grabbing off a woman, even then he is terrified to be left alone with her. If it were possible he would have me sit in the room while he puts on the performance. It would be like asking me to wait while he took a shave.

On his night off Van Norden generally manages to have at least fifty francs in his pocket, a circumstance which does not prevent him from making a touch whenever he encounters a prospect. "Hello," he says, "give me twenty francs . . . I need it." He has a way of looking panic-stricken at the same time. And if he meets with a rebuff he becomes insulting. "Well, you can buy a drink at least." And when he gets his drink he says more graciously—"Listen give me five francs then . . . give me *two* francs. . . ." We go from bar to bar looking for a little excitement and always accumulating a few more francs.

At the Coupole we stumble into a drunk from the newspaper. One of the upstairs guys. There's just been an accident at the office, he informs us. One of the proofreaders fell down the elevator shaft. Not expected to live.

At first Van Norden is shocked, deeply shocked. But when he learns that it was Peckover, the Englishman, he looks relieved. "The poor bastard," he says, "he's better off dead than alive. He just got his false teeth the other day too. . . ."

The allusion to the false teeth moves the man upstairs to tears. He relates in a slobbery way a little incident connected with the accident. He is upset about it, more upset about this little incident than about the catastrophe itself. It seems that Peckover, when he hit the bottom of the shaft, regained consciousness before anyone could reach him. Despite the fact that his legs were broken and his ribs busted, he had managed to rise to all fours and grope about for his false teeth. In the ambulance he was crying out in his delirium for the teeth he had lost. The incident was pathetic and ludicrous at the same time. The guy from upstairs hardly knew whether to laugh or to weep as he related it. It was a delicate moment because with a drunk like that, one false move and he'd crash a bottle over your skull. He had never been particularly friendly with Peckover—as a matter of fact, he had scarcely ever set foot in the proofreading department: there was an invisible wall like between the guys upstairs and the guys down below. But now, since he had felt the touch of death, he wanted to display his comradeship. He wanted to weep, if possible, to show that he was a regular guy. And Joe and I, who knew Peckover well and who knew also that he wasn't worth a good goddamn, even a few tears, we felt annoyed with this drunken sentimentality. We wanted to tell him so too, but with a guy like that you can't afford to be honest; you have to buy a wreath and go to the funeral and pretend that you're miserable. And you have to congratulate him too for the delicate obituary he's written. He'll be carrying his delicate little obituary around with him for months, praising the shit out of himself for the way he handled the situation. We felt all that, Joe and I, without saying a word to each other. We just stood there and listened with a murderous, silent contempt. And as soon as we could break away we did so; we left him there at the bar blubbering to himself over his Pernod.

Once out of his sight we began to laugh hysterically. The false teeth! No matter what we said about the poor devil, and we said some good things about him too, we always came back to the false teeth. There are people in this world who cut such a grotesque figure that even death renders them ridiculous. And the more horrible the death the more ridiculous they seem. It's no use trying to invest the end with a little dignity—you have to be a liar and a hypocrite to discover anything tragic in their going. And since we didn't have to put on a false front we could laugh about the incident to our heart's content. We laughed all night about it, and in between times we vented our scorn and disgust for the guys upstairs, the fatheads who were trying to persuade themselves, no doubt, that Peckover was a fine fellow and that his death was a catastrophe. All sorts of funny recollections came to our minds—the semicolons that he overlooked and for which they bawled the piss out of him. They made his life miserable with their fucking little semicolons and the fractions which he always got wrong. They were even going to fire him once because he came to work with a boozy breath. They despised him because he always looked so miserable and because he had eczema and dandruff. He was just a nobody, as far as they were concerned, but, now that he was dead, they would all chip in lustily and buy him a huge wreath and they'd put his name in big type in the obituary column. Anything to throw a little reflection on themselves; they'd make him out to be a *big* shit if they could. But unfortunately, with Peckover, there was little they could invent about him. He was a zero, and even the fact that he was dead wouldn't add a cipher to his name.

"There's only one good aspect to it," says Joe. "You may get his job. And if you have any luck, maybe you'll fall down the elevator shaft and break your neck too. We'll buy you a nice wreath, I promise you that."

Toward dawn we're sitting on the *terrasse* of the Dôme. We've forgotten about poor Peckover long ago. We've had a little excitement at the Bal Nègre and Joe's mind has slipped back to the eternal preoccupation: cunt. It's at this hour, when his night off is almost concluded, that his restlessness mounts to a fever pitch. He thinks of the women he passed up earlier in the evening and of the steady ones he might have had for the asking, if it weren't that he was fed up with them. He is reminded inevitably of his Georgia cunt—she's been hounding him lately, begging him to take her in, at least until she can find herself a job. "I don't mind giving her a feed once in a while," he says, "but I couldn't take her on as a steady thing . . . she'd ruin it for my other cunts." What gripes him most about her is that she doesn't put on any flesh. "It's like taking a skeleton to bed with you," he says. "The other night I took her on—out of pity—and what do you think the crazy bitch had done to herself? She had shaved it clean . . .

not a speck of hair on it. Did you ever have a woman who shaved her twat? It's repulsive, ain't it? And it's funny, too. Sort of mad like. It doesn't look like a twat any more: it's like a dead clam or something." He describes to me how, his curiosity aroused, he got out of bed and searched for his flashlight. "I made her hold it open and I trained the flashlight on it. You should have seen me . . . it was comical. I got so worked up about it that I forgot all about her. I never in my life looked at a cunt so seriously. You'd imagine I'd never seen one before. And the more I looked at it the less interesting it became. It only goes to show you there's nothing to it after all, especially when it's shaved. It's the hair that makes it mysterious. That's why a statue leaves you cold. Only once I saw a real cunt on a statue—that was by Rodin. You ought to see it some time . . . she has her legs spread wide apart. . . . I don't think there was any head on it. Just a cunt you might say. Jesus, it looked ghastly. The thing is this—they all look alike. When you look at them with their clothes on you imagine all sorts of things: you give them an individuality like, which they haven't got, of course. There's just a crack there between the legs and you get all steamed up about it—you don't even look at it half the time. You know it's there and all you think about is getting your ramrod inside; it's as though your penis did the thinking for you. It's an illusion! You get all burned up about nothing . . . about a crack with hair on it, or without hair. It's so absolutely meaningless that it fascinated me to look at it. I must have studied it for ten minutes or more. When you look at it that way, sort of detached like, you get funny notions in your head. All that mystery about sex and then you discover that it's nothing—just a blank. Wouldn't it be funny if you found a harmonica inside . . . or a calendar? But there's nothing there . . . nothing at all. It's disgusting. It almost drove me mad. . . .

Listen, do you know what I did afterwards? I gave her a quick lay and then I turned my back on her. Yeah, I picked up a book and I read. You can get something out of a book, even a bad book . . . but a cunt, it's just sheer loss of time. . . ."

It just so happened that as he was concluding his speech a whore gave us the eye. Without the slightest transition he says to me abruptly: "Would you like to give her a tumble? It won't cost much . . . she'll take the two of us on." And without waiting for a reply he staggers to his feet and goes over to her. In a few minutes he comes back. "It's all fixed," he says. "Finish your beer. She's hungry. There's nothing doing any more at this hour . . . she'll take the both of us for fifteen francs. We'll go to my room . . . it'll be cheaper."

On the way to the hotel the girl is shivering so that we have to stop and buy her a coffee. She's a rather gentle sort of creature and not at all bad to look at. She evidently knows Van Norden, knows there's nothing to expect from him but the fifteen francs. "You haven't got any dough," he says, mumbling to me under his breath. As I haven't a centime in my pocket I don't quite see the point of this, until he bursts out: "For Christ's sake, remember that we're broke. Don't get tenderhearted when we get upstairs. She's going to ask you for a little extra—I know this cunt! I could get her for ten francs, if I wanted to. There's no use spoiling them. . . ."

"*Il est méchant, celui-là,*" she says to me, gathering the drift of his remarks in her dull way.

"*Non, il n'est pas méchant, il est très gentil.*"

She shakes her head laughingly. "*Je le connais bien, ce type.*" And then she commences a hard luck story, about the hospital and the back rent and the baby in the country. But she doesn't overdo it. She knows that our ears are stopped; but the misery is there inside her, like a stone, and there's no room for any other thoughts. She isn't trying to make an appeal to our sympathies—she's just shifting this big weight inside her from one place to another. I rather like her. I hope to Christ she hasn't got a disease. . . .

In the room she goes about her preparations mechanically. "There isn't a crust of bread about by any chance?" she inquires, as she squats over the *bidet*. Van Norden laughs at this. "Here, take a drink," he says, shoving a bottle at her. She doesn't want anything to drink; her stomach's already on the bum, she complains.

"That's just a line with her," says Van Norden. "Don't let her work on your sympathies. Just the same, I wish she'd talk about something else. How the hell can you get up any passion when you've got a starving cunt on your hands?"

Precisely! We haven't any passion either of us. And as for her, one might as well expect her to produce a diamond necklace as to show a spark of passion. But there's the fifteen francs and something has to be done about it. It's like a state of war: the moment the condition is precipitated nobody thinks about anything but peace, about getting it over with. And yet nobody has the courage to lay down his arms, to say, "I'm fed up with it . . . I'm through." No, there's fifteen francs somewhere, which nobody gives a damn about any more and which nobody is going to get in the end anyhow, but the fifteen francs is like the primal cause of things and rather than listen to one's own voice, rather than walk out on the primal cause, one surrenders to the situation, one goes on butchering and butchering and the more cowardly one feels the more heroically does he behave, until a day when the bottom drops out and suddenly all the guns are silenced and the stretcher-bearers pick up the maimed and bleeding heroes and pin medals on their chest. Then one has the rest of his life to think about the fifteen francs. One hasn't any eyes or arms or legs, but he has the consolation of dreaming for the rest of his days about the fifteen francs which everybody has forgotten.

It's exactly like a state of war—I can't get it out of my head. The way she works over me, to blow a spark of passion into me, makes me think what a damned poor soldier I'd be if I was ever silly enough to be trapped like this and dragged to the front. I know for my part that I'd surrender everything, honor included, in order to get out of the mess. I haven't any stomach for it, and that's all there is to it. But she's got her mind set on the fifteen francs and if I don't want to fight about it she's going to make me fight. But you can't put fight into a man's guts if he hasn't any fight in him. There are some of us so cowardly that you can't ever make heroes of us, not even if you frighten us to death. We know too much, maybe. There are some of us who don't live in the moment, who live a little ahead, or a little behind. My mind is on the peace treaty all the time. I can't forget that it was the fifteen francs which started all the trouble. Fifteen francs! What does fifteen francs mean to me, particularly since it's not my fifteen francs?

Van Norden seems to have a more normal attitude about it. He doesn't care a rap about the fifteen francs either now; it's the situation itself which intrigues him. It seems to call for a show of mettle—his manhood is involved. The fifteen francs are lost, whether we succeed or not. There's something more involved—not just manhood perhaps, but will. It's like a man in the trenches again: he doesn't know any more why he should go on living, because if he escapes now he'll only be caught later, but he goes on just the same, and even though he has the soul of a cockroach and has admitted as much to himself, give him a gun or a knife or even just his bare nails, and he'll go on slaughtering and slaughtering, he'd slaughter a million men rather than stop and ask himself why.

As I watch Van Norden tackle her, it seems to me that

I'm looking at a machine whose cogs have slipped. Left to themselves, they could go on this way forever, grinding and slipping, without ever anything happening. Until a hand shuts the motor off. The sight of them coupled like a pair of goats without the least spark of passion, grinding and grinding away for no reason except the fifteen francs, washes away every bit of feeling I have except the inhuman one of satisfying my curiosity. The girl is lying on the edge of the bed and Van Norden is bent over her like a satyr with his two feet solidly planted on the floor. I am sitting on a chair behind him, watching their movements with a cool, scientific detachment; it doesn't matter to me if it should last forever. It's like watching one of those crazy machines which throw the newspaper out, millions and billions and trillions of them with their meaningless headlines. The machine seems more sensible, crazy as it is, and more fascinating to watch, than the human beings and the events which produced it. My interest in Van Norden and the girl is nil; if I could sit like this and watch every single performance going on at this minute all over the world my interest would be even less than nil. I wouldn't be able to differentiate between this phenomenon and the rain falling or a volcano erupting. As long as that spark of passion is missing there is no human significance in the performance. The machine is better to watch. And these two are like a machine which has slipped its cogs. It needs the touch of a human hand to set it right. It needs a mechanic.

I get down on my knees behind Van Norden and I examine the machine more attentively. The girl throws her head on one side and gives me a despairing look. "It's no use," she says. "It's impossible." Upon which Van Norden sets to work with renewed energy, just like an old billy goat. He's such an obstinate cuss that he'll break his horns rather than give up. And he's getting sore now because I'm tickling him in the rump.

"For God's sake, Joe, give it up! You'll kill the poor girl."

"Leave me alone," he grunts. "I almost got it in that time."

The posture and the determined way in which he blurts this out suddenly bring to my mind, for the second time, the remembrance of my dream. Only now it seems as though that broomstick, which he had so nonchalantly slung under his arm, as he walked away, is lost forever. It is like the sequel to the dream—the same Van Norden, but minus the primal cause. He's like a hero come back from the war, a poor maimed bastard living out the reality of his dreams. Wherever he sits himself the chair collapses; whatever door he enters the room is empty; whatever he puts in his mouth leaves a bad taste. Everything is just the same as it was before; the elements are unchanged, the dream is no different than the reality. Only, between the time he went to sleep and the time he woke up, his body was stolen. He's like a machine throwing out newspapers, millions and billions of them every day, and the front page is loaded with catastrophes, with riots, murders, explosions, collisions, but he doesn't feel anything. If somebody doesn't turn the switch off he'll never know what it means to die; you can't die if your own proper body has been stolen. You can get over a cunt and work away like a billy goat until eternity; you can go to the trenches and be blown to bits; nothing will create that spark of passion if there isn't the intervention of a human hand. Somebody has to put his hand into the machine and let it be wrenched off if the cogs are to mesh again. Somebody has to do this without hope of reward, without concern over the fifteen francs; somebody whose chest is so thin that a medal would make him hunchbacked. And somebody has to throw a feed into a starving cunt without fear of pushing it out again. Otherwise this show'll go on forever. There's no way out of the mess. . . .

"Gertrude Stein and Henry were two geniuses who couldn't be in the same room. When I came to Paris I tried to be the intermediary. I would say Gertrude, look, Henry's a friend of mine, he's been over here all these years, you're both from the States, he's sort of broke, why don't you pass him a meal once in awhile? And Gertrude would say: we're very particular who we pass meals to. She said, I have an instinctive feeling for when people are using me and when they really need a meal, and I cannot conceive of a situation where I would help Miller however desperate he might be."

Bern Porter
Observations from the Treadmill

3. Crazy Cock

Miller is not a writer whose life lends itself to clear and separated aesthetic periods, for it is characteristic of him to write in two directions at once. Even Tropic of Cancer, which is able to give the best impression of a single-minded intent, still presents its contrast of styles.

Nonetheless, there is some pattern to his life. Miller has his obsessions, and they are intense enough for him to spend a good part of his aesthetic career working them out. If there is a gauge which separates the artist from everybody else who works at being one, it is that the artist has risen precisely from therapy to art. He is no longer fixed at relieving one or another obsessional pressure on the ego by the act of expressing himself. The artist's ultimate interest is to put something together which is independent of the ego; such work can make you feel you are traveling through that fine and supple mood we may as well call the truth. Death in Venice or Daisy

Miller has that quality and The Red Pony by Steinbeck. Breakfast at Tiffany's by Truman Capote will offer it and Katherine Anne Porter's Noon Wine. There are a hundred or rather a thousand such pieces of literature and they are art. It is not to say that they are the greatest achievements of writing itself—nothing of Dostoyevsky, for example, could fit such a category of art, indeed it may be said that all of Dostoyevsky is therapy, except that he elevated the struggle from his ego to his soul, and so we can all partake of the therapy. Forever beyond art, happily, is genius.

On this herculean scale of measure, if considerably below Dostoyevsky, can Miller be found. His life impinges on his work ceaselessly, indeed his relation to the problems of his own life is so unremitting yet so scatterbrained that it is as if life is the only true spouse Henry Miller ever had. A crazy spouse, a confirmed nitwit in her lack of stability. He can never feel calm enough to live in the world of art. In this sense, everything Miller writes is therapy. No American author, not even Thomas Wolfe, emits so intense a message that the man will go mad if he stops writing, that his overcharged brain will simply burst. It is as if Miller was never able to afford the luxury of art—rather he had to drain the throttled heats of the ego each day. Yet his literary act takes on such intensity that we are compelled to awe as we read him. Awe can be a proper accompaniment to great art.

Never pausing to take a breath, it is as if Miller creates art as a species of spin-off from his more fundamental endeavor, which is to maintain some relation between his mind and that theatre beyond his mind which presumes to call itself reality.

That he was successful is part of his greatness. Most souls who go in for self-expression in order to relieve their suffering end on a treadmill. As they relieve themselves so do they repel readers. Excrement is excrement even when the *name is therapy. But Miller brought it off. His product transcended itself and became literary flesh. What he did was therapy in that he had to do it, but it rose above every limitation. Maybe it is because he kept one literary grace—he never justified himself (which is the predictable weakness of all therapy), rather he depended on a rigorous,* even delighted honesty in portraying his faults, in writing without shit, which is to say writing with the closest examination of each turd. Miller was a true American spirit. He knew that when you have a nation of transplants and weeds the best is always next to the worst, and right after shit comes Shinola. It was all equal to him because he understood that it was never equal—in the midst of heaven a rent, and out of the slime comes a pearl; he is a demon at writing about bad fucks with all the gusto others give to good ones, no fuck is in vain—the air may prove most transcendent at the edge of the spew, or if not, then the nausea it produces can let the mind clear out its vertigo. So he dived into the sordid, and portrayed men and women as they had hardly been painted before. In* Sexus *we will be treated to a girl having her period in the middle of an orgy, cock, balls, knees, thighs, cunt, and belly basted with blood, then soap and towels, a round of good-byes—a phrase or two later he is off on the beginning of a ten-page description of how he makes love to his wife which goes through many a mood, he will go right down to the depths, no cellar has maggots or rats big enough to frighten him, he can even write about the whipped-out flayed heel-ground butt of his own desire for a whore, about fucking when too exhausted to fuck, and come up with a major metaphor. (See p. 55 of this collection.)*

* Three excerpts from *Prisoner of Sex*, somewhat rewritten to fit the context of this text, appear as follows: p. 85, lines 6 through 28; p. 90, lines 29 through 34 to p. 91, lines 1 through 11; p. 92, line 17 to end of chapter.

If some ultimate simplicity saved him, some writer's instinct to know that no account of an unpleasant event could survive its evasions—few authors have the courage to work with that!—it is just as well to recognize that Miller was not necessarily born with such simplicity but achieved it out of his own literary struggles and was forever losing it and regaining it and finally forged his escape from his life by daring to live at the deepest level of honesty he could endure in his life. This is not to say that he was always more honest than anyone else—his evasions also stand out—but it is not how absolutely honest we are, so much as the torture we are willing to bear in the attempt to be honest which works as the lever of such literary deliverance. It is possible a coward attempting to be brave can light more iridescence in the cosmos than a brave man fulfilling a routine demand on his courage. The point is that Miller came out of a background which gave no medals for honesty, the parents from whom he emerged were at odds with each other, and his Brooklyn milieu, first Williamsburg then Bushwick at the turn of the century, was closed to the idea of literature itself.

Genius may depend on the ability to find a route between irreconcilables in oneself, and Miller's parents, by his description, were fundamentally apart. His father was a gentleman, a boss tailor, just so much of a gentleman as a custom tailor for gentlemen, a finely dressed German tradesman, progressively more devoted with each decade of his life to those sentiments of twilight which drinking with business cronies will arouse through elongated lunch hours that do not end until evening. A restaurant with a nice drinking clientele is Valhalla on long afternoons to middle-class men not getting along with their wives. Miller's mother was also German, junker in comparison to his father whose spirit next to hers might seem Viennese. A strong dour intolerant German woman, the mother was impeccably thrifty and irretrievably *hostile to any idea she had not heard every day for the last forty years. The only notion she and her husband share is their absolute anti-Semitism. There is not a single suggestion in all of Miller's writing that even one sexual vibration came from her ever into the family circle.*

> My people were entirely Nordic, which is to say *idiots*. Every wrong idea which has ever been expounded was theirs. Among them was the doctrine of cleanliness, to say nothing of righteousness. They were painfully clean. But inwardly they stank. Never once had they opened the door which leads to the soul; never once did they dream of taking a blind leap into the dark. After dinner the dishes were promptly washed and put in the closet; after the paper was read it was neatly folded and laid away on a shelf; after the clothes were washed they were ironed and folded and then tucked away in the drawers. Everything was for tomorrow, but tomorrow never came. The present was only a bridge and on this bridge they are still groaning, as the world groans, and not one idiot ever thinks of blowing up the bridge.
>
> *Tropic of Capricorn*

At one point when Miller was already thirty-five, twice-married and so penniless he and his second wife had to separate in order to live rent-free with their own parents, Miller trying to write would have to hear his mother say, "If anyone comes, a neighbor of one of our friends, put that typewriter away and hide in the closet. Don't let them know you're here." A mother's shame! "I stood in that closet sometimes for over an hour, the camphor balls choking me. . . . All my life she hated the idea of me being a writer."

His sister was mentally retarded. When they were children, the kids used to call her "Crazy Loretta." Miller at eighty reminisces about his mother and sister:

> . . . my sister couldn't attend school because she was so backward. So my mother decided to teach her herself.

> My mother was never meant to be a teacher. She was terrible. She used to scold her, crack her, fly into a rage. She'd say, "How much is two times two?" and my sister, who hadn't the faintest idea of the answer, would say, "Five, no—seven, no—three." Just wild. BANG. Another slap or crack. Then my mother would turn to me and say, "Why do I have to bear this cross? What did I do to be punished so?" asked *me*, a little boy, "*Why is God punishing me?*" You can see what kind of woman she was. Stupid? Worse than that . . . I never felt any warmth from her. She never kissed me, never hugged me. I don't ever remember going to her and putting my arms around her. I didn't know mothers did that till one day I visited a friend at his home. We were twelve years old. I went home from school with him and I heard his mother's greeting. "Jackie, oh Jackie," she says, "Oh darling, how are you, how have you been?" She puts her arms around him and kisses him. I never heard that kind of language—even that tone of voice. It was new to me. Of course, in that stupid German neighborhood, they were great disciplinarians, really brutal people.
>
> *My Life and Times*

How, in such a pass, does one arrive at a first love? He spends his adolescence "madly, passionately in love with my high school sweetheart." She is blonde with blue eyes. "I never went steady with her," he states at eighty. In his novels she reappears over and over. She is never aware of his existence. "That lasted three years! And it was a tremendous thing. Every evening after dinner I walked to her home and back again. It took almost an hour to reach her home, and all I did was walk past her house to see if by chance she might be at the window." At nineteen he meets an "attractive widow" old enough to be his mother and has his first affair, even lives*

---

* *My Life and Times by Henry Miller* (Chicago: Playboy Press, 1975), p. 185.

with the widow and her child for a period. He is in and out of City College—quits after the first two months of his Freshman year, goes in rigorously, Germanically, at keeping himself in top physical condition over the next seven years and one can believe it when his sexual exploits begin, for later he will stay up all night drinking, have three or four orgasms with one woman, come home and make love to his wife, pick up an hour of sleep and be off to work at his job—he is employment manager of messengers at Western Union. It is then 1920, and he is close to thirty. This Side of Paradise *is being published. Whereas Miller has spent his twenties in traveling through the west, working as a ranch hand, working in his father's shop, getting married in 1917, having a daughter, going through a dozen jobs, then another dozen, dreaming of writing, never daring to, carousing instead with friends and developing a powerful ability to cheat on his first wife.*

> The longer we lived together the worse it got. We had started out on the wrong foot and nothing could ever right the situation. Every friend or acquaintance my wife had was destined to betray her. Her pride and suspiciousness egged me on. Even when I took the baby out in the perambulator she kept her eye on me. She had good reason, I must admit, to be ever on the watch. Often I would leave the house, innocent like, with the baby carriage, to keep an appointment with one of her friends. Sometimes I'd park the carriage outside an apartment house and take her friend inside, under the stairs, for a quickie. Or, if there was a gathering at the house, I would go off with one of her friends to buy food or drink, and on the way I'd stand her up against a fence and do what I could. If I hadn't finally been caught with my pants down I think I'd have driven the poor woman stark mad. It was truly abominable the way I treated her, but I was simply powerless to act otherwise. There was something about her which inspired the most contemptible conduct.
>
> *The World of Sex*

If he had died before he was thirty, he would have been remembered as a neighborhood wit, a good pianist, a bad risk on a loan, a cheerful stud, a former "street car conductor, garbage collector, librarian, insurance man, book salesman" and assistant editor in a mail-order house. He was going nowhere. He was a brilliant conversationalist, but "being born in Brooklyn of parents who didn't have anything to do with artists, I never met any. I fought to meet anyone with any culture. To me being a writer was like saying, 'I'm going to be a saint, a martyr, a god.' It was just as big, just as far away, just as remote as that." He is now almost thirty—in a few years Hemingway will write The Sun Also Rises *and* Farewell to Arms, *and Fitzgerald* The Great Gatsby, *both authors full of accomplishment before they are thirty. Miller will only succeed in getting his first responsible job as the employment manager at Western Union.*

It is nonetheless the real beginning of his literary career. And his sexual career. Never has literature and sex lived in such symbiotic relation before—it is as if every stroke of his phallus is laying a future paragraph of phrases on his brain. He is the Grand Speleologist of the Vagina—out of the sensations of those caverns will he rediscover every item in the world. He may be the only writer in existence about whom we might as well suppose that without his prodigies of sex, he might have been able to produce no prodigies of literature. And without the successful practice of his literature we can wonder if his sexual vitality would have remained so long undiminished.

For Henry Miller had not set out to navigate through the world, but through himself, Henry Miller, with his brain and his balls and his daily life at the Cosmodemonic (read Western Union) telegraph office. One sloughed one's work and followed the line of one's sexual impulse without a backward look at what might be remotely desirable for soci-

ety. One set out to feed one's cock (as Renaissance man had set out to feed his brain) and the new effort was pioneer. Never before had a future literary man given that much attention to the vagaries and outright contradictions of a stiff prick without a modicum of conscience; no one had ever dared to assume that such a life might be as happy and amusing as the next, or that the paganism of a big-city fucker could have its own balance, and such a man might be therefore equipped to explore the sexual mysteries with his phallus as a searchlight, yes, all sexual experience was valid if one looked at it clearly, and no fuck was in vain.

Some, nonetheless, came close. Once he began to write, he would work the way he fucked, and like many another self-educated author, would rush to grab at every great and obscure literary name he had read as if they were all pieces of flesh on the great body of culture, or ineluctable wrinkles in the cuneiform labyrinth of the Great Twat of Knowledge. The titles of other books ululate through his work like oscillating hairs of the labia majorum. His cock seems covered with vibrations from a thousand cunts, and depression deep as the blackest chancres of the most venereal bogs will ride at times through his philosophy. He is even ready to believe that "the whole world, known and unknown, is out of kilter, screaming in pain and madness."* That is his depression; be certain he will rise from it. He gets, after all, the livid ache of the groin, 9/10ths cramp, 1/10th sugar, the phallus über alles of the insatiable hard-on. One crazy fuck begets another—that is the message, over and over. One is connecting into the electrical system of a world which runs cock-cunt-cock-cunt like the poles in a wiring circuit for a solder-it-yourself superheterodyne. Tapped into pain and madness, he is also part of the super-sending-and-receiving apparatus of all that palpitat-

---

* *Black Spring* (New York: Grove Press, Inc., 1963), p. 167.

ing noumenal world he senses just the other side of the wall of the cunt. No philosopher, he comes near to visions and bounces off them, buggers his own ideas, an indefatigable stud of a mind which will fuck everything before it, callipygous tissue, old core apples, used Kotex, armpits, bananas floating in grease. To enter Miller's mind is to write like him.

Sometimes, his writing even has the form of a fuck. All the roar of passion, the flaming poetry, the passing crazy wit, and not an instant of intellectual precision, no products of Mind but insights instead which smack the brain like a bouncy tit which plops full of fucky happy presence over your nostrils. Of course you can lose such insights as fast as you get them, the fuck is rolling down the river, and who looks back, ah, what tingles in the nose at rocks to come. Yes, one does well to recognize that the experience which makes his literature is precisely his sexual vigor, and he is next to no author without it. With it, he will spend a considerable part of his literary life exploring the vast watershed of sex from that relatively uncharted side which goes by the name of lust. It could be said that other writers from Casanova to Frank Harris had already made the same exploration, and they did, more or less. Less! It was with none of Miller's prodigious and poetic talent. That made it epic work for any man. Over the centuries, most poets have spent their lives on the familiar side of the watershed; they wrote of love. For lust is a world with vertiginous falls. It takes over the instinct to create life and converts it to a force. Curious force. Lust has all the attributes of junk. It dominates the mind, appropriates loyalties, generalizes character, leaches character out, rides on the fuel of any emotional gas—hatred, affection, curiosity, even boredom—yet lust can alter on the instant to love. Indeed, the more intense lust becomes, the more it is out of focus—the line of the ridge between lust and love is exactly where the light is blinding, and the ground remains unknown. Henry, *a hairy prospector, red eye full of lust, wandering those ridge lines during the early years of his literary life, got to know the mosquitoes in every swamp and could call to the ozones of cosmic lust on many a cloud-covered precipice. If cunts are only boscage and fodder for that lust they are also—it is the private little knowledge of lust—an indispensable step closer to the beyond. So, old Henry the ram, admits, "perhaps a cunt, smelly though it may be, is one of the prime symbols for the connection between all things."*

He has slipped the clue across. Here is a clue to the lust that drives a man to scour his balls and freak his back until he is ready to pass out from the drubbing he has given his organs. It is a clue which all but says that somewhere in the insane passions of all men is a huge desire to drive forward into the seat of creation, and there sink your cock to the hilt, sink it into as many hilts as will hold it. Since man is alienated from the nature which brought him forth, he must, if necessary, come close to blowing his head off in order to possess it. "Perhaps a cunt, smelly though it may be, is one of the prime symbols for the connection between all things." It is the horror of lust, and yet its justification, that wild as a blind maniac it still drives toward the creation. So Miller captured something in the sexuality of men as it had never been seen before, precisely that it was man's sense of awe before woman, his dread of her position one step closer to eternity (for in that step were her powers) which made men detest women, revile them, humiliate them, defecate symbolically upon them, do everything to reduce them so that one might dare to enter them and take pleasure of them. "His shit don't smell like ice cream either," says a private of a general in a novel, and it is the cry of an enlisted man whose ego needs equality to breathe. So do men look to destroy every quality in a woman which will give her the powers of a male, for she is in their eyes already armed with the power that she brought them forth, and that is a power beyond measure—the earliest etchings of memory go back to that woman between whose legs they were conceived, nurtured, and near strangled in the hours of birth. And if women were also born of woman, that could only compound the awe, for out of that process by which they had come in, so would something of the same come out of them; they were installed in the boxes-within-boxes of the universe, and man was only a box, all detached. So it is not unnatural that men, perhaps a majority of men, go through the years of their sex with women in some contract with lust which will enable them to be as fierce as their female when she is awash in the great ocean of the fuck. As it can appear to the man, great forces beyond his measure are calling to the woman then.

That was what Miller saw, and it is what he brought back to us: that there were mysteries in trying to explain the extraordinary fascination of an act we can abuse, debase, inundate, and drool upon, yet the act repeats an interest. It draws us toward obsession. It is the mirror of how we approach God through our imperfections, Hot, full of the shittiest lust. In all of his faceless, characterless, pullulating broads, in all those cunts which undulate with the movements of eels, in all those clearly described broths of soup and grease and marrow and wine which are all he will give us of them—their cunts are always closer to us than their faces—in all the indignities of position, the humiliation of situation, and the endless presentation of women as pure artifacts of farce, their asses all up in the air, still he screams his barbaric yawp of utter adoration for the power and the glory and the grandeur of the female in the universe, and it is his genius to show us that this power is ready to survive any context or any abuse.

From **Black Spring**

The day used to start like this: "Ask so-and-so for a little something on account, *but don't insult him!*" They were ticklish bastards, all these old farts we catered to. It was enough to drive any man to drink. There we were, just opposite the Olcott, Fifth Avenue tailors even though we weren't on the Avenue. A joint corporation of father and son, with mother holding the boodle.

Mornings, eight A.M. or thereabouts, a brisk intellectual walk from Delancey Street and the Bowery to just below the Waldorf. No matter how fast I walked old man Bendix was sure to be there ahead of me, raising hell with the cutter because neither of the bosses was on the job. How was it we could never get there ahead of that old buzzard Bendix? He had nothing to do, Bendix, but run from the tailor to the shirtmaker and from the shirtmaker to the jeweler's; his rings were either too loose or too tight, his watch was either twenty-five seconds slow or thirty-three seconds fast. He raised hell with everybody, including the family doctor, because the latter couldn't keep his kidneys clear of gravel. If we made him a sack coat in August by October it was too large for him, or too small. When he could find nothing to complain about he would dress on the right side so as to have the pleasure of bawling the pants maker out because he was strangling his, H. W. Bendix's, balls. A difficult guy. Touchy, whimsical, mean, crotchety, miserly, capricious, malevolent. When I look back on it all now, see the old man sitting down to table with his boozy breath and saying *shit why don't some one smile, why do you all look so glum,* I feel sorry for him and for all merchant tailors who have to kiss rich people's asses. If it hadn't been for the Olcott bar across the way and the sots he picked up there God knows what would have become of the old man. He certainly got no sympathy at home. My mother hadn't the least idea what it meant to be kissing rich people's backsides. All she knew how to do was to groan and lament all day, and with her groaning and lamenting she brought on the boozy breath and the potato dumplings grown cold. She got us so damned jumpy with her anxiety that we would choke on our own spittle, my brother and I. My brother was a half-wit and he got on the old man's nerves even more than H. W. Bendix with his "Pastor So-and-so's going to Europe. . . . Pastor So-and-so's going to open a bowling alley," etc. "Pastor So-and-so's an ass," the old man would say, "and why aren't the dumplings hot?"

There were three Bendixes—H. W., the grumpy one, A. F., whom the old man referred to in the ledger as Albert, and R.N., who never visited the shop because his legs were cut off, a circumstance, however, which did not prevent him from wearing out his trousers in due season. R. N. I never saw in the flesh. He was an item in the ledger which Bunchek the cutter spoke of glowingly because there was always a little schnapps about when it came time to try on the new trousers. The three brothers were eternal enemies; they never referred to one another in our presence. If Albert, who was a little cracked and had a penchant for dotted vests, happened to see a cutaway hanging on the rack with the words H. W. Bendix written in green ink on the try-on notice, he would give a feeble little grunt and say—"feels like spring today, eh?" There was not supposed to be a man by the name of H. W.

Bendix in existence, though it was obvious to all and sundry that we were not making clothes for ghosts.

Of the three brothers I liked Albert the best. He had arrived at that ripe age when the bones become as brittle as glass. His spine had the natural curvature of old age, as though he were preparing to fold up and return to the womb. You could always tell when Albert was arriving because of the commotion in the elevator—a great cussing and whining followed by a handsome tip which accompanied the process of bringing the floor of the elevator to a dead level with the floor of our tailor shop. If it could not be brought within a quarter of an inch exactitude there was no tip and Albert with his brittle bones and his bent spine would have a devil of a time choosing the right buttons to go with his dotted vest, his *latest* dotted vest. (When Albert died I inherited all his vests —they lasted me right through the war.) If it happened, as was sometimes the case, that the old man was across the street taking a little nip when Albert arrived, then somehow the whole day became disorganized. I remember periods when Albert grew so vexed with the old man that sometimes we did not see him for three days; meanwhile the vest buttons were lying around on little cards and there was talk of nothing but vest buttons, vest buttons, as if the vest itself didn't matter, only the buttons. Later, when Albert had grown accustomed to the old man's careless ways—they had been growing accustomed to each other for twenty-seven years—he would give us a ring to notify us that he was on the way. And just before hanging up he would add: "I suppose it's all right my coming in at eleven o'clock . . . it won't inconvenience you?" The purport of this little query was twofold. It meant—"I suppose you'll have the decency to be on hand when I arrive and not make me fiddle around for a half-hour while you swill it down with your cronies across the street." *And*, it also meant—

"At eleven o'clock I suppose there is little danger of bumping into a certain individual bearing the initials H. W.?" In the twenty-seven years during which we made perhaps 1,578 garments for the three Bendix brothers it so happened that they never met; not in our presence at least. When Albert died R. N. and H. W. both had mourning bands put on their sleeves, on all the left sleeves of their sack coats and overcoats—that is, those which were not black coats—but nothing was said of the deceased, nor even *who* he was. R. N., of course, had a good excuse for not going to the funeral—his legs were gone. H. W. was too mean and too proud to even bother offering an excuse.

About ten o'clock was the time the old man usually chose to go down for his first nip. I used to stand at the window facing the hotel and watch George Sandusky hoisting the big trunks on to the taxis. When there were no trunks to be hoisted George used to stand there with his hands clasped behind his back and bow and scrape to the clients as they swung in and out of the revolving doors. George Sandusky had been scraping and bowing and hoisting and opening doors for about twelve years when I first came to the tailor shop and took up my post at the front window. He was a charming, soft-spoken man with beautiful white hair, and strong as an ox. He had raised this ass-kissing business to an art. I was amazed one day when he came up the elevator and ordered a suit from us. In his off hours he was a gentleman, George Sandusky. He had quiet tastes—always a blue serge or an Oxford gray. A man who knew how to conduct himself at a funeral or a wedding.

After we got to know each other he gave me to understand that he had found Jesus. With the smooth tongue he had, and the brawn, and the active help of said Jesus he had managed to lay aside a nest egg, a little something to ward off the horrors of old age. He was the only man I ever met in that period who had not taken out life insurance. He maintained that God would look after those who were left behind just as He had looked after him, George Sandusky. He had no fear of the world collapsing upon his decease. God had taken care of everybody and everything up to date—no reason to suppose He would fall down on the job after George Sandusky's death. When one day George retired it was difficult to find a man to replace him. There was no one oily or unctuous enough to fill the bill. No one who could bow or scrape like George. The old man always had a great affection for George. He used to try to persuade him to take a drink now and then, but George always refused with that habitual and stubborn politeness which had endeared him to the Olcott guests.

The old man often had moods when he would ask anybody to take a drink with him, even such as George Sandusky. Usually late in the afternoon on a day when things were going wrong, when nothing but bills were coming in. Sometimes a week would pass without a customer showing up, or if one did show up it was only to complain, to ask for an alteration, to bawl the piss out of the coat maker, or to demand a reduction in the price. Things like this would make the old man so blue that all he could do was to put on his hat and go for a drink. Instead of going across the street as usual he would wander off base a bit, duck into the Breslin or the Broztell, sometimes getting as far off the path as the Ansonia where his idol, Julian Legree, kept a suite of rooms.

Julian, who was then a matinée idol, wore nothing but gray suits, every shade of gray imaginable, but only grays. He had that depressingly cheerful demeanor of the beefy-faced English actor who lounges about here and there swapping stories with woolen salesmen, liquor dealers, and others of no account. His accent alone was enough to make men swarm about him; it was English in the traditional stage sense, warm, soapy, glutinous English which gives to even the most insignificant thought an appearance of importance. Julian never said anything that was worth recording but that voice of his worked magic on his admirers. Now and then, when he and the old man were doing the rounds, they would pick up a derelict such as Corse Payton who belonged across the river in the ten-twenty-thirties. Corse Payton was the idol of Brooklyn! Corse Payton was to art what Pat McCarren was to politics.

What the old man had to say during these discussions was always a source of mystery to me. The old man had never read a book in his life, nor had he ever been to a play since the days when the Bowery gave way to Broadway. I can see him standing there at the free lunch counter—Julian was very fond of the caviar and the sturgeon that was served at the Olcott—sponging it up like a thirsty dog. The two matinée idols discussing Shakespeare—whether *Hamlet* or *Lear* was the greatest play ever written. Or else arguing the merits of Bob Ingersoll.

Behind the bar at that time were three doughty Irishmen, three low-down micks such as made the bars of that day the congenial haunts they were. They were so highly thought of, these three, that it was considered a privilege to have such as Patsy O'Dowd, for example, call you a goddamned degenerate cocksucking son of a bitch who hadn't sense enough to button up his fly. And if, in return for the compliment, you asked him if he wouldn't have a little something himself, said Patsy O'Dowd would coldly and sneeringly reply that only such as yourself were fit to pour such rotgut down your throat, and so saying he would scornfully lift your glass by the stem and wipe the mahogany because that was part of his job and he was paid to do it but be damned to you if you thought you could entice such as him to poison his intestines with the vile stuff. The more vicious his insults the more he was esteemed; financiers who were accustomed to having their asses wiped with silk handkerchiefs would drive all the way uptown, after the ticker closed down, in order to have this foulmouthed bastard of an Irish mick call them goddamned degenerate cocksucking sons of bitches. It was the end of a perfect day for them.

The boss of this jaunty emporium was a portly little man with aristocratic shanks and the head of a lion. He always marched with his stomach thrown forward, a little wine cask hidden under his vest. He usually gave a stiff, supercilious nod to the sots at the bar, unless they happened to be guests of the hotel, in which case he would pause a moment, extend three fat little fingers with blue veins and then, with a swirl of his mustache and a gingerly, creaky pirouette, he would whisk away. He was the only enemy the old man had. The old man simply couldn't stomach him. He had a feeling that Tom Moffatt looked down upon him. And so when Tom Moffatt came round to order his clothes the old man would tack on ten or fifteen per cent to cover the rents in his pride. But Tom Moffatt was a genuine aristocrat: he never questioned the price and he never paid his bills. If we dunned him he would get his accountant to find a discrepancy in our statements. And when it came time to order another pair of flannel trousers, or a cutaway, or a dinner jacket, he would sail in with his usual portly dignity, his stomach well forward, his mustache waxed, his shoes brightly polished and squeaky as always, and with an air of weary indifference, of aloof disdain, he would greet the old man as follows: "Well, have you straightened out that error yet?" Upon which the old man would fly into a rage and palm off a remnant or a piece of American goods on his enemy Tom Moffatt. A long correspondence ensued over the "little error" in our statements. The old man was beside himself. He hired an expert accountant who drew up statements three feet long—but to no avail. Finally the old man hit upon an idea.

Toward noon one day, after he had had his usual portion, after he had stood treat to all the woolen salesmen and the trimmings salesmen who were gathered at the bar, he quietly picked up the bar stubs and taking a little silver pencil which was attached to his watch chain he signed his name to the checks and sliding them across to Patsy O'Dowd he said: "Tell Moffatt to charge them up to my account." Then he quietly moved off and, inviting a few of his select cronies, he took a table in the dining room and commanded a spread. And when Adrian the frog presented the bill he calmly said: "Give me a pencil. There . . . them's my demi-quivers. Charge it up to my account." Since it was more pleasant to eat in the company of others he would always invite his cronies to lunch with him, saying to all and sundry—"if that bastard Moffatt won't pay for his clothes then we'll eat them." And so saying he would commandeer a juicy squab, or a lobster à la Newburg, and wash it down with a fine Moselle or any other vintage that Adrian the frog might happen to recommend.

To all this Moffatt, surprisingly enough, pretended to pay no heed. He continued to order his usual allotment of clothes for winter, spring, fall and summer, and he also continued to squabble about the bill which had become easier to do now since it was complicated with bar checks, telephone calls, squabs, lobsters, champagne, fresh strawberries, Benedictines, etc., etc. In fact, the old man was eating into that bill so fast that spindleshanks Moffatt couldn't wear his clothes out quickly enough. If he came in to order a pair of flannel trousers the old man had already eaten it the next day.

Finally Moffatt evinced an earnest desire to have the account straightened out. The correspondence ceased. Patting me on the back one day as I happened to be standing in the lobby he put on his most cordial manner and invited me upstairs to his private office. He said he had always regarded me as a very sensible young man and that we could probably straighten the matter out between ourselves, without bothering the old man. I looked over the accounts and I saw that the old man had eaten way into the minus side. I had probably eaten up a few raglans and shooting jackets myself. There was only one thing to do if we were to keep Tom Moffatt's despised patronage and that was to find an error in the account. I took a bundle of bills under my arm and promised the old geezer that I would look into the matter thoroughly.

The old man was delighted when he saw how things stood. We kept looking into the matter for years. Whenever Tom Moffatt came round to order a suit the old man would greet him cheerily and say: "Have you straightened out that little error yet? Now here's a fine Barathea weave that I laid aside for you. . . ." And Moffatt would frown and grimace and strut back and forth like a turkcy cock, his comb bristling, his thin little legs blue with malice. A half hour later the old man would be standing at the bar swilling it down. "Just sold Moffatt another dinner jacket," he would say. "By the way, Julian, what would you like to order for lunch today?"

It was toward noon, as I say, that the old man usually went down for an appetizer; lunch lasted anywhere from noon till four or five in the afternoon. It was marvelous the companionship the old man enjoyed in those days. After lunch the troupe would stagger out of the elevator, spitting and guffawing, their cheeks aflame, and lodge themselves in the big leather chairs beside the cuspidors. There was Ferd Pattee who sold silk linings and trimmings such as skeins of thread, buttons, chest padding, canvas, etc. A great hulk of a man, like a liner that's been battered by a typhoon, and always walking about in a somnambulistic state; so tired he was that he could scarcely move his lips, yet that slight movement of the lips kept everybody about him in stitches. Always muttering to himself—about cheeses particularly. He was passionate about cheese, about schmierkäse and limburger especially—the moldier the better. In between the cheeses he told stories about Heine and Schubert, or he would ask for a match just as he was about to break wind and hold it under his seat so that we could tell him the color of the flame. He never said good-by or see you tomorrow; he commenced talking where he had left off the day before, as though there had been no interruption of time. No matter whether it was nine in the morning or six in the evening he walked with the same exasperating slow shambling gait, muttering in his vici-kids, his head down, his linings and trimmings under his arm, his breath foul, his nose purple and translucent. Into the thickest traffic he would walk with head down, schmierkäse in one pocket and limburger in the other. Stepping out of the elevator he would say in that weary monotonous voice of his that he had some new linings and the cheese was fine last night were you thinking of returning the book he had loaned you and better pay up soon if you want more goods like to see some dirty pictures please scratch my back there a little higher that's it excuse me I'm going to fart now have you the time I can't waste all day here better tell the old man to put on his hat it's time to go for a drink. Still mumbling and grumbling he turns on his big scows and presses the elevator button while the old man with a straw hat on the back of his head is making a slide for the home plate from the back of the store, his face lit up with love and gratitude and saying: "Well, Ferd, how are you this morning? It's good to see you." And Ferd's big heavy mask of a face relaxes for a moment into a broad amiable grin. Just a second he holds it and then, lifting his voice he bellows at the top of his lungs—so that even Tom Moffatt across the way can hear it—"BETTER PAY UP SOON

WHAT THE HELL DO YOU THINK I'M SELLING THESE THINGS FOR?"

And as soon as the elevator has started down out comes little Rubin from the busheling room and with a wild look in his eye he says to me: "Would you like me to sing for you?" He knows damned well that I would. So, going back to the bench, he picks up the coat that he's stitching and with a wild Cossack shout he lets loose.

If you were to pass him in the street, little Rubin, you would say "dirty little kike," and perhaps he was a dirty little kike but he knew how to sing and when you were broke he knew how to put his hand in his pocket and when you were sad he was sadder still and if you tried to step on him he spat on your shoe and if you were repentant he wiped it off and he brushed you down and put a crease in your trousers like Jesus H. Christ himself couldn't do.

They were all midgets in the busheling room—Rubin, Rapp, and Chaimowitz. At noon they brought out big round loaves of Jewish bread which they smeared with sweet butter and slivers of lox. While the old man was ordering squabs and Rhine wine Bunchek the cutter and the three little bushelmen sat on the big bench among the goose irons and the legs and sleeves and talked earnestly and solemnly about things like the rent or the ulcers that Mrs. Chaimowitz had in her womb. Bunchek was an ardent member of the Zionist party. He believed that the Jews had a happy future ahead of them. But despite it all he could never properly pronounce a word like "screw." He always said: "He *scruled* her." Besides his passion for Zionism Bunchek had another obsession and that was to make a coat one day that would hug the neck. Nearly all the customers were round-shouldered and pot-bellied, especially the old bastards who had nothing to do all day but run from the shirtmaker to the tailor and from the tailor to the jeweler's and from the jeweler's to the dentist and from the dentist to the druggist. There were so many alterations to be made that by the time the clothes were ready to be worn the season had passed and they had to be put away until next year, and by next year the old bastards had either gained twenty pounds or lost twenty pounds and what with sugar in their urine and water in the blood it was hell to please them even when the clothes did fit.

Then there was Paul Dexter, a $10,000-a-year man but always out of work. Once he almost had a job, but it was $9,000 a year and his pride wouldn't permit him to accept it. And since it was important to be well groomed, in the pursuit of this mythical job, Paul felt it incumbent upon him to patronize a good tailor such as the old man. Once he landed the job everything would be settled in full. There was never any question about that in Paul's mind. He was thoroughly honest. But he was a dreamer. He came from Indiana. And like all dreamers from Indiana he had such a lovable disposition, such a smooth, mellow, honeyed way that if he had committed incest the world would have forgiven him. When he had on the right tie, when he had chosen the proper cane and gloves, when the lapels were softly rolled and the shoes didn't squeak, when he had a quart of rye under his belt and the weather wasn't too damp or dismal then there flowed from his personality such a warm current of love and understanding that even the trimmings salesmen, hardened as they were to soft language, melted in their boots. Paul, when all circumstances were favorably conjoined, could walk up to a man, any man on God's green earth and, taking him by the lapel of his coat, drown him in love. Never did I see a man with such powers of persuasion, such magnetism. When the flood began to rise in him he was invincible.

Paul used to say: "Start with Marcus Aurelius, or Epictetus, and the rest will follow." He didn't recommend studying Chinese or learning Provençal: he began with the fall of the Roman Empire. It was my great ambition in those days to win Paul's approbation, but Paul was difficult to please. He frowned when I showed him *Thus Spake Zarathustra*. He frowned when he saw me sitting on the bench with the midgets trying to expound the meaning of *Creative Evolution*. Above all, he loathed the Jews. When Bunchek the cutter appeared, with a piece of chalk and a tape measure slung around his neck, Paul became excessively polite and condescending. He knew that Bunchek despised him, but because Bunchek was the old man's right hand man he rubbed him down with oil, he larded him with compliments. So that eventually even Bunchek had to admit that there was something to Paul, some strange mark of personality which, despite his shortcomings, endeared him to every one.

Outwardly Paul was all cheerfulness. But at bottom he was morose. Every now and then Cora, his wife, would sail in with eyes brimming with tears and implore the old man to take Paul in hand. They used to stand at the round table near the window conversing in a low voice. She was a beautiful woman, his wife, tall, statuesque, with a deep contralto voice that seemed to quiver with anguish whenever she mentioned Paul''s name. I could see the old man putting his hand on her shoulder, soothing her, and promising her all sorts of things no doubt. She liked the old man, I could see that. She used to stand very close to him and look into his eyes in a way that was irresistible. Sometimes the old man would put his hat on and the two of them would go down the elevator together, arm in arm, as if they were going to a funeral. Off looking for Paul again. Nobody knew where to find him when he had a drinking fever on. For days on end he would disappear from sight. And then one day he would turn up, crestfallen, repentant, humiliated, and beg everybody's forgiveness. At the same time he would hand in his suit to be dry cleaned, to have the vomit stains removed, and a bit of expert repairing done at the knees.

It was after a bout that Paul talked most eloquently. He used to sit back in one of the deep leather chairs, the gloves in one hand, the cane between his legs, and discourse about Marcus Aurelius. He talked even better when he came back from the hospital, after he had had the fistula repaired. The way he lowered himself into the big leather chair made me think then that he came expressly to the tailor shop because nowhere else could he find such a comfortable seat. It was a painful operation either to sit down or to get up. But once accomplished Paul seemed to be in bliss and the words rolled off his tongue like liquid velvet. The old man could listen to Paul all day long. He used to say that Paul had the gift of gab, but that was only his inarticulate way of saying that Paul was the most lovable creature on God's earth and that he had a fire in his bowels. And when Paul was too conscience-stricken to order another suit the old man would coax him into it, saying to Paul all the while, "Nothing's too good for you, Paul . . . nothing!"

Paul must have recognized something of a kindred nature in the old man too. Never have I seen two men look at each other with such a warm glow of admiration. Sometimes they would stand there looking into each other's eyes adoringly until the tears came. In fact, neither of them was ashamed of showing his tears, something which seems to have gone out of the world now. I can see Paul's homely freckled face and his rather thick, blubbery lips twitching as the old man told him for the thousandth time what a great guy he was. Paul never spoke to the old man about things he wouldn't understand. But into the simple, everyday things which he discoursed about so earnestly he put such a wealth of tenderness that the old man's soul seemed to leave his body and when Paul was gone he was like a man bereaved. He would go then into the little cubbyhole of an office and he would sit there quietly all by himself staring ecstatically at the row of pigeon coops which were filled with letters unanswered and bills unpaid. It used to affect me so, to see him in one of these moods, that I would sneak quietly down the stairs and start to walk home, down the Avenue to the Bowery and along the Bowery to the Brooklyn Bridge, and then over the bridge past the string of cheap flops that extended from City Hall to Fulton Ferry. And if it were a summer's evening, and the entranceways crowded with loungers, I would look among these wasted figures searchingly, wondering how many Pauls there were among them and what it is about life that makes these obvious failures so endearing to men. The others, the successful ones, I had seen with their pants off; I had seen their crooked spines, their brittle bones, their varicose veins, their tumors, their sunken chests, their big breadbaskets which had grown shapeless with years of swilling it. Yes, all the silk-lined duffers I knew well—we had the best families in America on our roster. And what a pus and filth when they opened their dirty traps! It seemed as though when they had undressed before their tailor they felt compelled to unload the garbage which had accumulated in the plugged-up sinks which they had made of their minds. All the beautiful diseases of boredom and riches. Talked about themselves *ad nauseam.* Always "I," "I." I and my kidneys. I and my gout. I and my liverworst. When I think of Paul's dreadful hemorrhoids, of the marvelous fistula they repaired, of all the love and learning that issued from his grievous wounds, then I think that Paul was not of this age at all but sib brother to Moses Maimonides, he who under the Moors gave us those astounding treatises on "hemorrhoids, warts, carbuncles," etc.

In the case of all these men whom the old man so cherished death came quickly and unexpectedly. In Paul's case it happened while he was at the seashore. He was drowned in a foot of water. Heart failure, they said. And so, one fine day Cora came up the elevator, clad in her beautiful mourning garb, and wept all over the place. Never had she looked more beautiful to me, more svelte, more statuesque. Her ass particularly—I remember how caressingly the velvet clung to her figure. Again they stood near the round table at the front window, and this time she wept copiously. And again the old man put on his hat and down the elevator they went, arm in arm.

A short time later the old man, moved by some strange whim, urged me to call on Paul's wife and offer my condolences. When I rang the bell at her apartment I was trembling. I almost expected her to come out stark naked, with perhaps a mourning band around her breasts. I was infatuated with her beauty, with her years, with that somnolent, plantlike quality she had brought from Indiana and the perfume which she bathed in. She greeted me in a low-cut mourning gown, a beautiful clinging gown of black velvet. It was the first time I had ever had a tête-à-tête with a woman bereft, a woman whose breasts seemed to sob out loud. I didn't know what to say to her, especially about Paul. I stammered and blushed, and when she asked me to sit beside her on the couch I almost fell over her in my embarrassment.

Sitting there on the low sofa, the place flooded with soft lights, her big heaving loins rubbing against me, the Malaga pounding my temples and all this crazy talk about Paul and how good he was, I finally bent over and without saying a word I raised her dress and slipped it into her. And as I got it into her and began to work it around she took to moaning like, a sort of delirious, sorrowful guilt punctuated with gasps and little shrieks of joy and anguish, saying over and over again—"I never thought you would do this . . . I never thought you would do this!" And when it was all over she ripped off the velvet dress, the beautiful low-cut mourning gown, and she put my head down on her and she told me to kiss it and with her two strong arms she squeezed me almost in half and moaned and sobbed. And then she got up and she walked around the room naked for a while. And then finally she got down on her knees beside the sofa where I was stretched out and she said in a low tearful voice—"You promise me you'll love me always, won't you? You promise me?" And I said Yes with one hand working around in her crotch. Yes I said and I thought to myself what a sap you've been to wait so long. She was so wet and juicy down there, and so childlike, so trustful, why anybody could have come along and had what's what. She was a pushover.

Always merry and bright! Regularly, every season, there were a few deaths. Sometimes it was a good egg like Paul, or Julian Legree, sometimes a bartender who had picked his nose with a rusty nail—hail and hearty one day, dead the next—but regularly, like the movement of the seasons themselves, the old buzzards dropped off, one by one. *Alors*, nothing to do but draw a red line slantwise down the right-hand side of the ledger and mark "DEAD." Each death brought a little business—a new black suit or else mourning bands on the left sleeve of every coat. Those who ordered mourning bands were cheapskates, according to the old man. And so they were.

As the old 'uns died off they were replaced by young blood. *Young blood!* That was the war cry all along the Avenue, wherever there were silk-lined suits for sale. A fine bloody crew they were, the young bloods. Gamblers, racetrack touts, stockbrokers, ham actors, prize fighters, etc. Rich one day, poor the next. No honor, no loyalty, no sense of responsibility. A fine bunch of gangrened syphilitics they were, most of 'em.

Came back from Paris or Monte Carlo with dirty postcards and a string of big blue rocks in their groin. Some of them with balls as big as a lamb's fry.

One of them was the Baron Carola von Eschenbach. He had earned a little money in Hollywood posing as the Crown Prince. It was the period when it was considered riotously funny to see the Crown Prince plastered with rotten eggs. It must be said for the Baron that he was a good double for the Crown Prince. A death's head with arrogant nose, a waspish stride, a corseted waist, lean and ravished as Martin Luther, dour, glum, fanatical, with that brassy, fatuous glare of the Junker class. Before going to Hollywood he was just a nobody, the son of a German brewer in Frankfort. He wasn't even a baron. But afterwards, when he had been knocked about like a medicine ball, when his front teeth had been pushed down his throat and the neck of a broken bottle had traced a deep scar down his left cheek, afterwards when he had been taught to flaunt a red necktie, twirl a cane, clip his mustache short, like Chaplin, then he became somebody. Then he stuck a monocle in his eye and named himself Baron Carola von Eschenbach. And all might have gone beautifully for him had he not fallen for a redhaired walk-on who was rotting away with syphilis. That finished him.

Up the elevator he came one day in a cutaway and spats, a bright red rose in his buttonhole and the monocle stuck in his eye. Blithe and dapper he looked, and the card he took out of his wallet was handsomely engraved. It bore a coat of arms which had been in the family, so he said, for nine hundred years. "The family skeleton," he called it. The old man was highly pleased to have a baron among his clients, especially if he paid cash, as this one promised to do. And then too it was exhilarating to see the baron come sailing in with a pair of soubrettes on his arm—each time a different pair. Even more exhilarating when he invited them into the dressing room and asked them to help him off with his trousers. It was a European custom, he explained.

Gradually he got acquainted with all the old cronies who hung out in the front of the shop. He showed them how the Crown Prince walked, how he sat down, how he smiled. One day he brought a flute with him and he played the Lorelei on it. Another day he came in with a finger of his pigskin glove sticking out of his fly. Each day he had a new trick up his sleeve. He was gay, witty, amusing. He knew a thousand jokes, some that had never been told before. He was a riot.

And then one day he took me aside and asked me if I could lend him a dime—for carfare. He said he couldn't pay for the clothes he had ordered but he expected a job soon in a little movie house on Ninth Avenue, playing the piano. And then, before I knew it, he began to weep. We were standing in the dressing room and the curtains were drawn, fortunately. I had to lend him a handkerchief to wipe his eyes. He said he was tired of playing the clown, that he dropped in to our place every day because it was warm there and because we had comfortable seats. He asked me if I couldn't take him to lunch—he had had nothing but coffee and buns for the last three days.

I took him to a little German restaurant on Third Avenue, a bakery and restaurant combined. The atmosphere of the place broke him down completely. He could talk of nothing but the old days, the old days, the days before the war. He had intended to be a painter, and then the war came. I listened attentively and when he got through I proposed that he come to my home for dinner that evening—perhaps I could put him up with us. He was overwhelmed with gratitude. Sure, he would come—at seven o'clock *punkt*. Fine!

At the dinner table my wife was amused by his stories. I hadn't said anything about his being broke. Just that he was a baron—the Baron von Eschenbach, a friend of Charlie

Chaplin's. My wife—one of my first ones—was highly flattered to sit at the same table with a baron. And puritanical bastard that she was, she never so much as blushed when he told a few of his risqué stories. She thought they were delightful—*so European*. Finally, however, it came time to spill the beans. I tried to break the news gently, but how can you be gentle about a subject like syphilis? I didn't call it syphilis at first—I said "venereal disease." *Maladie intime, quoi!* But just that little word "venereal" sent a shudder through my wife. She looked at the cup he was holding to his lips and then she looked at me imploringly, as though to say—"how could you ask a man like that to sit at the same table with us?" I saw that it was necessary to bring the matter to a head at once. "The baron here is going to stay with us for a while," I said quietly. "He's broke and he needs a place to flop." My word, I never saw a woman's expression change so quickly. "*You!*" she said, "*you* ask *me* to do that? And what about the baby? You want us all to have syphilis, is that it? It's not enough that *he* has it—you want the baby to have it too!"

The baron of course was frightfully embarrassed by this outburst. He wanted to leave at once. But I told him to keep his shirt on. I was used to these scenes. Anyway, he got so wrought up that he began to choke over his coffee. I thumped him on the back until he was blue in the face. The rose fell out of his buttonhole on to the plate. It looked strange there, as though he had coughed it up out of his own blood. It made me feel so goddamned ashamed of my wife that I could have strangled her on the spot. He was still choking and sputtering as I led him to the bathroom. I told him to wash his face in cold water. My wife followed us in and watched in murderous silence as he performed his ablutions. When he had wiped his face she snatched the towel from his hands and, flinging the bathroom window open, flung it out. That made me furious. I told her to get the hell out of the bathroom and mind her own business. But the baron stepped between us and flung himself at my wife supplicatingly. "You'll see, my good woman, you, Henry, you won't have to worry about a thing. I'll bring all my syringes and ointments and I'll put them in a little valise—there, under the sink. You musn't turn me away, I have nowhere to go. I'm a desperate man. I'm alone in the world. You were so good to me before—why must you be cruel now? Is it my fault that I have the syph? Anybody can get the syph. It's human. You'll see, I'll pay you back a thousand times. I'll do anything for you. I'll make the beds, I'll wash the dishes. . . . I'll cook for you. . . ." He went on and on like that, never stopping to take a breath for fear that she would say No. And after he had gotten all through with his promises, after he had begged her forgiveness a hundred times, after he had knelt down and tried to kiss her hand which she drew away abruptly, he sat down on the toilet seat, in his cutaway and spats, and he began to sob, to sob like a child. It was ghastly, the sterile, white-enameled bathroom and the splintering light as if a thousand mirrors had been shattered under a magnifying glass, and then this wreck of a baron, in his cutaway and spats, his spine filled with mercury, his sobs coming like the short puffs of a locomotive getting under way. I didn't know what the hell to do. A man sitting on the toilet like that and sobbing—it got under my skin. Later I became inured to it. I got hard-boiled. I feel quite certain now that had it not been for the two hundred and fifty bed patients whom he was obliged to visit twice a day at the hospital in Lyons, Rabelais would never have been so boisterously gay. I'm sure of it.

Anyhow, apropos the sobs. . . . A little later, when another kid was on the way and no means of getting rid of it, though still hoping, still hoping that something would happen, a miracle perhaps, and her stomach blown up like a ripe watermelon, about the sixth or seventh month, as I say, she used to succumb to fits of melancholy and, lying on the bed with that watermelon staring her in the eye, she would commence to sob fit to break your heart. Maybe I'd be in the other room, stretched out on the couch, with a big, fat book in my hands, and those sobs of hers would make me think of the Baron Carola von Eschenbach, of his gray spats and the cutaway with braided lapels, and the deep red rose in his buttonhole. Her sobs were like music to my ears. Sobbing away for a little sympathy she was, and not a drop of sympathy in the house. It was pathetic. The more hysterical she grew the more deaf I became. It was like listening to the boom and sizzle of surf along the beach on a summer's night: the buzz of a mosquito can drown out the ocean's roar. Anyway, after she had worked herself up to a state of collapse, when the neighbors couldn't stand it any longer and there were knocks on the door, then her aged mother would come crawling out of the bedroom, with tears in her eyes would beg me to go in there and quiet her a bit. "Oh, leave her be," I'd say, "she'll get over it." Whereupon, ceasing her sobs for a moment the wife would spring out of bed, wild, blind with rage, her hair all down and tangled up, her eyes swollen and bleary, and still hiccoughing and sobbing she would commence to pound me with her fists, to lambast me until I became hysterical with laughter. And when she saw me rocking to and fro like a crazy man, when her arms were tired and her fists sore, she would yell like a drunken whore—"Fiend! Demon!"—and then slink off like a weary dog. Afterwards, when I had quieted her down a bit, when I realized that she really needed a kind word or two, I would tumble her on to the bed again and throw a good fuck into her. Blast me if she wasn't the finest piece of tail imaginable after those scenes of grief and anguish! I never heard a woman moan and gibber like she could. "*Do anything* to me!" she used to say. "Do what you want!" I could stand her on her head and blow into it, I could back-scuttle her, I could drag her past the parson's house, as they say, any goddamn thing at all—she was simply delirious with joy. Uterine hysteria, that's what it was! *And I hope God take me*, as the good master used to say, *if I am lying in a single word I say.*

(God, mentioned above, being defined by St. Augustine, as follows: "An infinite sphere, the center of which is everywhere, the circumference nowhere.")

However, *always merry and bright!* If it was before the war and the thermometer down to zero or below, if it happened to be Thanksgiving Day, or New Year's or a birthday, or just any old excuse to get together, then off we'd trot, the whole family, to join the other freaks who made up the living family tree. It always seemed astounding to me how jolly they were in our family despite the calamities that were always threatening. Jolly in spite of everything. There was cancer, dropsy, cirrhosis of the liver, insanity, thievery, mendacity, buggery, incest, paralysis, tapeworms, abortions, triplets, idiots, drunkards, ne'er-do-wells, fanatics, sailors, tailors, watchmakers, scarlet fever, whooping cough, meningitis, running ears, chorea, stutterers, jailbirds, dreamers, storytellers, bartenders—and finally there was Uncle George and Tante Melia. The morgue and the insane asylum. A merry crew and the table loaded with good things—with red cabbage and green spinach, with roast pork and turkey and sauerkraut, with kartoffelklösze and sour black gravy, with radishes and celery, with stuffed goose and peas and carrots, with beautiful white cauliflower, with apple sauce and figs from Smyrna, with bananas big as a blackjack, with cinnamon cake and Streussel Küchen, with chocolate layer cake and nuts, all kinds of nuts, walnuts, butternuts, almonds, pecans, hickory nuts, with lager beer and bottled beer, with white wines and red, with champagne, kümmel, malaga, port, with schnapps, with fiery cheeses, with dull, innocent store cheese, with flat Holland cheeses, with limburger and schmierkäse, with homemade wines, elderberry wine, with cider, hard and sweet, with rice pudding and tapioca, with roast chestnuts, mandarins, olives, pickles, with red caviar and black, with smoked sturgeon, with lemon meringue pie, with lady fingers and chocolate eclairs, with macaroons and cream puffs, with black cigars and long thin stogies, with Bull Durham and Long Tom and meerschaums, with corncobs and toothpicks, wooden toothpicks which gave you gum boils the day after, and napkins a yard wide with your initials stitched in the corner, and a blazing coal fire and the windows steaming, everything in the world before your eyes except a finger bowl.

From **Tropic of Capricorn**

Confusion is a word we have invented for an order which is not understood. I like to dwell on this period when things were taking shape because the order, if it were understood, must have been dazzling. In the first place there was Hymie, Hymie the bullfrog, and there were also his wife's ovaries which had been rotting away for a considerable time. Hymie was completely wrapped up in his wife's rotting ovaries. It was the daily topic of conversation; it took precedence now over the cathartic pills and the coated tongue. Hymie dealt in "sexual proverbs," as he called them. Everything he said began from or led up to the ovaries. Despite everything he was still nicking it off with the wife—prolonged snakelike copulations in which he would smoke a cigarette or two before uncunting. He would endeavor to explain to me how the pus from the rotting ovaries put her in heat. She had always been a good fuck, but now she was better than ever. Once the ovaries were ripped out there'd be no telling how she'd take it. She seemed to realize that too. Ergo, fuck away! Every night, after the dishes were cleared away, they'd strip down in their little birdlike apartment and lie together like a couple of snakes. He tried to describe it to me on a number of occasions—the way she fucked. It was like an oyster inside, an oyster with soft teeth that nibbled away at him. Sometimes it felt as though he were right inside her womb, so soft and fluffy it was, and those soft teeth biting away at his pecker and making him delirious. They used to lie scissors-fashion and look up at the ceiling. To keep from coming he would think about the office, about the little worries which plagued him and kept his bowels tied up in a knot. In between orgasms he would let his mind dwell on someone else, so that when she'd start working on him again he might imagine he was having a brand new fuck with a brand new cunt. He used to arrange it so that he could look out the window while it was going on. He was getting so adept at it that he could undress a woman on the boulevard there under his window and transport her to the bed; not only that, but he could actually make her change places with his wife, all without un-cunting. Sometimes he'd fuck away like that for a couple of hours and never even bother to shoot off. Why waste it! he would say.

Steve Romero, on the other hand, had a hell of a time holding it in. Steve was built like a bull and he scattered his seed freely. We used to compare notes sometimes sitting in the chop suey joint around the corner from the office. It was a strange atmosphere. Maybe it was because there was no wine. Maybe it was the funny little black mushrooms they served us. Anyway it wasn't difficult to get started on the subject. By the time Steve met us he would already have had his workout, a shower and a rubdown. He was clean inside and out. Almost a perfect specimen of a man. Not very bright, to be sure, but a good egg, a companion. Hymie, on the other hand, was like a toad. He seemed to come to the table direct from the swamps where he had passed a mucky day. Filth rolled off his lips like honey. In fact, you couldn't call it filth, in his case, because there wasn't any other ingredient with which you might compare it. It was all one fluid, a slimy, sticky substance made entirely of sex. When he looked at his food he saw it as potential sperm; if the weather were warm he would say it was good for the balls; if he took a trolley ride he knew in advance that the rhythmic movement of the trolley would stimulate his appetite, would give him a slow, "personal" hard on, as he put it. Why "personal" I never found out, but that was his expression. He liked to go out with us because we were always reasonably sure of picking up something decent. Left to himself he didn't always fare so well. With us he got a change of meat—Gentile cunt, as he put it. He liked Gentile cunt. Smelled sweeter, he said. Laughed easier too. . . . Sometimes in the very midst of things. The one thing he couldn't tolerate was dark meat. It amazed and disgusted him to see me traveling around with Valeska. Once he asked me if she didn't smell kind of extra strong like. I told him I liked it that way—strong and smelly, with lots of gravy around it. He almost blushed at that. Amazing how delicate he could be about some things. Food for example. Very finicky about his food. Perhaps a racial trait. Immaculate about his person, too. Couldn't stand the sight of a spot on his clean cuffs. Constantly brushing himself off, constantly taking his pocket mirror out to see if there was any food between his teeth. If he found a crumb he would hide his face behind the napkin and extract it with his pearlhandled toothpick. The ovaries of course he couldn't see. Nor could he smell them either, because his wife too was an immaculate bitch. Douching herself all day long in preparation for the evening nuptials. It was tragic, the importance she gave to her ovaries.

Up until the day she was taken to the hospital she was a regular fucking block. The thought of never being able to fuck again frightened the wits out of her. Hymie of course told her it wouldn't make any difference to him one way or the other. Glued to her like a snake, a cigarette in his mouth, the girls passing below on the boulevard, it was hard for him to imagine a woman not being able to fuck any more. He was sure the operation would be successful. *Successful!* That's to say that she'd fuck even better than before. He used to tell her that, lying on his back looking up at the ceiling. "You know I'll always love you," he would say. "Move over just a little bit, will you . . . there, like that . . . that's it. What was I saying? Oh yes . . . why sure, why should you worry about things like that? Of course I'll be true to you. Listen, pull away just a little bit . . . yeah, that's it . . . that's fine." He used to tell us about it in the chop suey joint. Steve would laugh like hell. Steve couldn't do a thing like that. He was too honest—especially with women. That's why he never had any luck. Little Curley, for example—Steve hated Curley—would always get what he wanted. . . . He was a born liar, a born deceiver. Hymie didn't like Curley much either. He said he was dishonest, meaning of course dishonest in money matters. About such things Hymie was scrupulous. What he disliked especially was the way Curley talked about his aunt. It was bad enough, in Hymie's opinion, that he should be screwing the sister of his own mother, but to make her out to be nothing but a piece of stale cheese, that was too much for Hymie. One ought to have a bit of respect for a woman, provided she's not a whore. If she's a whore that's different. Whores are not women. Whores are whores. That was how Hymie looked at things.

The real reason for this dislike, however, was that whenever they went out together Curley always got the best choice. And not only that, but it was usually with Hymie's money that Curley managed it. Even the way Curley asked for money irritated Hymie—it was like extortion, he said. He thought it was partly my fault, that I was too lenient with the kid. "He's got no moral character," Hymie would say. "And what about *you*, your moral character?" I would ask. "Oh *me!* Shit, I'm too old to have any moral character. But Curley's only a kid."

"You're jealous, that's what," Steve would say.

"*Me? Me* jealous of *him?*" And he'd try to smother the idea with a scornful little laugh. It made him wince, a jab like that. "Listen," he would say, turning to me, "did I ever act jealous toward you? Didn't I always turn a girl over to you if you asked me? What about that redhaired girl in SU office . . . you remember . . . the one with the big teats? Wasn't that a nice piece of ass to turn over to a friend? But I did it, didn't I? I did it because you said you liked big teats. But I wouldn't do it for Curley. He's a little crook. Let him do his own digging."

As a matter of fact, Curley was digging away very industriously. He must have had five or six on the string at one time, from what I could gather. There was Valeska, for example—he had made himself pretty solid with her. She was so damned pleased to have some one fuck her without blushing that when it came to sharing him with her cousin and then with the midget she didn't put up the least objection. What she liked best was to get in the tub and let him fuck her under water. It was fine until the midget got wise to it. Then there was a nice rumpus which was finally ironed out on the parlor floor. To listen to Curley talk he did everything but climb the chandeliers. And always plenty of pocket money to boot. Valeska was generous, but the cousin was a softy. If she came within a foot of a stiff prick she was like putty. An unbuttoned fly was enough to put her in a trance. It was almost shameful the things Curley made her do. He took pleasure in degrading her. I could scarcely blame him for it, she was such a prim, priggish bitch in her street clothes. You'd almost swear she didn't own a cunt, the way she carried herself in the street. Naturally, when he got her alone he made her pay for her highfalutin' ways. He went at it coldbloodedly. "Fish it out!" he'd say, opening his fly a little. "Fish it out with your tongue!" (He had it in for the whole bunch because, as he put it, they were sucking one another off behind his back.) Anyway, once she got the taste of it in her mouth you could do anything with her. Sometimes he'd stand her on her hands and push her around the room that way, like a wheelbarrow.

Or else he'd do it dog fashion, and while she groaned and squirmed he'd nonchalantly light a cigarette and blow smoke between her legs. Once he played her a dirty trick doing it that way. He had worked her up to such a state that she was beside herself. Anyway, after he had almost polished the ass off her with his back-scuttling he pulled out for a second, as though to cool his cock off, and then very slowly and gently he shoved a big long carrot up her twat. "That, Miss Abercrombie," he said, "is a sort of Doppelgänger to my regular cock," and with that he unhitches himself and yanks up his pants. Cousin Abercrombie was so bewildered by it all that she let a tremendous fart and out tumbled the carrot. At least, that's how Curley related it to me. He was an outrageous liar, to be sure, and there may not be a grain of truth in the yarn, but there's no denying that he had a flair for such tricks. As for Miss Abercrombie and her high-tone Narragansett ways, well, with a cunt like that one can always imagine the worst. By comparison Hymie was a purist. Somehow Hymie and his fat circumcised dick were two different things. When he got a personal hard on, as he said, he really meant that he was irresponsible. He meant that Nature was asserting itself—through his, Hymie Laubscher's, fat, circumcised dick. It was the same with his wife's cunt. It was something she wore between her legs, like an ornament. It was a part of Mrs. Laubscher but it wasn't Mrs. Laubscher personally, if you get what I mean.

Well, all this is simply by way of leading up to the general sexual confusion which prevailed at this time. It was like taking a flat in the Land of Fuck. The girl upstairs, for instance . . . she used to come down now and then, when the wife was giving a recital, to look after the kid. She was so obviously a simpleton that I didn't give her any notice at first. But like all the others she had a cunt too, a sort of impersonal personal cunt which she was unconsciously conscious of. The oftener she came down the more conscious she got, in her unconscious way. One night, when she was in the bathroom, after she had been in there a suspiciously long while, she got me to thinking of things. I decided to take a peep through the keyhole and see for myself what was what. Lo and behold, if she isn't standing in front of the mirror stroking and petting her little pussy. Almost talking to it, she was. I was so excited I didn't know what to do first. I went back into the big room, turned out the lights, and lay there on the couch waiting for her to come out. As I lay there I could still see that bushy cunt of hers and the fingers strumming it like. I opened my fly to let my pecker twitch about in the cool of the dark. I tried to mesmerize her from the couch, or at least I tried letting my pecker mesmerize her. "Come here, you bitch," I kept saying to myself, "come in here and spread that cunt over me." She must have caught the message immediately, for in a jiffy she had opened the door and was groping about in the dark to find the couch. I didn't say a word, I didn't make a move. I just kept my mind riveted on her cunt moving quietly in the dark like a crab. Finally she was standing beside the couch. She didn't say a word either. She just stood there quietly and as I slid my hand up her legs she moved one foot a little to open her crotch a bit more. I don't think I ever put my hand into such a juicy crotch in all my life. It was like paste running down her legs, and if there had been any billboards handy I could have plastered up a dozen or more. After a few moments, just as naturally as a cow lowering its head to graze, she bent over and put it in her mouth. I had my whole four fingers inside her, whipping it up to a froth. Her mouth was stuffed full and the juice pouring down her legs. Not a word out of us, as I say. Just a couple of quiet maniacs working away in the dark like gravediggers. It was a fucking Paradise and I knew it, and I was ready and willing to fuck my brains away if necessary. She was probably the best fuck I ever had. She never once opened her trap —not that night, nor the next night, nor any night. She'd steal down like that in the dark, soon as she smelled me there alone, and plaster her cunt all over me. It was an enormous cunt, too, when I think back on it. A dark, subterranean labyrinth fitted up with divans and cosy corners and rubber teeth and syringas and soft nestles and eiderdown and mulberry leaves. I used to nose in like the solitary worm and bury myself in a little cranny where it was absolutely silent, and so soft and restful that I lay like a dolphin on the oyster banks. A slight twitch and I'd be in the Pullman reading a newspaper or else up an impasse where there were mossy round cobblestones and little wicker gates which opened and shut automatically. Sometimes it was like riding the shoot-the-shoots, a steep plunge and then a spray of tingling sea crabs, the bulrushes swaying feverishly and the gills of tiny fishes lapping against me like harmonica stops. In the immense black grotto there was a silk-and-soap organ playing a predaceous black music. When she pitched herself high, when she turned the juice on full, it made a violaceous purple, a deep mulberry stain like twilight, a ventriloqual twilight such as dwarfs and cretins enjoy when they menstruate. It made me think of cannibals chewing flowers, of Bantus running amuck, of wild unicorns rutting in rhododendron beds. Everything was anonymous and unformulated, John Doe and his wife Emmy Doe; above us the gas tanks and below the marine life. Above the belt, as I say, she was batty. Yes, absolutely cuckoo, though still abroad and afloat. Perhaps that was what made her cunt so marvelously impersonal. It was one cunt out of a million, a regular Pearl of the Antilles, such as Dick Osborn discovered when reading Joseph Conrad. In the broad Pacific of sex she lay, a gleaming silver reef surrounded with human anemones, human starfish, human madrepores. Only an Osborn could have discovered her, given the proper latitude and longitude of cunt. Meeting her in the daytime, watching her slowly going daft, it was like trapping a weasel when night came on. All I had to do was to lie down in the dark with my fly open and wait. She was like Ophelia suddenly resurrected among the Kaffirs. Not a word of any language could she remember, especially not English. She was a deaf-mute who had lost her memory, and with the loss of memory she had lost her frigidaire, her curling irons, her tweezers and handbag. She was even more naked than a fish, except for the tuft of hair between her legs. And she was even slipperier than a fish because after all a fish has scales and she had none. It was dubious at times whether I was in her or she in me. It was open warfare, the newfangled Pancrace, with each one biting his own ass.

* * *

It is customary to blame everything on the war. I say the war had nothing to do with me, with my life. At a time when others were getting themselves comfortable berths I was taking one miserable job after another, and never enough in it to keep body and soul together. Almost as quickly as I was hired I was fired. I had plenty of intelligence but I inspired distrust. Wherever I went I fomented discord—not because I was idealistic but because I was like a searchlight exposing the stupidity and futility of everything. Besides, I wasn't a good ass licker. That marked me, no doubt. People could tell at once when I asked for a job that I really didn't give a damn whether I got it or not. And of course I generally didn't get it. But after a time the mere looking for a job became an activity, a pastime, so to speak. I would go in and ask for most anything. It was a way of killing time—no worse, as far as I could see, than work itself. I was my own boss and I had my own hours, but unlike other bosses I entrained only my own ruin, my own bankruptcy. I was not a corporation or a trust or a state or a federation or a polity of nations—I was more like God, if anything.

This went on from about the middle of the war until . . . well, until one day I was trapped. Finally the day came when I did desperately want a job. I needed it. Not having another minute to lose, I decided that I would take the last job on earth, that of messenger boy. I walked into the employment bureau of the telegraph company—the Cosmodemonic Telegraph Company of North America—toward the close of the day, prepared to go through with it. I had just come from the public library and I had under my arm some fat books on economics and metaphysics. To my great amazement I was refused the job.

The guy who turned me down was a little runt who ran the switchboard. He seemed to take me for a college student, though it was clear enough from my application that I had long left school. I had even honored myself on the application with a Ph.D. degree from Columbia University. Apparently that passed unnoticed, or else was suspiciously regarded by this runt who had turned me down. I was furious, the more so because for once in my life I was in earnest. Not only that, but I had swallowed my pride, which in certain peculiar ways is rather large. My wife of course gave me the usual leer and sneer. I had done it as a gesture, she said. I went to bed thinking about it, still smarting, getting angrier and angrier as the night wore on. The fact that I had a wife and child to support didn't bother me so much; people didn't offer you jobs because you had a family to support, that much I understood too well. No, what rankled was that they had rejected *me*, Henry V. Miller, a competent, superior individual who had asked for the lowest job in the world. That burned me up. I couldn't get over it. In the morning I was up bright and early, shaved, put on my best clothes and hotfooted it to the subway. I went immediately to the main offices of the telegraph company . . . up to the twenty-fifth floor or wherever it was that the president and the vice-presidents had their cubicles. I asked to see the president. Of course the president was either out of town or too busy to see me, but wouldn't I care to see the vice-president, or his secretary rather. I saw the vice-president's secretary, an intelligent, considerate sort of chap, and I gave him an earful. I did it adroitly, without too much heat, but letting him understand all the while that I wasn't to be put out of the way so easily.

When he picked up the telephone and demanded the general manager I thought it was just a gag, that they were going to pass me around like that from one to the other until I'd get fed up. But the moment I heard him talk I changed my opinion. When I got to the general manager's office, which was in another building uptown, they were waiting for me. I sat down in a comfortable leather chair and accepted one of the big cigars that were thrust forward. This individual seemed at once to be vitally concerned about the matter. He wanted me to tell him all about it, down to the last detail, his big hairy ears cocked to catch the least crumb of information which would justify something or other which was formulating itself inside his dome. I realized that by some accident I had really been instrumental in doing him a service. I let him wheedle it out of me to suit his fancy, observing all the time which way the wind was blowing. And as the talk progressed I noticed that he was warming up to me more and more. At last some one was showing a little confidence in me! That was all I required to get started on one of my favorite lines. For, after years of job hunting I had naturally become quite adept: I knew not only what *not* to say, but I knew also what to imply, what to insinuate. Soon the assistant manager was called in and asked to listen to my story. By this time I knew what the story was. I understood that Hymie—"that little kike," as the general manager called him—had no business pretending that he was the employment manager. Hymie had usurped his prerogative, that much was clear. It was also clear that Hymie was a Jew and that Jews were not in good odor with the general manager, nor with Mr. Twilliger, the vice-president, who was a thorn in the general manager's side.

Perhaps it was Hymie, "the dirty little kike," who was responsible for the high percentage of Jews on the messenger force. Perhaps Hymie was really the one who was doing the hiring at the employment office—at Sunset Place, they called it. It was an excellent opportunity, I gathered, for Mr. Clancy, the general manager, to take down a certain Mr. Burns who, he informed me, had been the employment manager for some thirty years now and who was evidently getting lazy on the job.

The conference lasted several hours. Before it was terminated Mr. Clancy took me aside and informed me that he was going to make *me* the boss of the works. Before putting me into office, however, he was going to ask me as a special favor, and also as a sort of apprenticeship which would stand me in good stead, to work as a special messenger. I would receive the salary of employment manager, but it would be paid me out of a separate account. In short I was to float from office to office and observe the way affairs were conducted by all and sundry. I was to make a little report from time to time as to how things were going. And once in a while, so he suggested, I was to visit him at his home on the q.t. and have a little chat about the conditions in the hundred and one branches of the Cosmodemonic Telegraph Company in New York City. In other words I was to be a spy for a few months and after that I was to have the run of the joint. Maybe they'd make me a general manager too one day, or a vice-president. It was a tempting offer, even if it was wrapped up in a lot of horseshit. I said Yes.

In a few months I was sitting at Sunset Place hiring and firing like a demon. It was a slaughterhouse, so help me God.

The thing was senseless from the bottom up. A waste of men, material and effort. A hideous farce against a backdrop of sweat and misery. But just as I had accepted the spying so I accepted the hiring and firing and all that went with it. I said Yes to everything. If the vice-president decreed that no cripples were to be hired I hired no cripples. If the vice-president said that all messengers over forty-five were to be fired without notice I fired them without notice. I did everything they instructed me to do, but in such a way that they had to pay for it. When there was a strike I folded my arms and waited for it to blow over. But I first saw to it that it cost them a good penny. The whole system was so rotten, so inhuman, so lousy, so hopelessly corrupt and complicated, that it would have taken a genius to put any sense or order into it, to say nothing of human kindness or consideration. I was up against the whole system of American labor, which is rotten at both ends. I was the fifth wheel on the wagon and neither side had any use for me, except to exploit me. In fact, everybody was being exploited—the president and his gang by the unseen powers, the employees by the officials, and so on and around, in and out and through the whole works. From my little perch at Sunset Place I had a bird's eye view of the whole American society. It was like a page out of the telephone book. Alphabetically, numerically, statistically, it made sense. But when you looked at it up close, when you examined the pages separately, or the parts separately, when you examined one lone individual and what constituted him, examined the air he breathed, the life he led, the chances he risked, you saw something so foul and degrading, so low, so miserable, so utterly hopeless and senseless, that it was worse than looking into a volcano. You could see the whole American life—economically, politically, morally, spiritually, artistically, statistically, pathologically. It looked like a grand chancre on a worn-out cock. It looked worse than that, really, because you couldn't even see anything resembling a cock any more. Maybe in the past this thing had life, did produce something, did at least give a moment's pleasure, a moment's thrill. But looking at it from where I sat it looked rottener than the wormiest cheese. The wonder was that the stench of it didn't carry 'em off. . . . I'm using the past tense all the time, but of course it's the same now, maybe even a bit worse. At least now we're getting it full stink.

By the time Valeska arrived on the scene I had hired several army corps of messengers. My office at Sunset Place was like an open sewer, and it stank like one. I had dug myself into the first-line trench and I was getting it from all directions at once. To begin with, the man I had ousted died of a broken heart a few weeks after my arrival. He held out just long enough to break me in and then he croaked. Things happened so fast that I didn't have a chance to feel guilty. From the moment I arrived at the office it was one long uninterrupted pandemonium. An hour before my arrival—I was always late—the place was already jammed with applicants. I had to elbow my way up the stairs and literally force my way in to get to my desk. Before I could take my hat off I had to answer a dozen telephone calls. There were three telephones on my desk and they all rang at once. They were bawling the piss out of me before I had even sat down to work. There wasn't even time to take a crap—until five or six in the afternoon. Hymie was worse off than I because he was tied to the switchboard. He sat there from eight in the morning until six, moving waybills around. A waybill was a messenger loaned by one office to another office for the day or a part of the day. None of the hundred and one offices ever had a full staff; Hymie had to play chess with the waybills while I worked like a madman to plug up the gaps. If by a miracle I succeeded of a day in filling all the vacancies, the next morning would find the situation exactly the same—or worse. Perhaps twenty per cent of the force was steady; the rest was driftwood. The steady ones drove the new ones away. The steady ones earned forty to fifty dollars a week, sometimes sixty or seventy-five, sometimes as much as a hundred dollars a week, which is to say that they earned far more than the clerks and often more than their own managers. As for the new ones, they found it difficult to earn ten dollars a week. Some of them worked an hour and quit, often throwing a batch of telegrams in the garbage can or down the sewer. And whenever they quit they wanted their pay immediately, which was impossible, because in the complicated bookkeeping which ruled no one could say what a messenger had earned until at least ten days later. In the beginning I invited the applicant to sit down beside me and I explained everything to him in detail. I did that until I lost my voice. Soon I learned to save my strength for the grilling that was necessary. In the first place, every other boy was a born liar, if not a crook to boot. Many of them had already been hired and fired a number of times. Some found it an excellent way to find another job, because their duty brought them to hundreds of offices which normally they would never have set foot in. Fortunately McGovern, the old trusty who guarded the door and handed out the application blanks, had a camera eye. And then there were the big ledgers behind me, in which there was a record of every applicant who had ever passed through the mill. The ledgers were very much like a police record; they were full of red ink marks, signifying this or that delinquency. To judge from the evidence I was in a tough spot. Every other name involved a theft, a fraud, a brawl, or dementia or perversion or idiocy. "Be careful—so-and-so is an epileptic!" "Don't hire this man—he's a nigger!" "Watch out—X has been in Dannemora—or else in Sing Sing."

If I had been a stickler for etiquette nobody would ever have been hired. I had to learn quickly, and not from the records or from those about me, but from experience. There were a thousand and one details by which to judge an applicant: I had to take them all in at once, and quickly, because in one short day, even if you are as fast as Jack Robinson, you can only hire so many and no more. And no matter how many I hired it was never enough. The next day it would begin all over again. Some I knew would last only a day, but I had to hire them just the same. The system was wrong from start to finish, but it was not my place to criticize the system. It was mine to hire and fire. I was in the center of a revolving disk which was whirling so fast that nothing could stay put. What was needed was a mechanic, but according to the logic of the higher-ups there was nothing wrong with the mechanism, everything was fine and dandy except that things were temporarily out of order. And things being temporarily out of order brought on epilepsy, theft, vandalism, perversion, niggers, Jews, whores and whatnot—sometimes strikes and lockouts. Whereupon, according to this logic, you took a big broom and you swept the stable clean, or you took clubs and guns and you beat sense into the poor idiots who were suffering from the illusion that things were fundamentally wrong. It was good now and then to talk of God, or to have a little community sing—maybe even a bonus was justifiable now and then, that is when things were getting too terribly bad for words. But on the whole, the important thing was to keep hiring and firing; as long as there were men and ammunition we were to advance, to keep mopping up the trenches. Meanwhile Hymie kept taking cathartic pills—enough to blow out his rear end if he had had a rear end, but he hadn't one any more, he only imagined he was taking a crap, he only imagined he was shitting on his can. Actually the poor bugger was in a trance. There were a hundred and one offices to look after and each one had a staff of messengers which was mythical, if not hypothetical, and whether the messengers were real or unreal, tangible or intangible, Hymie had to shuffle them about from morning to night while I plugged up the holes, which was also imaginary because who could say when a recruit had been dispatched to an office whether he would arrive there today or tomorrow or never. Some of them got lost in the subway or in the labyrinths under the skyscrapers; some rode around on the elevated line all day because with a uniform it was a free ride and perhaps they had never enjoyed riding around all day on the elevated lines. Some of them started for Staten Island and ended up in Canarsie, or else were brought back in a coma by a cop. Some forgot where they lived and disappeared completely. Some whom we hired for New York turned up in Philadelphia a month later, as though it were normal and according to Hoyle. Some would start for their destination and on the way decide that it was easier to sell newspapers and they would sell them, in the uniform we had given them, until they were picked up. Some went straight to the observation ward, moved by some strange preservative instinct.

When he arrived in the morning Hymie first sharpened his pencils; he did this religiously no matter how many calls were coming in, because, as he explained to me later, if he didn't sharpen the pencils first thing off the bat they would never get sharpened. The next thing was to take a glance out the window and see what the weather was like. Then, with a freshly sharpened pencil he made a little box at the head of the slate which he kept beside him and in it he gave the weather report. This, he also informed me, often turned out to be a useful alibi. If the snow were a foot thick or the ground covered with sleet, even the devil himself might be excused for not shuffling the waybills around more speedily, and the employment manager might also be excused for not filling up the holes on such days, no? But why he didn't take a crap first instead of plugging in on the switchboard soon as his pencils were sharpened was a mystery to me. That too he explained to me later. Anyway, the day always broke with confusion, complaints, constipation and vacancies. It also began with loud smelly farts, with bad breaths, with ragged nerves, with epilepsy, with meningitis, with low wages, with back pay that was overdue, with worn-out shoes, with corns and bunions, with flat feet and broken arches, with pocketbooks missing and fountain pens lost or stolen, with telegrams floating in the sewer, with threats from the vice-president and advice from the managers, with wrangles and disputes, with cloudbursts and broken telegraph wires, with new methods of efficiency and old ones that had been discarded, with hope for better times and a prayer for the bonus which never came. The new messengers were going over the top and getting machine-gunned; the old ones were digging in deeper and deeper, like rats in a cheese. Nobody was satisfied, especially not the public. It took ten minutes to reach San Francisco over the wire, but it might take a year to get the message to the man whom it was intended for—or it might never reach him.

The Y. M. C. A., eager to improve the morale of working boys everywhere in America, was holding meetings at noon hour and wouldn't I like to send a few spruce-looking boys to hear William Carnegie Asterbilt Junior give a five-minute talk on service. Mr. Mallory of the Welfare League would like to know if I could spare a few minutes some time to tell me about the model prisoners who were on parole and who would be glad to serve in any capacity, even as messengers. Mrs. Guggenhoffer of the Jewish Charities would be very grateful if I would aid her in maintaining some broken-down homes which had broken down because everybody was either infirm, crippled or disabled in the family. Mr. Haggerty of the Runaway Home for Boys was sure he had just the right youngsters for me, if only I would give them a chance; all of them had been mistreated by their stepfathers or stepmothers. The

Mayor of New York would appreciate it if I would give my personal attention to the bearer of said letter whom he could vouch for in every way—but why the hell he didn't give said bearer a job himself was a mystery. Man leaning over my shoulder hands me a slip of paper on which he has just writ-ten—"Me understand everything but me no hear the voices." Luther Winifred is standing beside him, his tattered coat fastened together with safety pins. Luther is two-sevenths pure Indian and five-sevenths German-American, so he ex-plains. On the Indian side he is a Crow, one of the Crows from Montana. His last job was putting up window shades, but there is no ass in his pants and he is ashamed to climb a ladder in front of a lady. He got out of the hospital the other day and so he is still a little weak, but he is not too weak to carry messages, so he thinks.

And then there is Ferdinand Mish—how could I have forgotten him? He has been waiting in line all morning to get a word with me. I never answered the letters he sent me. Was that just? he asks me blandly. Of course not. I remember vaguely the last letter which he sent me from the Cat and Dog Hospital on the Grand Concourse, where he was an attendant. He said he repented that he had resigned his post "but it was on account of his father being too strick over him, not giving him any recreation or outside pleasure." "I'm twenty-five now," he wrote, "and I don't think I should ought to be sleeping no more with my father, do you? I know you are said to be a very fine gentleman and I am now self-dependent, so I hope . . ." McGovern, the old trusty, is standing by Ferdinand's side waiting for me to give him the sign. He wants to give Ferdinand the bum's rush—he remem-bers him from five years ago when Ferdinand lay down on the sidewalk in front of the main office in full uniform and threw an epileptic fit. No, shit, I can't do it! I'm going to give him a chance, the poor bastard. Maybe I'll send him to Chinatown where things are fairly quiet. Meanwhile while Ferdinand is changing into a uniform in the back room, I'm getting an earful from an orphan boy who wants to "help make the company a success." He says that if I give him a chance he'll pray for me every Sunday when he goes to church, except the Sundays when he has to report to his parole officer. He didn't do nothing, it appears. He just pushed the fellow and the fellow fell on his head and got killed. *Next:* An ex-consul from Gibraltar. Writes a beautiful hand—too beautiful. I ask him to see me at the end of the day—something fishy about him. Meanwhile Ferdinand's thrown a fit in the dressing room. Lucky break! If it had happened in the subway, with a number on his hat and everything, I'd have been canned. *Next:* A guy with one arm and mad as hell because McGovern is showing him the door. "What the hell! I'm strong and healthy, ain't I?" he shouts, and to prove it he picks up a chair with his good arm and smashes it to bits. I get back to the desk and there's a telegram lying there for me. I open it. It's from George Blasini, ex-messenger No. 2459 of S.W. office. "I am sorry that I had to quit so soon, but the job was not fitted for my character idleness and I am a true lover of labor and frugality but many a time we be unable to control or subdue our personal pride." Shit!

In the beginning I was enthusiastic, despite the damper above and the clamps below. I had ideas and I executed them, whether it pleased the vice-president or not. Every ten days or so I was put on the carpet and lectured for having "too big a heart." I never had any money in my pocket but I used other people's money freely. As long as I was the boss I had credit. I gave money away right and left; I gave my clothes away and my linen, my books, everything that was superfluous. If I had had the power I would have given the company away to the poor buggers who pestered me. If I was asked for a dime

I gave a half dollar, if I was asked for a dollar I gave five. I didn't give a fuck how much I gave away, because it was easier to borrow and give than to refuse the poor devils. I never saw such an aggregation of misery in my life, and I hope I'll never see it again. Men are poor everywhere—they always have been and they always will be. And beneath the terrible poverty there is a flame, usually so low that it is almost invisible. But it is there and if one has the courage to blow on it it can become a conflagration. I was constantly urged not to be too lenient, not to be too sentimental, not to be too charitable. Be firm! Be hard! they cautioned me. Fuck that! I said to myself, I'll be generous, pliant, forgiving, tolerant, tender. In the beginning I heard every man to the end; if I couldn't give him a job I gave him money, and if I had no money I gave him cigarettes or I gave him courage. But I gave! The effect was dizzying. Nobody can estimate the results of a good deed, of a kind word. I was swamped with gratitude, with good wishes, with invitations, with pathetic, tender little gifts. If I had had real power instead of being the fifth wheel on a wagon, God knows what I might not have accomplished. I could have used the Cosmodemonic Telegraph Company of North America as a base to bring all humanity to God; I could have transformed North and South America alike, and the Dominion of Canada too. I had the secret in my hand: it was to be generous, to be kind, to be patient. I did the work of five men. I hardly slept for three years. I didn't own a whole shirt and often I was so ashamed of borrowing from my wife, or robbing the kid's bank, that to get the carfare to go to work in the morning I would swindle the blind newspaperman at the subway station. I owed so much money all around that if I were to work for twenty years I would not have been able to pay it back. I took from those who had and I gave to those who needed, and it was the right thing to do, and I would do it all over again if I were in the same position.

I even accomplished the miracle of stopping the crazy turnover, something that nobody had dared to hope for. Instead of supporting my efforts they undermined me. According to the logic of the higher-ups the turnover had ceased because the wages were too high. So they cut the wages. It was like kicking the bottom out of a bucket. The whole edifice tumbled, collapsed on my hands. And, just as though nothing had happened they insisted that the gaps be plugged up immediately. To soften the blow a bit they intimated that I might even increase the percentage of Jews, I might take on a cripple now and then, if he were capable, I might do this and that, all of which they had informed me previously was against the code. I was so furious that I took on anything and everything; I would have taken on broncos and gorillas if I could have imbued them with the modicum of intelligence which was necessary to deliver messages. A few days previously there had been only five or six vacancies at closing time. Now there were three hundred, four hundred, five hundred—they were running out like sand. It was marvelous. I sat there and without asking a question I took them on in carload lots—niggers, Jews, paralytics, cripples, ex-convicts, whores, maniacs, perverts, idiots, any fucking bastard who could stand on two legs and hold a telegram in his hand. The managers of the hundred and one offices were frightened to death. I laughed. I laughed all day long thinking what a fine stinking mess I was making of it. Complaints were pouring in from all parts of the city. The service was crippled, constipated, strangulated. A mule could have gotten there faster than some of the idiots I put into harness.

The best thing about the new day was the introduction of female messengers. It changed the whole atmosphere of the joint. For Hymie especially it was a godsend. He moved his switchboard around so that he could watch me while juggling the waybills back and forth. Despite the added work he had a permanent erection. He came to work with a smile and he smiled all day long. He was in heaven. At the end of the day I always had a list of five or six who were worth trying out. The game was to keep them on the string, to promise them a job but to get a free fuck first. Usually it was only necessary to throw a feed into them in order to bring them back to the office at night and lay them out on the zinc-covered table in the dressing room. If they had a cosy apartment, as they sometimes did, we took them home and finished it in bed. If they liked to drink Hymie would bring a bottle along. If they were any good and really needed some dough Hymie would flash his roll and peel off a five spot or a ten spot, as the case might be. It makes my mouth water when I think of that roll he carried about with him. Where he got it from I never knew, because he was the lowest-paid man in the joint. But it was always there, and no matter what I asked for I got. And once it happened that we did get a bonus and I paid Hymie back to the last penny—which so amazed him that he took me out that night to Delmonico's and spent a fortune on me. Not only that, but the next day he insisted on buying me a hat and shirts and gloves. He even insinuated that I might come home and fuck his wife, if I liked, though he warned me that she was having a little trouble at present with her ovaries.

In addition to Hymie and McGovern I had as assistants a pair of beautiful blondes who often accompanied us to dinner in the evening. And there was O'Mara, an old friend of mine who had just returned from the Philippines and whom I made my chief assistant. There was also Steve Romero, a prize bull whom I kept around in case of trouble. And O'Rourke, the company detective, who reported to me at the close of day when he began his work. Finally I added another man to the staff—Kronski, a young medical student, who was diabolically interested in the pathological cases of which we had plenty. We were a merry crew, united in our desire to fuck the company at all costs. And while fucking the company we fucked everything in sight that we could get hold of, O'Rourke excepted, as he had a certain dignity to maintain, and besides he had trouble with his prostate and had lost all interest in fucking. But O'Rourke was a prince of a man, and generous beyond words. It was O'Rourke who often invited us to dinner in the evening and it was O'Rourke we went to when we were in trouble.

That was how it stood at Sunset Place after a couple of years had rolled by. I was saturated with humanity, with experiences of one kind and another. In my sober moments I made notes which I intended to make use of later if ever I should have a chance to record my experiences. I was waiting for a breathing spell. And then by chance one day, when I had been put on the carpet for some wanton piece of negligence, the vice-president let drop a phrase which stuck in my crop. He had said that he would like to see some one write a sort of Horatio Alger book about the messengers; he hinted that perhaps I might be the one to do such a job. I was furious to think what a ninny he was and delighted at the same time because secretly I was itching to get the thing off my chest. I thought to myself—you poor old futzer, you, just wait until I get it off my chest. . . . I'll give you an Horatio Alger book . . . just you wait! My head was in a whirl leaving his office. I saw the army of men, women and children that had passed through my hands, saw them weeping, begging, beseeching, imploring, cursing, spitting, fuming, threatening. I saw the tracks they left on the highways, the freight trains lying on the floor, the parents in rags, the coal box empty, the sink running over, the walls sweating and between the cold beads of sweat the cockroaches running like mad; I saw them hobbling along like twisted gnomes or falling backwards in the epileptic frenzy, the mouth twitching, the slaver pouring from the lips, the limbs writhing; I saw the walls giving way and the pest pouring out like a winged fluid, and the men higher up with their ironclad logic, waiting for it to blow over, waiting for everything to be patched up, waiting contentedly, smugly, with big cigars in their mouths and their feet on the desk, saying things were temporarily out of order. I saw the Horatio Alger hero, the dream of a sick America, mounting higher and higher, first messenger, then operator, then manager, then chief, then superintendent, then vice-president, then president, then trust magnate, then beer baron, then Lord of all the Americas, the money god, the god of gods, the clay of clay, nullity on high, zero with ninety-seven thousand decimals fore and aft. You shits, I said to myself, I will give you the picture of twelve little men, zeros without decimals, ciphers, digits, the twelve uncrushable worms who are hollowing out the base of your rotten edifice. I will give you Horatio Alger as he looks the day after the Apocalypse, when all the stink has cleared away.

From all over the earth they had come to me to be succored. Except for the primitives there was scarcely a race which wasn't represented on the force. Except for the Ainus, the Maoris, the Papuans, the Veddas, the Lapps, the Zulus, the Patagonians, the Igorots, the Hottentots, the Tuaregs, except for the lost Tasmanians, the lost Grimaldi men, the lost Atlanteans, I had a representative of almost every species under the sun. I had two brothers who were still sun-worshipers, two Nestorians from the old Assyrian world; I had two Maltese twins from Malta and a descendant of the Mayas from Yucatan; I had a few of our little brown brothers from the Philippines and some Ethiopians from Abyssinia; I had men from the pampas of Argentina and stranded cowboys from Montana; I had Greeks, Letts, Poles, Croats, Slovenes, Ruthenians, Czechs, Spaniards, Welshmen, Finns, Swedes, Russians, Danes, Mexicans, Puerto Ricans, Cubans, Uruguayans, Brazilians, Australians, Persians, Japs, Chinese, Javanese, Egyptians, Africans from the Gold Coast and the Ivory Coast, Hindus, Armenians, Turks, Arabs, Germans, Irish, English, Canadians—and plenty of Italians and plenty of Jews. I had only one Frenchman that I can recall and he lasted about three hours. I had a few American Indians, Cherokees mostly, but no Tibetans, and no Eskimos: I saw names I could never have imagined and handwriting which ranged from cuneiform to the sophisticated and astoundingly beautiful calligraphy of the Chinese. I heard men beg for work who had been Egyptologists, botanists, surgeons, gold miners, professors of Oriental languages, musicians, engineers, physicians, astronomers, anthropologists, chemists, mathematicians, mayors of cities and governors of states, prison wardens, cowpunchers, lumberjacks, sailors, oyster pirates, stevedores, riveters, dentists, painters, sculptors, plumbers, architects, dope peddlers, abortionists, white slavers, sea divers, steeplejacks, farmers, cloak and suit salesmen, trappers, lighthouse keepers, pimps, aldermen, senators, every bloody thing under the sun, and all of them down and out, begging for work, for cigarettes, for carfare, *for a chance, Christ Almighty, just another chance!* I saw and got to know men who were saints, if there are saints in this world; I saw and spoke to savants, crapulous and uncrapulous ones; I listened to men who had the divine fire in their bowels, who could have convinced God Almighty that they were worthy of another chance, but not the vice-president of the Cosmococcic Telegraph Company. I sat riveted to my desk and I traveled around the world at lightning speed, and I learned that everywhere it is the same—hunger, humiliation, ignorance, vice, greed, extortion, chicanery, torture, despotism: the inhumanity of man to man: the fetters, the harness, the halter, the bridle, the whip, the spurs. The finer the caliber the worse off the man. Men were walking the streets of New

York in that bloody, degrading outfit, the despised, the lowest of the low, walking around like auks, like penguins, like oxen, like trained seals, like patient donkeys, like big jackasses, like crazy gorillas, like docile maniacs nibbling at the dangling bait, like waltzing mice, like guinea pigs, like squirrels, like rabbits, and many and many a one was fit to govern the world, to write the greatest book ever written. When I think of some of the Persians, the Hindus, the Arabs I knew, when I think of the character they revealed, their grace, their tenderness, their intelligence, *their holiness,* I spit on the white conquerors of the world, the degenerate British, the pigheaded Germans, the smug, self-satisfied French. The earth is one great sentient being, a planet saturated through and through with man, a live planet expressing itself falteringly and stutteringly; it is not the home of the white race or the black race or the yellow race or the lost blue race, but the home of *man* and all men are equal before God and will have their chance, if not now then a million years hence. The little brown brothers of the Philippines may bloom again one day and the murdered Indians of America north and south may also come alive one day to ride the plains where now the cities stand belching fire and pestilence. Who has the last say? *Man!* The earth is his because he *is* the earth, its fire, its water, its air, its mineral and vegetable matter, its spirit which is cosmic, which is imperishable, which is the spirit of all the planets, which transforms itself through him, through endless signs and symbols, through endless manifestations. Wait, you cosmococcic telegraphic shits, you demons on high waiting for the plumbing to be repaired, wait, you dirty white conquerors who have sullied the earth with your cloven hoofs, your instruments, your weapons, your disease germs, wait, all you who are sitting in clover and counting your coppers, it is not the end. The last man will have his say before it is finished. Down to the last sentient molecule justice must be done—*and will be done!* Nobody is getting away with anything, least of all the cosmococcic shits of North America.

When it came time for my vacation—I hadn't taken one for three years, I was so eager to make the company a success! —I took three weeks instead of two and I wrote the book about the twelve little men. I wrote it straight off, five, seven, sometimes eight thousand words a day. I thought that a man, to be a writer, must do at least five thousand words a day. I thought he must say everything all at once—in one book—and collapse afterwards. I didn't know a thing about writing. I was scared shitless. But I was determined to wipe Horatio Alger out of the North American consciousness. I suppose it was the worst book any man has ever written. It was a colossal tome and faulty from start to finish. But it was my first book and I was in love with it. If I had had the money, as Gide had, I would have published it at my own expense. If I had had the courage that Whitman had, I would have peddled it from door to door. Everybody I showed it to said it was terrible. I was urged to give up the idea of writing. I had to learn, as Balzac did, that one must write volumes before signing one's own name. I had to learn, as I soon did, that one must give up everything and not do anything else but write, that one must write and write and write, even if everybody in the world advises you against it, even if nobody believes in you. Perhaps one does it just because nobody believes; perhaps the real secret lies in making people believe. That the book was inadequate, faulty, bad, *terrible*, as they said, was only natural. I was attempting at the start what a man of genius would have undertaken only at the end. I wanted to say the last word at the beginning. It was absurd and pathetic. It was a crushing defeat, but it put iron in my backbone and sulphur in my blood. I knew at least what it was to fail. I knew what it was to attempt something big. Today, when I think of the circumstances under which I wrote that book, when I think of the overwhelming material which I tried to put into form, when I think of what I hoped to encompass, I pat myself on the back, I give myself a double A. I am proud of the fact that I made such a miserable failure of it; had I succeeded I would have been a monster. Sometimes, when I look over my notebooks, when I look at the names alone of those whom I thought to write about, I am seized with vertigo. Each man came to me with a world of his own; he came to me and unloaded it on my desk; he expected me to pick it up and put it on my shoulders. I had no time to make a world of my own: I had to stay fixed like Atlas, my feet on the elephant's back and the elephant on the tortoise's back. To inquire on what the tortoise stood would be to go mad.

I didn't dare to think of anything then except the "facts." To get beneath the facts I would have had to be an artist, and one doesn't become an artist overnight. First you have to be crushed, to have your conflicting points of view annihilated. You have to be wiped out as a human being in order to be born again an individual. You have to be carbonized and mineralized in order to work upwards from the last common denominator of the self. You have to get beyond pity in order to feel from the very roots of your being. One can't make a new heaven and earth with "facts." There are no "facts"—there is only *the fact* that man, every man everywhere in the world, is on his way to ordination. Some men take the long route and some take the short route. Every man is working out his destiny in his own way and nobody can be of help except by being kind, generous and patient. In my enthusiasm certain things were then inexplicable to me which now are clear. I think, for example, of Carnahan, one of the twelve little men I had chosen to write about. He was what is called a model messenger. He was a graduate of a prominent university, had a sound intelligence and was of exemplary character. He worked eighteen and twenty hours a day and earned more than any messenger on the force. The clients whom he served wrote letters about him, praising him to the skies; he was offered good positions which he refused for one reason or another. He lived frugally, sending the best part of his wages to his wife and children who lived in another city. He had two vices—drink and the desire to succeed. He could go for a year without drinking, but if he took one drop he was off. He had cleaned up twice in Wall Street and yet, before coming to me for a job, he had gotten no further than to be a sexton of a church in some little town. He had been fired from that job because he had broken into the sacramental wine and rung the bells all night long. He was truthful, sincere, earnest. I had implicit confidence in him and my confidence was proven by the record of his service which was without a blemish. Nevertheless he shot his wife and children in cold blood and then he shot himself. Fortunately none of them died; they all lay in the hospital together and they all recovered. I went to see his wife, after they had transferred him to jail, to get her help. She refused categorically. She said he was the meanest, cruelest son of a bitch that ever walked on two legs—she wanted to see him hanged. I pleaded with her for two days, but she was adamant. I went to the jail and talked to him through the mesh. I found that he had already made himself popular with the authorities, had already been granted special privileges. He wasn't at all dejected. On the contrary, he was looking forward to making the best of his time in prison by "studying up" on salesmanship. He was going to be the best salesman in America after his release. I might almost say that he seemed happy. He said not to worry about him, he would get along all right. He said everybody was swell to him and that he had nothing to complain about. I left him somewhat in a daze. I went to a nearby beach and decided to take a swim. I saw everything with new eyes. I almost forgot to return home, so absorbed had I become in my speculations about this chap. Who could say that everything that happened to him had not happened for the best? Perhaps he might leave the prison a full-fledged evangelist instead of a salesman. Nobody could predict what he might do. And nobody could aid him because he was working out his destiny in his own private way.

There was another chap, a Hindu named Guptal. He was not only a model of good behavior—he was a saint. He had a passion for the flute which he played all by himself in his miserable little room. One day he was found naked, his throat slit from ear to ear, and beside him on the bed was his flute. At the funeral there were a dozen women who wept passionate tears, including the wife of the janitor who had murdered him. I could write a book about this young man who was the gentlest and the holiest man I ever met, who had never offended anybody and never taken anything from anybody, but who had made the cardinal mistake of coming to America to spread peace and love.

There was Dave Olinski, another faithful, industrious messenger who thought of nothing but work. He had one fatal weakness—he talked too much. When he came to me he had already been around the globe several times and what he hadn't done to make a living isn't worth telling about. He knew about twelve languages and he was rather proud of his linguistic ability. He was one of those men whose very willingness and enthusiasm is their undoing. He wanted to help everybody along, show everybody how to succeed. He wanted more work than we could give him—he was a glutton for work. Perhaps I should have warned him, when I sent him to his office on the East Side, that he was going to work in a tough neighborhood, but he pretended to know so much and he was so insistent on working in that locality (because of his linguistic ability) that I said nothing. I thought to myself—you'll find out quickly enough for yourself. And sure enough, he was only there a short time when he got into trouble. A tough Jewboy from the neighborhood walked in one day and asked for a blank. Dave, the messenger, was behind the desk. He didn't like the way the man asked for the blank. He told him he ought to be more polite. For that he got a box in the ears. That made him wag his tongue some more, whereupon he got such a wallop that his teeth flew down his throat and his jawbone was broken in three places. Still he didn't know enough to hold his trap. Like the damned fool that he was he goes to the police station and registers a complaint. A week later, while he's sitting on a bench snoozing, a gang of roughnecks break into the place and beat him to a pulp. His head was so battered that his brains looked like an omelette. For good measure they emptied the safe and turned it upside down. Dave died on the way to the hospital. They found five hundred dollars hidden away in the toe of his sock. . . . Then there was Clausen and his wife Lena. They came in together when he applied for the job. Lena had a baby in her arms and he had two little ones by the hand. They were sent to me by some relief agency. I put him on as a night messenger so that he'd have a fixed salary. In a few days I had a letter from him, a batty letter in which he asked me to excuse him for being absent as he had to report to his parole officer. Then another letter saying that his wife had refused to sleep with him because she didn't want any more babies and would I please come to see them and try to persuade her to sleep with him. I went to his home—a cellar in the Italian quarter. It looked like a bughouse. Lena was pregnant again, about seven months under way, and on the verge of idiocy. She had taken to sleeping on the roof because it was too hot in the cellar, also because she didn't want him to touch her any more. When I said it wouldn't make any difference now she just looked at me and grinned. Clausen had been in the war and maybe the gas had made him a bit goofy—at any rate he was foaming at the mouth. He said he would brain her if she didn't stay off that roof. He insinuated that she was sleeping up there in order to carry on with the coal man who lived in the attic. At this Lena smiled again with that mirthless batrachian grin. Clausen lost his temper and gave her a swift kick in the ass. She went out in a huff taking the brats with her. He told her to stay out for good. Then he opened a drawer and pulled out a big Colt. He was keeping it in case he needed it some time, he said. He showed me a few knives, too, and a sort of blackjack which he had made himself. Then he began to weep. He said his wife was making a fool of him. He said he was sick of working for her because she was sleeping with everybody in the neighborhood. The kids weren't his because he couldn't make a kid any more even if he wanted to. The very next day, while Lena was out marketing, he took the kids up to the roof and with the blackjack he had shown me he beat their brains out. Then he jumped off the roof head first. When Lena came home and saw what happened she went off her nut. They had to put her in a strait jacket and call for the ambulance. . . . There was Schuldig, the rat who had spent twenty years in prison for a crime he had never committed. He had been beaten almost to death before he confessed; then solitary confinement, starvation, torture, perversion, dope. When they finally released him he was no longer a human being. He described to me one night his last thirty days in jail, the agony of waiting to be released. I have never heard anything like it; I didn't think a human being could survive such anguish. Freed, he was haunted by the fear that he might be obliged to commit a crime and be sent back to prison again. He complained of being followed, spied on, perpetually tracked. He said "they" were tempting him to do things he had no desire to do. "They" were the dicks who were on his trail, who were paid to bring him back again. At night, when he was asleep, they whispered in his ear. He was powerless against them because they mesmerized him first. Sometimes they placed dope under his pillow, and with it a revolver or a knife. They wanted him to kill some innocent person so that they would have a solid case against him this time. He got worse and worse. One night, after he had walked around for hours with a batch of telegrams in his pocket, he went up to a cop and asked to be locked up. He couldn't remember his name or address or even the office he was working for. He had completely lost his identity. He repeated over and over—"I'm innocent. . . . I'm innocent." Again they gave him the third degree. Suddenly he jumped up and shouted like a madman —"I'll confess . . . I'll confess"—and with that he began to reel off one crime after another. He kept it up for three hours. Suddenly, in the midst of a harrowing confession, he stopped short, gave a quick look about, like a man who has suddenly come to, and then, with the rapidity and the force which only a madman can summon he made a tremendous leap across the room and crashed his skull against the stone wall. . . . I relate these incidents briefly and hurriedly as they flash through my mind; my memory is packed with thousands of such details, with a myriad faces, gestures, tales, confessions all entwined and interlaced like the stupendous reeling façade of some Hindu temple made not of stone but of the experience of human flesh, a monstrous dream edifice built entirely of reality and yet not reality itself but merely the vessel in which the mystery of the human being is contained.

* * *

For the time being she's all right, Valeska, seeing as how she's six feet under and by now perhaps picked clean by the worms. When she was in the flesh she was picked clean too, by the human worms who have no respect for anything which has a different tint, a different odor.

The sad thing about Valeska was the fact that she had nigger blood in her veins. It was depressing for everybody around her. She made you aware of it whether you wished to be or no. The nigger blood, as I say, and the fact that her mother was a trollop. The mother was white, of course. Who the father was nobody knew, not even Valeska herself.

Everything was going along smoothly until the day an officious little Jew from the vice-president's office happened to espy her. He was horrified, so he informed me confidentially, to think that I had employed a colored person as my secretary. He spoke as though she might contaminate the messengers. The next day I was put on the carpet. It was exactly as though I had committed sacrilege. Of course I pretended that I hadn't observed anything unusual about her, except that she was extremely intelligent and extremely capable. Finally the president himself stepped in. There was a short interview between him and Valeska during which he very diplomatically proposed to give her a better position in Havana. No talk of the blood taint. Simply that her services had been altogether remarkable and that they would like to promote her—to Havana. Valeska came back to the office in a rage. When she was angry she was magnificent. She said she wouldn't budge. Steve Romero and Hymie were there at the time and we all went out to dinner together. During the course of the evening we got a bit tight. Valeska's tongue was wagging. On the way home she told me that she was going to put up a fight; she wanted to know if it would endanger my job. I told her quietly that if she were fired I would quit too. She pretended not to believe it at first. I said I meant it, that I didn't care what happened. She seemed to be unduly impressed; she took me by the two hands and she held them very gently, the tears rolling down her cheeks.

That was the beginning of things. I think it was the very next day that I slipped her a note saying that I was crazy about her. She read the note sitting opposite me and when she was through she looked me square in the eye and said she didn't believe it. But we went to dinner again that night and we had more to drink and we danced and while we were dancing she pressed herself against me lasciviously. It was just the time, as luck would have it, that my wife was getting ready to have another abortion. I was telling Valeska about it as we danced. On the way home she suddenly said—"Why don't you let me lend you a hundred dollars?" The next night I brought her home to dinner and I let her hand the wife the hundred dollars. I was amazed how well the two of them got along. Before the evening was over it was agreed upon that Valeska would come to the house the day of the abortion and take care of the kid. The day came and I gave Valeska the afternoon off. About an hour after she had left I suddenly decided that I would take the afternoon off also. I started toward the burlesque on Fourteenth Street. When I was about a block from the theater I suddenly changed my mind. It was just the thought that if anything happened—if the wife were to kick off—I wouldn't feel so damned good having spent the afternoon at the burlesque. I walked around a bit, in and out of the penny arcades, and then I started homeward.

It's strange how things turn out. Trying to amuse the kid I suddenly remembered a trick my grandfather had shown me when I was a child. You take the dominoes and you make tall battleships out of them; then you gently pull the tablecloth on which the battleships are floating until they come to the edge of the table when suddenly you give a brisk tug and they fall onto the floor. We tried it over and over again, the three of us, until the kid got so sleepy that she toddled off to the next room and fell asleep. The dominoes were lying all over the floor and the tablecloth was on the floor too. Suddenly Valeska was leaning against the table, her tongue halfway down my throat, my hand between her legs. As I laid her back on the table she twined her legs around me. I could feel one of the dominoes under my feet—part of the fleet that we had destroyed a dozen times or more. I thought of my grandfather sitting on the bench, the way he had warned my mother one day that I was too young to be reading so much, the pensive look in his eyes as he pressed the hot iron against the wet seam of a coat; I thought of the attack on San Juan Hill which the Rough Riders had made, the picture of Teddy charging at the head of his volunteers in the big book which I used to read beside the workbench; I thought of the battleship "Maine" that floated over my bed in the little room with the iron-barred window, and of Admiral Dewey and of Schley and Sampson; I thought of the trip to the Navy Yard which I never made because on the way my father suddenly remembered that we had to call on the doctor that afternoon and when I left the doctor's office I didn't have any more tonsils nor any more faith in human beings. . . . We had hardly finished when the bell rang and it was my wife coming home from the slaughterhouse. I was still buttoning my fly as I went through the hall to open the gate. She was as white as flour. She looked as though she'd never be able to go through another one. We put her to bed and then we gathered up the dominoes and put the tablecloth back on the table.

* * *

Chaos! A howling chaos! No need to choose a particular day. Any day of my life—back there—would suit. Every day of my life, my tiny, microcosmic life, was a reflection of the outer chaos. Let me think back. . . . At seven-thirty the alarm went off. I didn't bounce out of bed. I lay there till eight-thirty, trying to gain a little more sleep. Sleep—how could I sleep? In the back of my mind was an image of the office where I was already due. I could see Hymie arriving at eight sharp, the switchboard already buzzing with demands for help, the applicants climbing up the wide wooden stairway, the strong smell of camphor from the dressing room. Why get up and repeat yesterday's song and dance? As fast as I hired them they dropped out. Working my balls off and not even a clean shirt to wear. Mondays I got my allowance from the wife—carfare and lunch money. I was always in debt to her and she was in debt to the grocer, the butcher, the landlord, and so on. I couldn't be bothered shaving—there wasn't time enough. I put on the torn shirt, gobble up the breakfast, and borrow a nickel for the subway. If she were in a bad mood I would swindle the money from the newsdealer at the subway. I get to the office out of breath, an hour behind time and a dozen calls to make before I even talk to an applicant. While I make one call there are three other calls waiting to be answered. I use two telephones at once. The switchboard is buzzing. Hymie is sharpening his pencils between calls. McGovern the doorman is standing at my elbow to give me a word of advice about one of the applicants, probably a crook, who is trying to sneak back under a false name. Behind me the cards and ledgers containing the name of every applicant who had ever passed through the machine. The bad ones are starred in red ink; some of them have six aliases after their names. Meanwhile the room is crawling like a hive. The room stinks with sweat, dirty feet, old uniforms, camphor, lysol, bad breaths. Half of them will have to be turned away—not that we don't need them, but that even under the worst conditions they just won't do. The man in front of my desk, standing at the rail with palsied hands and bleary eyes, is an ex-mayor of New York City. He's seventy now and would be glad to take anything. He has wonderful letters of recommendation, but we can't take any one over forty-five years of age. Forty-five in New York is the deadline. The telephone rings and it's a smooth secretary from the Y.M.C.A. Wouldn't I make an exception for a boy who has just walked into his office—a boy who was in the reformatory for a year or so. *What did he do?* He tried to rape his sister. An Italian, of course. O'Mara, my assistant, is putting an applicant through the third degree. He suspects him of being an epileptic. Finally he succeeds and for good measure the boy throws a fit right there in the office. One of the women faints. A beautiful looking young woman with a handsome fur around her neck is trying to persuade me to take her on. She's a whore clean through and I know if I put her on there'll be hell to pay. She wants to work in a certain building uptown—because it is near home, she says. Nearing lunch time and a few cronies are beginning to drop in. They sit around watching me work, as if it were a vaudeville performance. Kronski, the medical student, arrives; he says one of the boys I've just hired has Parkinson's disease. I've been so busy I haven't had a chance to go to the toilet. All the telegraph operators, all the managers, suffer from hemorrhoids, so O'Rourke tells me. He's been having electrical massages for the last two years, but nothing works. Lunch time and there are six of us at the table. Some one will have to pay for me, as usual. We gulp it down and rush back. More calls to make, more applicants to interview. The vice-president is raising hell because we can't keep the force up to normal. Every paper in New York and for twenty miles outside New York carries long ads demanding help. All the schools have been canvassed for part-time messengers. All the charity bureaus and relief societies have been invoked. They drop out like flies. Some of them don't even last an hour. It's a human flour mill. And the saddest thing about it is that it's totally unnecessary. But that's not my concern. Mine is to do or die, as Kipling says. I plug on, through one victim after another, the telephone ringing like mad, the place smelling more and more vile, the holes getting bigger and bigger. Each one is a human being asking for a crust of bread; I have his height, weight, color, religion, education, experience, etc. All the data will go into a ledger to be filed alphabetically and then chronologically. Names and dates. Fingerprints too, if we had the time for it. So that what? So that the American people may enjoy the fastest form of communication known to man, so that they may sell their wares more quickly, so that the moment you drop dead in the street your next of kin may be apprised immediately, that is to say, within an hour, unless the messenger to whom the telegram is entrusted decides to throw up the job and throw the whole batch of telegrams in the garbage can. Twenty million Christmas blanks, all wishing you a Merry Christmas and a Happy New Year, from the directors and president and vice-president of the Cosmodemonic Telegraph Company, and maybe the telegram reads "Mother dying, come at once," but the clerk is too busy to notice the message and if you sue for damages, spiritual damages, there is a legal department trained expressly to meet such emergencies and so you can be sure that your mother will die and you will have a Merry Christmas and Happy New Year just the same. The clerk, of course, will be fired and after a month or so he will come back for a messenger's job and he will be taken on and put on the night shift near the docks where nobody will recognize him, and his wife will come with the brats to thank the general manager, or perhaps the vice-president himself, for the kindness and consideration shown. And then one day everybody will be heartily surprised that said messenger robbed the till and O'Rourke will be asked to take the night train for Cleveland or Detroit and to track him down even if it costs ten thousand dollars. And then the vice-president will issue an order that no more Jews are to be hired, but after three or four days he will let up a bit because there are nothing but Jews coming for the job. And because it's getting so very tough and the timber so damned scarce I'm on the point of hiring a midget from the circus and I probably would have hired him if he hadn't broken down and confessed that he was a she. And to make it worse Valeska takes "it" under her wing, takes "it" home that night and under pretense of sympathy gives "it" a thorough examination, including a vaginal exploration with the index finger of the right hand. And the midget becomes very amorous and finally very jealous. It's a trying day and on the way home I bump into the sister of one of my friends and she insists on taking me to dinner. After dinner we go to a movie and in the dark we begin to play with each other and finally it gets to such a point that we leave the movie and go back to the office where I lay her out on the zinc-covered table in the dressing room. And when I get home, a little after midnight, there's a telephone call from Valeska and she wants me to hop into the subway immediately and come to her house, it's very urgent. It's an hour's ride and I'm dead weary, but she said it was urgent and so I'm on the way. And when I get there I meet her cousin, a rather attractive young woman, who, according to her own story, had just had an affair with a strange man because she was tired of being a virgin. And what was all the fuss about? Why this, that in her eagerness she had forgotten to take the usual precautions, and maybe now she was pregnant and then what? They wanted to know what I thought should be done and I said: "*Nothing.*" And then Valeska takes me aside and she asks me if I wouldn't care to sleep with her cousin, to break her in, as it were, so that there wouldn't be a repetition of that sort of thing.

The whole thing was cockeyed and we were all laughing hysterically and then we began to drink—the only thing they had in the house was kümmel and it didn't take much to put us under. And then it got more cockeyed because the two of them began to paw me and neither one would let the other do anything. The result was I undressed them both and put them to bed and they fell asleep in each other's arms. And when I walked out, toward five A.M., I discovered I didn't have a cent in my pocket and I tried to bum a nickel from a taxi driver but nothing doing so I took off my fur-lined overcoat and I gave it to him—for a nickel. When I got home my wife was awake and sore as hell because I had stayed out so long. We had a hot discussion and finally I lost my temper and I clouted her and she fell on the floor and began to weep and sob and then the kid woke up and hearing the wife bawling she got frightened and began to scream at the top of her lungs. The girl upstairs came running down to see what was the matter. She was in her kimono and her hair was hanging down her back. In the excitement she got close to me and things happened without either of us intending anything to happen. We put the wife to bed with a wet towel around her forehead and while the girl upstairs was bending over her I stood behind her and lifting her kimono I got it into her and she stood there a long time talking a lot of foolish, soothing nonsense. Finally I climbed into bed with the wife and to my utter amazement she began to cuddle up to me and without saying a word we locked horns and we stayed that way until dawn. I should have been worn out, but instead I was wide-awake, and I lay there beside her planning to take the day off and look up the whore with the beautiful fur whom I was talking to earlier in the day. After that I began to think about another woman, the wife of one of my friends who always twitted me about my indifference. And then I began to think about one after the other—all those whom I had passed up for one reason or another—until finally I fell sound asleep and in the midst of it I had a wet dream. At seven-thirty the alarm went off as usual and as usual I looked at my torn shirt hanging over the chair and I said to myself what's the use and I turned over. At eight o'clock the telephone rang and it was Hymie. Better get over quickly, he said, because there's a strike on. And that's how it went, day after day, and there was no reason for it, except that the whole country was cockeyed and what I relate was going on everywhere, either on a smaller scale or a larger scale, but the same thing everywhere, because it was all chaos and all meaningless.

It went on and on that way, day in and day out for almost five solid years. The continent itself perpetually wracked by cyclones, tornadoes, tidal waves, floods, droughts, blizzards, heat waves, pests, strikes, hold-ups, assassinations, suicides . . . a continuous fever and torment, an eruption, a whirlpool. I was like a man sitting in a lighthouse: below me the wild waves, the rocks, the reefs, the debris of shipwrecked fleets. I could give the danger signal but I was powerless to avert catastrophe. I *breathed* danger and catastrophe. At times the sensation of it was so strong that it belched like fire from my nostrils. I longed to be free of it all and yet I was irresistibly attracted. I was violent and phlegmatic at the same time. I was like the lighthouse itself—secure in the midst of the most turbulent sea. Beneath me was solid rock, the same shelf of rock on which the towering skyscrapers were reared. My foundations went deep into the earth and the armature of my body was made of steel riveted with hot bolts. Above all I was an eye, a huge searchlight which scoured far and wide, which revolved ceaselessly, pitilessly. This eye so wide-awake seemed to have made all my other faculties dormant; all my powers were used up in the effort to see, to take in the drama of the world.

If I longed for destruction it was merely that this eye might be extinguished. I longed for an earthquake, for some cataclysm of nature which would plunge the lighthouse into the sea. I wanted a metamorphosis, a change to fish, to leviathan, to destroyer. I wanted the earth to open up, to swallow everything in one engulfing yawn. I wanted to see the city buried fathoms deep in the bosom of the sea. I wanted to sit in a cave and read by candlelight. I wanted that eye extinguished so that I might have a chance to know my own body, my own desires. I wanted to be alone for a thousand years in order to reflect on what I had seen and heard—*and in order to forget.* I wanted something of the earth which was not of man's doing, something absolutely divorced from the human of which I was surfeited. I wanted something purely terrestrial and absolutely divested of idea. I wanted to feel the blood running back into my veins, even at the cost of annihilation. I wanted to shake the stone and the light out of my system. I wanted the dark fecundity of nature, the deep well of the tomb, silence, or else the lapping of the black waters of death. I wanted to be that night which the remorseless eye illuminated, a night diapered with stars and trailing comets. To be of night so frighteningly silent, so utterly incomprehensible and eloquent at the same time. Never more to speak or to listen or to think. To be englobed and encompassed and to encompass and to englobe at the same time. No more pity, no more tenderness. To be human only terrestrially, like a plant or a worm or a brook. To be decomposed, divested of light and stone, variable as the molecule, durable as the atom, heartless as the earth itself.

* * *

It was just about a week before Valeska committed suicide that I ran into Mara. The week or two preceding that event was a veritable nightmare. A series of sudden deaths and strange encounters with women. First of all there was Pauline Janowski, a little Jewess of sixteen or seventeen who was without a home and without friends or relatives. She came to the office looking for a job. It was toward closing time and I didn't have the heart to turn her down cold. For some reason or other I took it into my head to bring her home for dinner and if possible try to persuade the wife to put her up for a while. What attracted me to her was her passion for Balzac. All the way home she was talking to me about *Lost Illusions*. The car was packed and we were jammed so tight together that it didn't make any difference what we were talking about because we were both thinking of only one thing. My wife of course was stupefied to see me standing at the door with a beautiful young girl. She was polite and courteous in her frigid way but I could see immediately that it was no use asking her to put the girl up. It was about all she could do to sit through the dinner with us. As soon as we had finished she excused herself and went to the movies. The girl started to weep. We were still sitting at the table, the dishes piled up in front of us. I went over to her and I put my arms around her. I felt genuinely sorry for her and I was perplexed as to what to do for her. Suddenly she threw her arms around my neck and she kissed me passionately. We stood there a long while embracing each other and then I thought to myself no, it's a crime, and besides maybe the wife didn't go to the movies at all, maybe she'll be ducking back any minute. I told the kid to pull herself together, that we'd take a trolley ride somewhere. I saw the child's bank lying on the mantelpiece and I took it to the toilet and emptied it silently. There was only about seventy-five cents in it. We got on a trolley and went to the beach. Finally we found a deserted spot and we lay down in the sand. She was hysterically passionate and there was nothing to do but to do it. I thought she would reproach me afterwards, but she didn't. We lay there a while and she began talking about Balzac again. It seems she had ambitions to be a writer herself. I asked her what she was going to do. She said she hadn't the least idea. When we got up to go she asked me to put her on the highway. Said she thought she would go to Cleveland or some place. It was after midnight when I left her standing in front of a gas station. She had about thirty-five cents in her pocketbook. As I started homeward I began cursing my wife for the mean bitch that she was. I wished to Christ it was she whom I had left standing on the highway with no place to go to. I knew that when I got back she wouldn't even mention the girl's name.

I got back and she was waiting up for me. I thought she was going to give me hell again. But no, she had waited up because there was an important message from O'Rourke. I was to telephone him soon as I got home. However, I decided not to telephone. I decided to get undressed and go to bed. Just when I had gotten comfortably settled the telephone rang. It was O'Rourke. There was a telegram for me at the office—he wanted to know if he should open it and read it to me. I said of course. The telegram was signed Monica. It was from Buffalo. Said she was arriving at the Grand Central in the morning with her mother's body. I thanked him and went back to bed. No questions from the wife. I lay there wondering what to do. If I were to comply with the request that would mean starting things all over again. I had just been thanking my stars that I had gotten rid of Monica. And now she was coming back with her mother's corpse. Tears and reconciliation. No, I didn't like the prospect at all. Supposing I didn't show up? There was always somebody around to take care of a corpse. Especially if the bereaved were an attractive young blonde with sparkling blue eyes. I wondered if she'd go back to her job in the restaurant. If she hadn't known Greek and Latin I would never have been mixed up with her. But my curiosity got the better of me. And then she was so goddamned poor, that too got me. Maybe it wouldn't have been so bad if her hands hadn't smelled greasy. That was the fly in the ointment—the greasy hands. I remember the first night I met her and we strolled through the park. She was ravishing to look at, and she was alert and intelligent. It was just the time when women were wearing short skirts and she wore them to advantage. I used to go to the restaurant night after night just to watch her moving around, watch her bending over to serve or stooping down to pick up a fork. And with the beautiful legs and the bewitching eyes a marvelous line about Homer, with the pork and sauerkraut a verse of Sappho's, the Latin conjugations, the odes of Pindar, with the dessert perhaps *The Rubaiyat* or *Cynara.* But the greasy hands and the frowsy bed in the boarding house opposite the marketplace—Whew! I couldn't stomach it. The more I shunned her the more clinging she became. Ten-page letters about love with footnotes on *Thus Spake Zarathustra.* And then suddenly silence and me congratulating myself heartily. No, I couldn't bring myself to go to the Grand Central Station in the morning. I rolled over and I fell sound asleep. In the morning I would get the wife to telephone the office and say I was ill. I hadn't been ill now for over a week—it was coming to me.

At noon I find Kronski waiting for me outside the office. He wants me to have lunch with him . . . there's an Egyptian girl he wants me to meet. The girl turns out to be a Jewess, but she came from Egypt and she looks like an Egyptian. She's hot stuff and the two of us are working on her at once. As I was supposed to be ill I decided not to return to the office but to take a stroll through the East Side. Kronski was going back to cover me up. We shook hands with the girl and we each went our separate ways. I headed toward the river where it was cool, having forgotten about the girl almost immediately. I sat on the edge of the pier with my legs dangling over the stringpiece. A scow passed with a load of red bricks. Suddenly Monica came to my mind. Monica arriving at the Grand Central Station with a corpse. A corpse f. o. b. New York! It seemed so incongruous and ridiculous that I burst out laughing. What had she done with it? Had she checked it or had she left it on a siding? No doubt she was cursing me out roundly. I wondered what she would really think if she could have imagined me sitting there at the dock with my legs dangling over the stringpiece. It was warm and sultry despite the breeze that was blowing off the river. I began to snooze. As I dozed off Pauline came to my mind. I imagined her walking along the highway with her hand up. She was a brave kid, no doubt about it. Funny that she didn't seem to worry about getting knocked up. Maybe she was so desperate she didn't care. And Balzac! That too was highly incongruous. Why Balzac? Well, that was her affair. Anyway she'd have enough to eat with, until she met another guy. But a kid like that thinking about becoming a writer! Well, why not? Everybody had illusions of one sort or another. Monica too wanted to be a writer. Everybody was becoming a writer. A writer! Jesus, how futile it seemed!

I dozed off. . . . When I woke up I had an erection. The sun seemed to be burning right into my fly. I got up and I washed my face at the drinking fountain. It was still as hot and sultry as ever. The asphalt was soft as mush, the flies were biting, the garbage was rotting in the gutter. I walked about between the pushcarts and looked at things with an empty eye. I had a sort of lingering hard on all the while, but no definite object in mind. It was only when I got back to Second Avenue that I suddenly remembered the Egyptian Jewess from lunch time. I remembered her saying that she lived over the Russian restaurant near Twelfth Street. Still I hadn't any definite idea of what I was going to do. Just browsing about, killing time. My feet nevertheless were dragging me northward, toward Fourteenth Street. When I got abreast of the Russian restaurant I paused a moment and then I ran up the stairs three at a time. The hall door was open. I climbed up a couple of flights scanning the names on the doors. She was on the top floor and there was a man's name under hers. I knocked softly. No answer. I knocked again, a little harder. This time

I heard some one moving about. Then a voice close to the door, asking who is it and at the same time the knob turning. I pushed the door open and stumbled into the darkened room. Stumbled right into her arms and felt her naked under the half-opened kimono. She must have come out of a sound sleep and only half realized who was holding her in his arms. When she realized it was me she tried to break away but I had her tight and I began kissing her passionately and at the same time backing her up toward the couch near the window. She mumbled something about the door being open but I wasn't taking any chance on letting her slip out of my arms. So I made a slight detour and little by little I edged her toward the door and made her shove it to with her ass. I locked it with my one free hand and then I moved her into the center of the room and with the free hand I unbuttoned my fly and got my pecker out and into position. She was so drugged with sleep that it was almost like working on an automaton. I could see too that she was enjoying the idea of being fucked half asleep. The only thing was that every time I made a lunge she grew more wide-awake. And as she grew more conscious she became more frightened. It was difficult to know how to put her to sleep again without losing a good fuck. I managed to tumble her on to the couch without losing ground and she was hot as hell now, twisting and squirming like an eel. From the time I had started to maul her I don't think she had opened her eyes once. I kept saying to myself—"an Egyptian fuck . . . an Egyptian fuck"—and so as not to shoot off immediately I deliberately began thinking about the corpse that Monica had dragged to the Grand Central Station and about the thirty-five cents that I had left with Pauline on the highway. Then bango! A loud knock on the door and with that she opens her eyes wide and looks at me in utmost terror. I started to pull away quickly but to my surprise she held me tight. "Don't move," she whispered in my ear. "Wait!" There was another loud knock and then I heard Kronski's voice saying "It's me, Thelma . . . it's me, *Izzy*." At that I almost burst out laughing. We slumped back again into a natural position and as her eyes softly closed I moved it around inside her, gently, so as not to wake her up again. It was one of the most wonderful fucks I ever had in my life. I thought it was going to last forever. Whenever I felt in danger of going off I would stop moving and think—think for example of where I would like to spend my vacation, if I got one, or think of the shirts lying in the bureau drawer, or the patch in the bedroom carpet just at the foot of the bed. Kronski was still standing at the door—I could hear him changing about from one position to another. Every time I became aware of him standing there I jibbed her a little for good measure and in her half sleep she answered back, humorously, as though she understood what I meant by this put-and-take language. I didn't dare to think what she might be thinking or I'd have come immediately. Sometimes I skirted dangerously close to it, but the saving trick was always Monica and the corpse at the Grand Central Station. The thought of that, the humorousness of it, I mean, acted like a cold douche.

When it was all over she opened her eyes wide and stared at me, as though she were taking me in for the first time. I hadn't a word to say to her; the only thought in my head was to get out as quickly as possible. As we were washing up I noticed a note on the floor near the door. It was from Kronski. His wife had just been taken to the hospital—he wanted her to meet him at the hospital. I felt relieved! It meant that I could break away without wasting any words.

The next day I had a telephone call from Kronski. His wife had died on the operating table. That evening I went home for dinner; we were still at the table when the bell rang. There was Kronski standing at the gate looking absolutely sunk. It was always difficult for me to offer words of condolence; with him it was absolutely impossible. I listened to my wife uttering her trite words of sympathy and I felt more than ever disgusted with her. "Let's get out of here," I said.

We walked along in absolute silence for a while. At the park we turned in and headed for the meadows. There was a heavy mist which made it impossible to see a yard ahead. Suddenly, as we were swimming along, he began to sob. I stopped and turned my head away. When I thought he had finished I looked around and there he was staring at me with a strange smile. "It's funny," he said, "how hard it is to accept death." I smiled too now and put my hand on his shoulder. "Go on," I said, "talk your head off. Get it off your chest." We started walking again, up and down over the meadows, as though we were walking under the sea. The mist had become so thick that I could just barely discern his features. He was talking quietly and madly. "I knew it would happen," he said. "It was too beautiful to last." The night before she was taken ill he had had a dream. He dreamt that he had lost his identity. "I was stumbling around in the dark calling my own name. I remember coming to a bridge, and looking down into the water I saw myself drowning. I jumped off the bridge head first and when I came up I saw Yetta floating under the bridge. She was dead." And then suddenly he added: "You were there yesterday when I knocked at the door, weren't you? I knew you were there and I couldn't go away. I knew too that Yetta was dying and I wanted to be with her, but I was afraid to go alone." I said nothing and he rambled on. "The first girl I ever loved died in the same way. I was only a kid and I couldn't get over it. Every night I used to go to the cemetery and sit by her grave. People thought I was out of my mind. I guess I was out of my mind. Yesterday, when I was standing at the door, it all came back to me. I was back in Trenton, at the grave, and the sister of the girl I loved was sitting beside me. She said it couldn't go on that way much longer, that

I would go mad. I thought to myself that I really was mad and to prove it to myself I decided to do something mad and so I said to her it isn't *her* I love, it's *you,* and I pulled her over me and we lay there kissing each other and finally I screwed her, right beside the grave. And I think that cured me because I never went back there again and I never thought about her any more—until yesterday when I was standing at the door. If I could have gotten hold of you yesterday I would have strangled you. I don't know why I felt that way but it seemed to me that you had opened up a tomb, that you were violating the dead body of the girl I loved. That's crazy, isn't it? And why did I come to see you tonight? Maybe it's because you're absolutely indifferent to me . . . because you're not a Jew and I can talk to you . . . because you don't give a damn, and you're right. . . . Did you ever read *The Revolt of the Angels?*"

We had just arrived at the bicycle path which encircles the park. The lights of the boulevard were swimming in the mist. I took a good look at him and I saw that he was out of his head. I wondered if I could make him laugh. I was afraid, too, that if he once got started laughing he would never stop. So I began to talk at random, about Anatole France at first, and then about other writers, and finally, when I felt that I was losing him, I suddenly switched to General Ivolgin, and with that he began to laugh, not a laugh either, but a cackle, a hideous cackle, like a rooster with its head on the block. It got him so badly that he had to stop and hold his guts; the tears were streaming down his eyes and between the cackles he let out the most terrible, heartrending sobs. "I knew you would do me good," he blurted out, as the last outbreak died away. "I always said you were a crazy son of a bitch. . . . You're a Jew bastard yourself, only you don't know it. . . . Now tell me, you bastard, how was it yesterday? Did you get your end in? Didn't I tell you she was a good lay?

And do you know who she's living with? Jesus, you were lucky you didn't get caught. She's living with a Russian poet —you know the guy, too. I introduced you to him once at the Café Royal. Better not let him get wind of it. He'll beat your brains out . . . and then he'll write a beautiful poem about it and send it to her with a bunch of roses. Sure, I knew him out in Stelton, in the anarchist colony. His old man was a Nihilist. The whole family's crazy. By the way, you'd better take care of yourself. I meant to tell you that the other day, but I didn't think you would act so quickly. You know she may have syphilis."

4. Narcissism

The gusto of Miller's relation to sex is so outside the clam-like formulations of conventional psychoanalysis that it is probably incumbent to make a pass at the psychology of his sexual patterns. Some possible psychology, at any rate. Who can conceive today of a man without a psychology? On the other hand, let it be done in modesty. To analyze the sexuality of another person, any other person, is unattractive; it is not even a question of taste but philosophy. The implicit assumption is that the person who performs the analysis is sexually superior to the subject. One is equal at such times to a writer for Time who assigns objectivity to himself.

To analyze anyone's sexuality assumes we know what sex is about; even the assumption is offensive. But to suggest we know the psychological patterns of a great writer is doubly irritating. As soon talk about the real secret in the reflexes of a great athlete. Nonetheless, by the style of this apology, it is obvious some attempt is going to be made. There is a modern vanity which thrusts us into the dissection of our betters. Besides, in the case of Henry Miller, a species of cop-out exists. To the degree we come to know Miller's psychic apparatus, we can claim sympathy with the difficulty of what he managed to achieve.

Told often enough by the victim, Miller comes from a mother from whom he admits to receiving no love. In his childhood he is, so far as his parents have influence, hermetically *sealed against sexuality. Whatever sex is, it is on the other side of the wall. His first and fundamental relation to a woman is detestation. A grand beginning! To it he adds the formative logic of an eight-year-old. To anyone familiar with Miller, the next scene is peculiarly subdued in the writing. If he is telling the truth (and on reflection we can hardly be certain he is), then he killed a boy in a gang fight at the age of eight by hitting him in the temple with a stone.*

> I'm thinking now about the rock fight one summer's afternoon long long ago when I was staying with my Aunt Caroline up near Hell Gate. My cousin Gene and I had been corralled by a gang of boys while we were playing in the park. We didn't know which side we were fighting for but we were fighting in dead earnest amidst the rock pile by the river bank. We had to show even more courage than the other boys because we were suspected of being sissies. That's how it happened that we killed one of the rival gang. Just as they were charging us my cousin Gene let go at the ringleader and caught him in the guts with a handsome-sized rock. I let go almost at the same instant and my rock caught him in the temple and when he went down he lay there for good and not a peep out of him. A few minutes later the cops came and the boy was found dead. He was eight or nine years old, about the same age as us. What they would have done to us if they had caught us I don't know. Anyway, so as not to arouse any suspicion we hurried home; we had cleaned up a bit on the way and had combed our hair. We walked in looking almost as immaculate as when we had left the house. Aunt Caroline gave us our usual two big slices of sour rye with fresh butter and a little sugar over it and we sat there at the kitchen table listening to her with an angelic smile. It was an extremely hot day and she thought we had better stay in the house, in the big front room where the blinds had been pulled down, and play marbles with our little friend Joey Kasselbaum. Joey had the reputation of being a little back-

> ward and ordinarily we would have trimmed him, but that afternoon, by a sort of mute understanding, Gene and I allowed him to win everything we had. Joey was so happy that he took us down to his cellar later and made his sister pull up her dress and show us what was underneath. Weesie, they called her, and I remember that she was stuck on me instantly. I came from another part of the city, so far away it seemed to them, that it was almost like coming from another country. They even seemed to think that I talked differently from them. Whereas the other urchins used to pay to make Weesie lift her dress, for us it was done with love. After a while we persuaded her not to do it any more for the other boys—we were in love with her and we wanted her to go straight.
>
> *Tropic of Capricorn*

After war and good chow comes this natural readiness for love. The story offers a bit of help in accounting for the good humor in the murderous cold accounts he will later give of women's reactions as he is tooling them, a good Brooklyn substitute for fornication. Three-quarters of the women to whom he makes love are tooled quicker than they are fucked. Miller comes after all out of a milieu where sex has something wrong with it if it is not sordid. The last contractive spasm of the Victorian age may have been throttling the sexuality of Miller's parents and the parents of everyone around him (as if every late Victorian working-class and middle-class Brooklyn parent had a nightmarish vision of a disordered sexual chaos to come), but the children were loose. Sex was stinky-pinky back in Brooklyn at the turn of the century (and for a good part of the next forty years). Sex and filth were components of the same equation, as related as mass and energy—tender sex was a flower you shoved up a girl's ass. Sex was a function of filth; filth was a function of sex—no surprise that sex was getting ready for the automobile, and the smell of gasoline would prove the new aphrodisiac. Henry Miller's milieu was incapable of experiencing sex without the power relation of sex. In a fight one man may beat another man's head against the ground. In sex, in dirty sex, the tastes are ground into the other's mouth and cowardice is expiated by going down. Beyond dirt is karma.

They weren't thinking of karma, however, in Miller's Brooklyn. Sex was hunting season. "How far did you get with her?" went the question. "Hit a triple." Which is to say my hand got into her wet pussy. Needless to say, in the land of the filthy fuck, all pussies are wet. Sexuality was a river of grease in the crack of the taboo.

That was his environment. With a sexy loving mother, he would still have seen sex as dirty. With his own home-grown family strictures against sexuality, a part of Miller had to see sex as equal to disembowelling a garbage can. It is his achievement that he didn't end as a rapist, a suicide, or a monk. Instead he made what moves he could to extricate himself from a doomed relation to sexuality. If he never succeeded altogether in being able to love a woman, or at least never so deeply that he could enter the literary lists against Lawrence (whom he tried to write about for years), he did pry himself out of a sexual pit and it was a true climb up the inside of a chimney: he proceeded to have his first serious affair with that woman old enough to be his mother. All the while he was still feeling love for the blonde blue-eyed near-mythical girl he could not have and never touched. At least he has forged an ideal of love. Of course, he will never reach that love and on the consequence will never cease in some classic part of himself to pine for the girl.

> From the rear windows of the flat we occupied, my mistress and I, I could look into the bedroom of the one I loved, the one I swore to love forever. She was married and had a child. At the time I was ignorant of the fact that she was living in this house across the

yard; I never dreamed that it was *she* whose silhouette loomed before my eyes, and *me* filled with blackest misery. If only I had known, how grateful I would have been to sit forever before the window, aye, even in muck and filth. No, never once during those agonizing sessions did I suspect that she was there, less than a stone's throw away, almost within my grasp. *Almost!* If only, when calling her name in vain, I had thought to open the window! She would have heard. She might have answered.

Crawling into bed with the other I would pass heart-breaking hours wondering about the one who was lost to me. Exhausted, I would fall back into the deep pit. What an abominable form of suicide! I not only destroyed myself and the love that devoured me, I destroyed everything that came my way, including the one who clung to me desperately in sleep. I had to annihilate the world which had made me its victim.

The World of Sex

Still, he has moved from his family's detestation of sex to some sense of sexual pleasure however full of misery. After a few years he will marry a woman he never fails to describe as a prissy and/or puritanical bitch.

With this one the war of the sexes began in earnest. Her musical talent, which was the magnet of attraction, soon took second place. She was an hysterical, lascivious, puritanical bitch whose crack was hidden beneath a tangled mat of hair that looked for all the world like a sporran. The first time my fingers came in contact with it was of an evening during the early days of our courtship. She had stretched herself out on the radiator to warm up. She had nothing on but a silk dressing gown. The tuft of hair between her legs stood out so prominently that it almost looked as if she had a head of cauliflower hidden beneath her wrap. To her horror and amazement I made a grab for it. She was that startled I thought she would jump out of her skin. There was nothing for it but to grab my hat and coat and—bolt. In the hallway, at the head of the stairs, she caught up with me; she was still trembling, still dazed, but obviously unwilling to let me depart in such precipitate fashion. Under a flickering gas jet I held her in my arms and did my best to soothe her ruffled feelings. She responded with warm embraces. I concluded that everything was okey-dokey again. (A few more minutes, thought I to myself, and we'll be back in her snug little room making honey.) Unbuttoning my overcoat as discreetly as possible, I opened my fly. Then I gently took her hand and closed it around my pecker. That was the climax! With a shudder she let go of it and burst into a spasm of tears. I left her there in the hallway and, scampering down the long flight of stairs, I fled into the street. The following day I received a letter saying that she hoped never to see me again.

A few days later, however, I was back. Again she stretched out on the radiator, clad only in the silk dressing gown. This time I was a little more tactful. Casually, as it were, I ran my fingers lightly over the dressing gown. Her thick bush seemed to be full of electricity; the hair stood up stiff and crackly, like a wire sponge. It was necessary, in this approach, to maintain a running stream of chatter about music and other lofty subjects, while stroking her in absent-minded fashion. By resorting to this dodge I enabled her, or so I surmised, to tell herself that there was no harm in such deportment. In the kitchen later she showed me a few stunts she had learned in boarding school; these acrobatic enticements served, of course, to reveal her figure to full advantage. Every time her dressing sack fell open it disclosed the rich growth of fungus which was her secret pride. Tantalizing, to say the least.

Things went on this way for several weeks before she forgot herself. Even then she didn't abandon herself completely. The first time she lay down for it she insisted that I try to do it through her night gown. Not only was she mortally afraid of being knocked up, she wanted to test me. Should I give in to her whims and caprices, she would be able and willing to trust me all the way. That was her logic.

Gradually, very gradually, she began to react like a normal human being. Occasionally I would pay her a call in the middle of the day. I always had to proffer the excuse that I came to hear her play. It would never do to walk in and grab hold of her immediately. If I took a seat in the corner and listened to her attentively she might stop half way through a sonata and come over to me of her own accord, let me run my hand up her leg, and finally straddle me. With the orgasm she would sometimes have a weeping fit. Doing it in broad daylight always awakened her sense of guilt. (The way she voiced it was that it deteriorated her keyboard technique.) Anyway, the better the fuck the worse she felt afterwards. "You don't really care for *me*," she would say. "All you're after is sex." By dint of repeating it a thousand times it became a fact. I was already fed up with her by the time we legalized the relationship.

The World of Sex

It remains a curious relation. He detests his wife but loves to fuck her. There is nothing in literature to compare to the accounts he gives in Tropic of Capricorn *and* Sexus *of making love to other women—they read like round by round AP wire stories. Returning to his wife, he will have a predictable itch to make love to her even if she is asleep. Then he meets June, and a short time later leaves his wife. By every one of his descriptions he is altogether in love with June (who is first called Mara, then Mona, in* Tropic of Cancer, Capricorn *and* The Rosy Crucifixion*). Still he continues to fuck his ex-wife. He enjoys her more than ever. It is as if every man must have in addition to everything else a sexy statue—some embodiment (here prissy) of all the non-sexuality and anti-sexuality imbibed from all the cold and disinterested women of childhood, and yet succeed somehow in converting that cold marble to flesh sweet and happy at room temperature. So* he makes love to his ex-wife like a pirate opening a chest or a terrorist blowing up a factory, a sex murderer whose weapon is his phallus. It is social artifice he would slay first, and hypocrisy, and all the cancers of bourgeois suffocation. "Take that, you cunt," is his war cry. Yet the enigma of woman's nature (if she has, that is, a nature, and is not merely a person altogether equal, hoof to human hoof, with man), the enigma, if it exists, is that women respond to him, of course they do, it is the simple knowledge of the street that murderers are even sexier than athletes. Something in a woman wishes to be killed went the old wisdom before Women's Liberation wiped that out, something in a woman wishes to be killed, and it is obvious what does—she would like to lose the weakest part of herself, have it ploughed under, ground under, kneaded, tortured, squashed, sliced, banished, and finally immolated. Burn out my dross is the unspoken cry of his girls—in every whore is an angel burning her old rags.

It is a pure period of his life. He is in sex for the kill and will later write about it better than anyone ever has. (The kill.) But we are far from arriving at the truth of him. He is not Henry Miller who can sublimate murder into sex, and nothing more. No, he is Henry Miller, the man of metamorphoses. The first of the lovers in him, and it will never leave him altogether, is the stud with a rock for a cock and a rock for a heart—so he will present himself. That is the first manifest of himself as a lover. Others are to follow.

June (Mona) has been met in a dancehall in 1923. She is to prove the love of his life. In writing about that love, he begins an infatuation with the number seven equal to Mann's in The Magic Mountain. He speaks of the first seven days of their meeting, and the seven years of their relation (which came to an end of sorts in 1930 when he went off to Europe alone—although they were to live together on and off for another few years). He must bring himself up to the point of trying to write about her at least seven times. In Tropic of Cancer he is about to begin more than once, and Tropic of Capricorn could be described as a book written entirely around the difficulty of trying to write about her. Forget the number seven—it will still take six years from the time of their divorce in 1934 before he can undertake to describe their affair and marriage in anything like novelistic fashion, and The Rosy Crucifixion, which just about covers the day-to-day movement of their five years of excursions and capers together in New York is a novel of 1600 pages. If the first book Sexus was begun in 1940 it was not finished until 1945, and Plexus took from 1947 to 1949. Nexus, the final volume, was not even started until 1952 nor done until 1959. He has spent close to twenty years on his magnum opus! Of course, he has written other books in the same time, The Air-Conditioned Nightmare, The Time of the Assassins, The Books in My Life, Big Sur and The Oranges of Hieronymus Bosch plus some smaller works, but in comparison to the prodigies of talent he exhibited in the thirties with Tropic of Cancer, Black Spring and Tropic of Capricorn, he is something like half the writer stretched out to twice the length.

He is also, of course, now old for a writer. His work on The Rosy Crucifixion corresponds almost exactly to his fifties and his sixties. He is not far from seventy when he is done, yet the mysteries of his relation with Mona have so beguiled him that he has spent thirty-six obsessive years living with her and writing about her and never succeeds, never quite, in making her real to us, as novelistically real as Anna Karenina or Emma Bovary. She hovers in that space between the actual and the fictional where everything is just out of focus. Indeed Anaïs Nin in one page of her diary succeeds in making Mona as vivid as Miller ever can. (Yet, no more real.)

Henry came to Louveciennes with June.

As June walked toward me from the darkness of the garden into the light of the door, I saw for the first time the most beautiful woman on earth. A startlingly white face, burning dark eyes, a face so alive I felt it would consume itself before my eyes. Years ago I tried to imagine a true beauty; I created in my mind an image of just such a woman. I had never seen her until last night. Yet I knew long ago the phosphorescent color of her skin, her huntress profile, the evenness of her teeth. She is bizarre, fantastic, nervous, like someone in a high fever. Her beauty drowned me. As I sat before her, I felt I would do anything she asked of me. Henry suddenly faded. She was color and brilliance and strangeness. By the end of the evening I had extricated myself from her power. She killed my admiration by her talk. Her talk. The enormous ego, false, weak, posturing. She lacks the courage of her personality, which is sensual, heavy with experience. Her role alone preoccupies her. She invents drama in which she always stars. I am sure she creates genuine dramas, genuine chaos and whirlpools of feelings, but I feel that her share in it is a pose. That night, in spite of my response to her, she sought to be whatever she felt I wanted her to be. She is an actress every moment. I cannot grasp the core of June. Everything Henry had said about her is true.

By the end of the evening I felt as Henry did, fascinated with her face and body which promises so much, but hating her invented self which hides the true one.

The Diary of Anaïs Nin

Curious! If we fix on Miller's mind rather than June's beauty, Nin could be giving a description of his talent: startling, burning, phosphorescent, bizarre, fantastic, nervous, in high fever, *full of* color, brilliance *and* strangeness *but possessed of an* enormous ego, false, weak, posturing *and finally* lacking the courage of its personality, *leaving behind* chaos *and* whirlpools of feeling. Yet it may be all a pose. One cannot grasp the core of Henry Miller, and one can come near to hating (his) invented self which hides the true one.

It works. If one is to judge Miller's talent by the vices of his mind, the result is not unequal to the flaws in June's beauty. No wonder they have seven years together. It is a relation which proves obsessive but consistently changeable; fixed in compulsion yet stripped of roots; emotional as blood and yet as insecure as emotion itself. She will take him a long way in seven good and bad years from the cold mean calculating street-fucker, the hard-nosed Brooklyn hard-on by which he was still picturing himself when they met. He is one stud who has met more than his equal. She is more enterprising than he, wiser about the world, more subtly aggressive, a better hustler. Before a year is out, she has convinced him to quit work and try to write while she will make their living. If ever there is an inner movement in his life, it is here, indeed we are witness to his first metamorphosis. He shifts from an intelligent and second-rate promoter of bad debts, and some riotous Brooklyn nights, to a faithful and tortured young writer helplessly in love with a Junoesque woman whose maddening lack of center leads him into an intuition of his own lack of identity. He comes to discover all those modern themes which revolve around the discovery of oneself. Soon he will dive into the pit of recognizing that there may not be a geological fundament in the psyche one can call identity. Like June, he will have to re-create himself each morning, and soon realizes he has been doing it all his life. He has never looked back in moral guilt because whatever act he committed yesterday, and it could have been atrocious, heinous, or incommensurately disloyal to what he thought he believed or loved, it hardly mattered. He could look yesterday's act in the eye because the man who did it was no longer himself. In the act of doing it, he became another *man, free to go in another direction. It can be 180° away from yesterday's attempt. Tomorrow he may be close again to the man he was day before yesterday, but never the same. He has passed from the sublimation of murder (by way of a sullen intent cock) to the liberation of the self from every cancer-habit of the past. Since he has a life full of adventure, debts, mishaps and constant on-coming lack of funds, since June brings in their living as irregularly as changes in the weather, so there is no nicety to his liberation, no, Miller's psychic life is equal to a scatback scampering upfield on a punt return. He can lose ten yards as easily as gain them. And his head is forever ringing from the last concussion.*

His confusion, however, is great; his passivity feels pervasive. He has changed from a stand-up hallway-fucker to a somewhat indolent husband-pimp. His wife is having the adventures, and he is home doing the writing, sometimes the cooking. He is in the untidy situation of a man who lives with a Brooklyn moral code for sex, "If she won't screw, she's frigid; if she does, she's a whore," yet the wife is a consummate liar, and makes money off men to the tune of hundred dollar bills dropped in from the sky, never tells him how, a woman even more changeable than himself and vastly more bisexual—their love will crash finally when she brings home a girl to live with them, and becomes hooked on the girl. Sixteen hundred pages of The Rosy Crucifixion *will founder on Miller's inability to penetrate these depths, or even come near them. He was brought up by a moral code which taught that love was attached to the living room; one's family was one's house. The living room carpet was one's rock. Now he floats in a fluid as limitless as amniotic fluid. He has no limbs and his feet are over his head, his eyes smell sounds and his nose hears colors, he is living with a woman even more incredible than himself. All the while he is becoming an artist. He is moving away from the use of himself as a skilled and stealthy* sex murderer who can instill small deaths into every hot and humping fornication. Now, he is emerging as a narcissist at loose in the uncategorizability of his own experience.

It is too simple to think of the narcissist as someone in love with himself. One can detest oneself intimately and still be a narcissist. What characterizes narcissism is the fundamental relation. It is with oneself. The same dialectic of love and hate that mates feel for one another is experienced within the self. But then a special kind of insanity calls to the narcissist. The inner dialogue hardly ever ceases. Like animals are each half of themselves and forever scrutinizing the other. So two narcissists in love are the opposite of two mates who may feel a bond powerful as the valence holding the atoms of a molecule together. Narcissists, in contrast, are linked up into themselves. They do not join each other so much as approach one another like crystals brought into juxtaposition. They have a passionate affair to the degree each allows the other to resonate more fully than when alone. Two narcissists might live together for fifty years in every appearance of matrimonial solidity (although it probably helps if money is present) but essentially, no matter how considerate they may be of one another, the courtesies come more from a decision to be good to the other than issuing from a love which will go forth whether one wills it or not. The narcissistic relation insists that the other continue to be good for one's own resonance. In the profoundest sense, one narcissist is never ready to die for the other. It is not love we may encounter so much as fine tuning. Small wonder that the coming together of narcissists is the natural matrimony of the Technological Century. Small wonder that Henry Miller, the last great American pioneer, is first to boff and bang his way across this last psychological frontier, there first with the most. No love in literature is so long recounted as his 1600-page affair and marriage and separation from his Mona. The Rosy Crucifixion becomes one of the greatest failures in the history of the novel, a literary cake large as the Himalayas which fails to rise. And across half at least of its sixteen hundred pages are peaks and avenues and haunches and battlements and arêtes and basins and summits and valleys of writing so good one shakes one's head. Pity the poor aspiring mediocrity of a writer who reads Miller without protection—he will never write another word if he has any decency left. Pity for that matter the good writer. At times Miller is too good.

Yet The Rosy Crucifixion is one of the monumental failures of world literature. For those sixteen hundred pages, Miller knocks on the door of ultimate meaning and it never opens a crack. By the end he is where he was at the beginning at least so far as sexual satori is concerned. I-got-laid-and-it-was-wondrous is the opening theme of the book, and by the end not one new philosophical connection has been laid onto that first lay. Miller and the reader know no more of the intimate wonders beneath the first wonder after the book is done.

An obvious critical impulse is to decide the work is too long. But on examination it cannot be cut. Rather, as it stands, it is too fragmentary. Perhaps it should be a novel of four thousand pages. What Miller has bogged into (precisely because he is the first American to make the attempt) is the uncharted negotiations of the psyche when two narcissists take the vow of love. Yet it is finally his own novelistic terrain. Since he has always eschewed politics as a literary subject (he merely issues calumnies against it), since he therefore has also eschewed the incomparably finicky and invaluable literary task of trying to place people in society, he never really writes about society except through metaphor. Since he is a great writer, his metaphors occasionally produce the whole and entire machine of society until it passes over one's brain like an incubus. He does this with his vision of the Cosmodemonic Telegraph Company and the unforgettable metaphor in Tropic of Cancer when Miller and Van Norden are exhaustedly fucking a worn-out whore like men standing up in the trenches.

His preference, however, is to create his literary world through the visions of dreams and the tides of whatever myths he finds appropriate to his use. Since that has to be a perfumed and farty literary game unless there is real novelistic meat on each mythic tendon, Miller naturally goes to sex for his meat. He is not a social writer, but a sexual writer. Even Lawrence never let go of the idea that through sex he could still delineate society; Miller, however, went further. Sex, he assumed, was a natural literary field for the novel, as clear and free and open to a land-grab as any social panorama. One could capture the sex-life of two people in all its profundity and have quite as much to say about the cosmos as any literary plot laid out the other way with its bankers and beggars, ladies and whores, clerks and killers. The real novel, went Miller's assumption, could short-circuit society. Give us the cosmos head on. Give it to us by way of a cunt impaled on a cock.

That is a herculean assumption. Because you need the phallus of Hercules to bring it off (and conceivably the brain of Einstein). A writer works with what he is given, and in Miller's case, for cosmic blast-off, he had a narcissistic cunt on a narcissistic cock and thirty-six years of bewilderment from the day of meeting his love to the hour he finished writing of her. She was so changeable went his everlasting lament.

It is hard enough for a man twisting a pencil through the traps and loops of his handwriting to get a character onto an empty page, but to create someone who shifts all the time! As soon teach one's spine to wind like a snake. The narcissist is always playing roles, and if there is any character harder for an author to create than that writer greater than himself, it may be a great actor. We do not even begin to comprehend the psychology of actors.

The narcissist suffers from too much inner dialogue. The eye of one's consciousness is forever looking at one's own action. Yet these words turn us away from the psychic reality. The narcissist is not self-absorbed so much as one self is absorbed in studying the other. The narcissist is the scientist and the experiment in one. Other people exist for their ability to excite one presence or another in oneself. And are valued for that. Are even loved for that. Of course, they are loved as an actor loves an audience.

Since the amount of stimulation we may offer ourselves is obviously limited, the underlying problem of the narcissist is boredom. So there are feverish and/or violent attempts to shift the given, to alter the context in which one self is forever regarding the other. It is a reason why narcissists are forever falling in and out of love, jobs, places and addictions. Promiscuity is the happy opportunity to try a new role. Vanity is the antidote to claustrophobia. Miller complains bitterly of June's lack of center, her incapacity to tell the truth or even recognize it. "I want the key," he says once to Anaïs Nin, "the key to the lies." As if necessarily blind to himself (for every artist lives in a self-induced blindness which establishes a foundation for his shifting effort) Miller never wants to recognize that the key may be simple. Every day is a scenario for June. On the best of days she creates a life into which she can fit for a few hours. She can feel real love and real hate for strangers, and leave the circle of her own self-absorption. Through scenarios, she can in an hour arrive at depths of emotion other people voyage toward for years, but the scenario once concluded, so, too, is the love for that day. The passing actor she was playing with is again a stranger. It is useless to speak of whether she loves or does not love Miller.

It depends on whether he is a part of her scenario that day. So is it also useless to speak of her lives. They are no more real to her than last year's role for an actor. It is the scenario that is her truth and her life. That is her liberty from the prison cell of the narcissist.

Indeed, part of Miller's continuing literary obsession with his second wife for close to thirty more years is due to the variety of her roles. Each offered a new role for Miller to play opposite. To be living as a detective one day and as a criminal the next is to keep one's interest in one's own personality alive.

Narcissists, after all, do not hand emotion back and forth through their bodies so much as they induce emotion in one another through their minds. It is not their own flesh nor the other's which is felt so quickly as the vibrancy of the role. Their relations are at once more electric and more empty, more perfect and more hollow. So it is possible that narcissism is a true disease, a biological displacement of the impulse to develop which could bear the same relation to love that onanism does to copulation, or cancer to the natural growth of tissue. As we come a little nearer to the recognition that the base beneath all disease, the ultimate disease, is insanity or cancer, and other illnesses may even be bulwarks against some irreversible revolt of the flesh or the mind once they have determined to grow in ways and into places flesh and mind have never grown before, so to the narcissist, there is always the unconscious terror that isolation, if unrelieved, must end in one arm or the other of the ultimate disease.

The paradox is that no love can prove so intense, therefore, as the love of two narcissists for each other. So much depends on it. Each—the paradox turns upon itself—is capable of offering deliverance to the other. To the degree that they tune each other superbly well they begin to create what had before been impossible—they begin to have a skill which enables them to enter the world. (For it is not love of the self but dread at the world outside the self which is the seed of narcissism.) So narcissists can end by having a real need of each other. That is, of course, hardly the characteristic relation. The love of most narcissists tends to become comic, since seen from the outside, their suffering manages to be equalled only by the rapidity with which they recover from suffering.

Of course, the reality is considerably more painful. Given the delicacy of every narcissist and the timidity which created their detachment, we can recognize that the intensity of their relations has to be with themselves. They need an excess of control over external events for their own self-protection. Not too removed in analogy is that excess of control which technology is forever trying to exact from nature, even as the love affairs of technology give back in recollection their own comic atrocity: defoliation of the land in Vietnam, or computerized dating services.

To the degree, however, that narcissism is an affliction of the talented, the stakes are not small, and the victims are playing their own serious game in the midst of the scenarios. If one can only break out of the penitentiary of self-absorption, there are artistic wonders, conceivably, to achieve. Indeed, for a narcissist to stay in love with someone else for a long period is to speak of the fine art of the beloved. They can tune, after all, the unspeakably complex machine of oneself.

Miller may have been playing, therefore, for the highest stakes we can conceive. He had the energy, the vision, the talent, and the outrageous individuality to have some chance of becoming the greatest writer in America's history, a figure equal to Shakespeare. (For Americans.) Of course, to invoke such contrasts is to mock them. A writer cannot live too seriously with the idea that he will or will not beat Tolstoy—he has rather some sense of a huge and not impossible literary destiny in the reverberations of his own ambition; he feels his talent, perhaps, as a trust; so he sees his loves as evil when they balk him. He is living, after all, with his own secret plot. He knows that a writer of the largest dimension can alter the nerves and marrow of a nation; no one, in fact, can measure what collective loss of inner life would have come to English people if Shakespeare had failed to write.

In those seven years with June, Miller was shaping the talent with which he would go out into the world. It is part of the total ambiguity with which he has surrounded himself (despite the ten thousand intimate details he offers of his life) that we do not know by the end of The Rosy Crucifixion whether she breathed a greater life into his talent or exploited him. We do not know if Mona was a Great Ice Lady who chilled a part of him forever, or a beautiful much-abused piece of earth-mother. We do not know if Miller could have become something like an American Shakespeare capable of writing about tyrants and tycoons (instead, repetitively, of his own liberation) if he had never met Mona, whether, that is, she left him frozen in obsession, and The Rosy Crucifixion could have become the most important American novel ever written if not for her; or—we are left wide open—the contrary is the true possibility and he might never have written at all if he had not met her, certainly never become a writer of the major dimension he achieved. All we know is that after seven years of living with her, he went off to Paris alone and learned to live by himself. He had escaped his mother, the blonde with the blue eyes, the reproachful widow, his first wife, and even could work after separation from Mona. He had come into that magical confluence of his life where he could extract a clean and unforgettable esthetic from ogres and sewers. And June after their separation, and divorce in 1934, sinks from view. The last we hear of her is by way of a line in a one-page letter full of news to Anaïs Nin somewhere in the winter of

1954–55. "June, by the way," he writes, "was taken to a mental institution some months ago. Must stop—mailman due any minute. Henry."

We will not know if brutality or stoicism is the foundation of the line, nor will we have a clue to whether he weakened her in their seven years or if she would have been considerably more damaged without him. In The Diary of Anaïs Nin *(1931–1935) there is a heartbreaking comment made by June after she has read some of what Miller has finally written about her. "I expected Henry to do wonderful things with my life," she says. "But instead he reduced it all, vulgarized it, made it shabby and ugly." It is the cry of everyone who has ever been written about when the author failed to share the inner eye of the model. In another place, Anaïs Nin will write of June,*

> She died in Paris. She died the night she read Henry's book (the manuscript version of *Tropic of Cancer*) because of his brutality. She wept and repeated over and over again, "It is not me, it is not me he is writing about. It's a distortion. He says I live in delusions, but it is he, it is he who does not see me, or anyone as I am, as they are. He makes everything ugly."
>
> *The Diary of Anaïs Nin*

Yet even Anaïs Nin, firm as a countess in her percipience, veers first to one side of the marriage in her sympathy, then the other.

> June, having no core of strength, can only prove it by her power to destroy others. Henry, until he knew me, could only assert his strength by attacking June. He caricatured her; she weakened him by protecting him. They devoured each other. And when they succeed in destroying each other, they weep. June wanted Henry to be a Dostoevsky, but she did all she could to make it impossible. She really wanted him to sing her praises, to paint her as an admirable character. It is

only in the light of this that she judges Henry's book a failure. It failed to aggrandize June.

The Diary of Anaïs Nin

Each evaluation overthrows the consistency of the previous one. A clue to the endless mirrors of Miller's relation to June shimmers through this earlier extract from the same diary.

Yesterday Henry came to Louveciennes. A new Henry, or, rather, the Henry I sensed behind the one generally known, the Henry behind the one he has written down. This Henry can understand: he is sentient.

He looked so serious. His violence has burnt itself out. The coarseness, in the alchemy, became strength. He had received a letter from June, in pencil, irregular, mad, like a child's moving, simple cries, of her love for him. "Such a letter blots out everything." I felt the moment had come to expose the June I knew, to give him June, "because it will make you love her more. It's a beautiful June. Other days I felt you might laugh at my portrait, jeer at its naïveté. Today I know you won't."

I let him read all I had written about June.

What is happening? He is deeply moved, torn apart. He believes.

"It is in this way that I should have written about June," he says. "The other is incomplete, superficial. You have got her."

"You leave softness, tenderness out of your work, you write down only the hatred, the rebellions, the violence. I have only inserted what you leave out. What you leave out is not because you don't feel it, or know it, or understand, as you think. It is left out only because it is more difficult to express, and so far, your writing has come out of violence and anger."

I confide in him completely, in the profound Henry. He is won over. He says, "Such love is wonderful. I do not hate or despise that. I see what you give each other. I see it so well. Let me read on. This is a revelation to me." I tremble while he is reading. He understands too well. Suddenly he says, "Anaïs, I have just realized that what I give is something coarse and plain, compared to that. I realize that when June returns. . . ."

I stop him. "You don't know what you have given me! It is not coarse and plain." And then I add, "You see a beautiful June now."

"No, I hate her."

"You hate her?"

"Yes, I hate her," Henry says, "because I see by your notes that we are her dupes, that you are duped, that there is a pernicious, destructive direction to her lies. Insidiously, they are meant to deform me in your eyes, and you in my eyes. If June returns, she will poison us against each other. I fear that."

"There is a friendship between us, Henry, which is not possible for June to understand."

"For that she will hate us, and she will combat us with her own tools."

"What can she use against our understanding of each other?"

"Lies," said Henry.

The Diary of Anaïs Nin

He is speaking like a man who is now in love with Anaïs Nin. It is a worthy Jamesian dialogue. He has come a long way from the boy who has no relation to his mother. But as we shall see in the sections on Mona which follow (and they were written ten years after these entries from Anaïs Nin's diary) a part of Miller has been amputated forever from any comfort in the idea that woman has a character as large as man. No matter. We will not know all of Mona, but we will live through enough to stimulate any knowledge we have acquired already about the dimensions of a heroine.*

---

* In compensation, he will see Woman with a nature large as Nature itself.

From **Tropic of Capricorn**

I remember how the second time I met her she told me that she had never expected to see me again, and the next time I saw her she said she thought I was a dope fiend, and the next time she called me a god, and after that she tried to commit suicide and then I tried and then she tried again, and nothing worked except to bring us closer together, so close indeed that we interpenetrated, exchanged personalities, name, identity, religion, father, mother, brother. Even her body went through a radical change, not once but several times. At first she was big and velvety, like the jaguar, with that silky, deceptive strength of the feline species, the crouch, the spring, the pounce; then she grew emaciated, fragile, delicate, almost like a cornflower, and with each change thereafter she went through the subtlest modulations—of skin, muscle, color, posture, odor, gait, gesture, et cetera. She changed like a chameleon. Nobody could say what she really was like because with each one she was an entirely different person. After a time she didn't even know herself what she was like. She had begun this process of metamorphosis before I met her, as I later discovered. Like so many women who think themselves ugly she had willed to make herself beautiful, dazzlingly beautiful. To do this she first of all renounced her name, then her family, her friends, everything which might attach her to the past. With all her wits and faculties she devoted herself to the cultivation of her beauty, of her charm, which she already possessed to a high degree but which she had been made to believe were nonexistent. She lived constantly before the mirror, studying every movement, every gesture, every slightest grimace. She changed her whole manner of speech, her diction, her intonation, her accent, her phraseology. She conducted herself so skilfully that it was impossible even to broach the subject of origins. She was constantly on her guard, even in her sleep. And, like a good general, she discovered quickly enough that the best defense is attack. She never left a single position unoccupied; her outposts, her scouts, her sentinels were stationed everywhere. Her mind was a revolving searchlight which was never dimmed.

Blind to her own beauty, her own charm, her own personality, to say nothing of her identity, she launched her full powers toward the fabrication of a mythical creature, a Helen, a Juno, whose charms neither man nor woman would be able to resist. Automatically, without the slightest knowledge of legend, she began to create little by little the ontological background, the mythic sequence of events preceeding the conscious birth. She had no need to remember her lies, her fictions—she had only to bear in mind her role. There was no lie too monstrous for her to utter, for in her adopted role she was absolutely faithful to herself. She did not have to *invent* a past: she *remembered* the past which belonged to her. She was never outflanked by a direct question since she never presented herself to an adversary except obliquely. She presented only the angles of the ever-turning facets, the blinding prisms of light which she kept constantly revolving. She was never a being, such as might finally be caught in repose, but the mechanism itself, relentlessly operating the myriad mirrors which would reflect the myth she had created. She had no poise whatsoever; she was eternally poised above her multiple identities in the vacuum of the self. She had not intended to make herself a legendary figure, she had merely wanted her beauty to be recognized. But in the pursuit of beauty, she soon forgot her quest entirely, became the victim of her own creation. She became so stunningly beautiful that at times she was frightening, at times positively uglier than the ugliest woman in the world. She could inspire horror and dread, especially when her charm was at its height. It was as though the will, blind and uncontrollable, shone through the creation, exposing the monster which it is.

In the dark, locked away in the black hole with no world looking on, no adversary, no rivals, the blinding dynamism of the will slowed down a bit, gave her a molten copperish glow, the words coming out of her mouth like lava, her flesh clutching ravenously for a hold, a perch on something solid and substantial, something in which to reintegrate and repose for a few moments. It was like a frantic long-distance message, an S O S from a sinking ship. At first I mistook it for passion, for the ecstasy produced by flesh rubbing against flesh. I thought I had found a living volcano, a female Vesuvius. I never thought of a human ship going down in an ocean of despair, in a Sargasso of impotence. Now I think of that black star gleaming through the hole in the ceiling, that fixed star which hung above our conjugal cell, more fixed, more remote than the Absolute, and I know it was her, emptied of all that was properly herself: a dead black sun without aspect. I know that we were conjugating the verb love like two maniacs trying to fuck through an iron grate. I said that in the frantic grappling in the dark I sometimes forgot her name, what she looked like, who she was. It's true. I overreached myself in the dark. I slid off the flesh rails into the endless space of sex, into the channel-orbits established by this one and that one: Georgiana, for instance, of only a brief afternoon, Thelma, the Egyptian whore, Carlotta, Alannah, Una, Mona, Magda, girls of six or seven; waifs, will-o'-the-wisps, faces, bodies, thighs, a subway brush, a dream, a memory, a desire, a longing.

* * *

The dance hall was just opposite the side entrance of the theater where I used to sit in the afternoons instead of looking for work. It was a street of theaters and I used to sit there for hours at a time dreaming the most violent dreams. The whole theatrical life of New York was concentrated in that one street, so it seemed. It was Broadway, it was success, fame, glitter, paint, the asbestos curtain and the hole in the curtain. Sitting on the steps of the theater I used to stare at the dance hall opposite, at the string of red lanterns which even in the summer afternoons were lit up. In every window there was a spinning ventilator which seemed to waft music into the street, where it was broken by the jangled din of traffic. Opposite the other side of the dance hall was a comfort station and here too I used to sit now and then, hoping either to make a woman or make a touch. Above the comfort station, on the street level, was a kiosk with foreign papers and magazines; the very sight of these papers, of the strange languages in which they were printed, was sufficient to dislocate me for the day.

Without the slightest premeditation I climbed the stairs to the dance hall, went directly to the little window of the booth where Nick, the Greek, sat with a roll of tickets in front of him. Like the urinal below and the steps of the theater, this hand of the Greek now seems to me a separate and detached thing—the enormous hairy hand of an ogre borrowed from some horrible Scandinavian fairy tale. It was the hand which spoke to me always, the hand which said "Miss Mara will not be here tonight," or "Yes, Miss Mara is coming late tonight."

It was this hand which I dreamt of as a child when I slept in the bedroom with the barred window. In my fevered sleep suddenly this window would light up, to reveal the ogre clutching at the bars. Night after night the hairy monster visited me, clutching at the bars and gnashing its teeth. I would awake in a cold sweat, the house dark, the room absolutely silent.

Standing at the edge of the dance floor I notice her coming toward me; she is coming with sails spread, the large full face beautifully balanced on the long, columnar neck. I see a woman perhaps eighteen, perhaps thirty, with blue-black hair and a large white face, a full white face in which the eyes shine brilliantly. She has on a tailored blue suit of duveteen. I remember distinctly now the fullness of her body, and that her hair was fine and straight, parted on the side, like a man's. I remember the smile she gave me—knowing, mysterious, fugitive—a smile that sprang up suddenly, like a puff of wind.

The whole being was concentrated in the face. I could have taken just the head and walked home with it; I could have put it beside me at night, on a pillow, and made love to it. The mouth and the eyes, when they opened up, the whole being glowed from them. There was an illumination which came from some unknown source, from a center hidden deep in the earth. I could think of nothing but the face, the strange, womblike quality of the smile, the engulfing immediacy of it. The smile was so painfully swift and fleeting that it was like the flash of a knife. This smile, this face, was borne aloft on a long white neck, the sturdy, swanlike neck of the medium—and of the lost and the damned.

I stand on the corner under the red lights, waiting for her to come down. It is about two in the morning and she is signing off. I am standing on Broadway with a flower in my buttonhole, feeling absolutely clean and alone. Almost the whole evening we have been talking about Strindberg, about a character of his named Henriette. I listened with such tense alertness that I fell into a trance. It was as if, with the opening phrase, we had started on a race—in opposite directions. Henriette! Almost immediately the name was mentioned she began to talk about herself, without ever quite losing hold of Henriette. Henriette was attached to her by a long, invisible string which she manipulated imperceptibly with one finger, like the street hawker who stands a little removed from the black cloth on the sidewalk, apparently indifferent to the little mechanism which is jiggling on the cloth, but betraying himself by the spasmodic movement of the little finger to which the black thread is attached. Henriette is me, my real self, she seemed to be saying. She wanted me to believe that Henriette was really the incarnation of evil. She said it so naturally, so innocently, with an almost subhuman candor—how was I to believe that she meant it? I could only smile as though to show her I was convinced.

Suddenly I feel her coming. I turn my head. Yes, there she is coming full on, the sails spread, the eyes glowing. For the first time I see now what a carriage she has. She comes forward like a bird, a human bird wrapped in a soft fur. The engine is going full steam: I want to shout, to give a blast that will make the whole world cock its ears. What a walk! It's not a walk, it's a glide. Tall, stately, full-bodied, self-possessed, she cuts the smoke and jazz and red-light glow like the queen mother of all the slippery Babylonian whores. On the corner of Broadway just opposite the comfort station, this is happening. Broadway—it's her realm. This is Broadway, this is New York, this is America. She's America on foot, winged and sexed. She is the lubet, the abominate and the sublimate—with a dash of hydrochloric acid, nitroglycerin, laudanum and powdered onyx. Opulence she has, and magnificence; it's America right or wrong, and the ocean on either side. For the first time in my life the whole continent hits me full force, hits me between the eyes. This is America, buffaloes or no buffaloes, America the emery wheel of hope and disillusionment. Whatever made America made her, bone, blood, muscle, eyeball, gait, rhythm, poise, confidence, brass and hollow gut. She's almost on top of me, the full face gleaming like calcium. The big soft fur is slipping from her shoulder. She doesn't notice it. She doesn't seem to care if her clothes should drop off. She doesn't give a fuck about anything. It's America moving like a streak of lightning toward the glass warehouse of red-blooded hysteria. Amurrica, fur or no fur, shoes or no shoes. Amurrica C.O.D. *And scram, you bastards, before we plug you!* It's got me in the guts, I'm quaking. Something's coming to me and there's no dodging it. She's coming head on, through the plate glass window. If she would only stop a second, if she would only let me be for just one moment. But no, not a single moment does she grant me. Swift, ruthless, imperious, like Fate itself she is on me, a sword cutting me through and through. . . .

She has me by the hand, she holds it tight. I walk beside her without fear. Inside me the stars are twinkling; inside me a great blue vault where a moment ago the engines were pounding furiously.

One can wait a whole lifetime for a moment like this. The woman whom you never hoped to meet now sits before you, and she talks and looks exactly like the person you dreamed about. But strangest of all is that you never realized before that you had dreamed about her. Your whole past is like a long sleep which would have been forgotten had there been no dream. And the dream too might have been forgotten had there been no memory, but remembrance is there in the blood and the blood is like an ocean in which everything is washed away but that which is new and more substantial even than life: REALITY.

We are seated in a little booth in the Chinese restaurant

across the way. Out of the corner of my eye I catch the flicker of the illuminated letters running up and down the sky. She is still talking about Henriette, or maybe it is about herself. Her little black bonnet, her bag and fur are lying beside her on the bench. Every few minutes she lights a fresh cigarette which burns away as she talks. There is no beginning nor end; it spurts out of her like a flame and consumes everything within reach. No knowing how or where she began. Suddenly she is in the midst of a long narrative, a fresh one, but it is always the same. Her talk is as formless as dream: there are no grooves, no walls, no exits, no stops. I have the feeling of being drowned in a deep mesh of words, of crawling painfully back to the top of the net, of looking into her eyes and trying to find there some reflection of the significance of her words—but I can find nothing, nothing, except my own image wavering in a bottomless well. Though she speaks of nothing but herself I am unable to form the slightest image of her being. She leans forward, with elbows on the table, and her words inundate me; wave after wave rolling over me and yet nothing builds up inside me, nothing that I can seize with my mind. She's telling me about her father, about the strange life they led at the edge of Sherwood Forest where she was born, or at least she *was* telling me about this, but now it's about Henriette again, or is it Dostoevski?—I'm not sure—but anyway, suddenly I realize that she's not talking about any of these any more but about a man who took her home one night and as they stood on the stoop saying good-night he suddenly reached down and pulled up her dress. She pauses a moment as though to reassure me that this is what she means to talk about. I look at her bewilderedly. I can't imagine by what route we got to this point. *What man?* What had he been saying to her? I let her continue, thinking that she will probably come back to it, but no, she's ahead of me again and now it seems the man, *this* man, is already dead, a suicide, and she is trying to make me understand that it was an awful blow to her, but what she really seems to convey is that she is proud of the fact that she drove a man to suicide. I can't picture the man as dead; I can only think of him as he stood on her stoop lifting her dress, a man without a name but alive and perpetually fixed in the act of bending down to lift up her dress. There is another man who was her father and I see him with a string of race horses, or sometimes in a little inn just outside Vienna; rather I see him on the roof of the inn flying kites to while the time away. And between this man who was her father and the man with whom she was madly in love I can make no separation. He is someone in her life about whom she would rather not talk, but just the same she comes back to him all the time, and though I'm not sure that it was *not* the man who lifted up her dress neither am I sure that it wasn't the man who committed suicide. Perhaps it's the man whom she started to talk about when we sat down to eat. Just as we were sitting down I remember now that she began to talk rather hectically about a man whom she had just seen entering the cafeteria. She even mentioned his name, but I forgot it immediately. But I remember her saying that she had lived with him and that he had done something which she didn't like—she didn't say what—and so she had walked out on him, left him flat, without a word of explanation. And then, just as we were entering the chop suey joint, they ran into each other and she was still trembling over it as we sat down in the little booth. . . . For one long moment I have the most uneasy sensation. Maybe every word she uttered was a lie!

From **Sexus**

It must have been a Thursday night when I met her for the first time—at the dance hall. I reported to work in the morning, after an hour or two's sleep, looking like a somnambulist. The day passed like a dream. After dinner I fell asleep on the couch and awoke fully dressed about six the next morning. I felt thoroughly refreshed, pure at heart, and obsessed with one idea—to have her at any cost. Walking through the park I debated what sort of flowers to send with the book I had promised her (*Winesburg, Ohio*). I was approaching my thirty-third year, the age of Christ crucified. A wholly new life lay before me, had I the courage to risk all. Actually there was nothing to risk: I was at the bottom rung of the ladder, a failure in every sense of the word.

It was a Saturday morning, then, and for me Saturday has always been the best day of the week. I come to life when others are dropping off with fatigue; my week begins with the Jewish day of rest. That this was to be the grand week of my life, to last for seven long years, I had no idea of course. I knew only that the day was auspicious and eventful. To make the fatal step, to throw everything to the dogs, is in itself an emancipation: the thought of consequences never entered my head. To make absolute, unconditional surrender to the woman one loves is to break every bond save the desire not to lose her, which is the most terrible bond of all.

I spent the morning borrowing right and left, dispatched

the book and flowers, then sat down to write a long letter to be delivered by a special messenger. I told her that I would telephone her later in the afternoon. At noon I quit the office and went home. I was terribly restless, almost feverish with impatience. To wait until five o'clock was torture. I went again to the park, oblivious of everything as I walked blindly over the downs to the lake where the children were sailing their boats. In the distance a band was playing; it brought back memories of my childhood, stifled dreams, longings, regrets. A sultry, passionate rebellion filled my veins. I thought of certain great figures in the past, of all that they had accomplished at my age. What ambitions I may have had were gone; there was nothing I wanted to do except to put myself completely in her hands. Above everything else I wanted to hear her voice, know that she was still alive, that she had not already forgotten me. To be able to put a nickel in the slot every day of my life henceforth, to be able to hear her say hello, that and nothing more was the utmost I dared hope for. If she would promise me that much, and keep her promise, it wouldn't matter what happened.

Promptly at five o'clock I telephoned. A strangely sad, foreign voice informed me that she was not at home. I tried to find out when she would be home but I was cut off. The thought that she was out of reach drove me frantic. I telephoned my wife that I would not be home for dinner. She greeted the announcement in her usual disgusted way, as though she expected nothing more of me than disappointments and postponements. "Choke on it, you bitch," I thought to myself as I hung up, "at least I know that I don't want you, any part of you, dead or alive." An open trolley was coming along; without a thought of its direction I hopped aboard and made for the rear seat. I rode around for a couple of hours in a deep trance; when I came to I recognized an Arabian ice cream parlor near the water-front, got off, walked to the wharf and sat on a string-piece looking up at the humming fret-work of the Brooklyn Bridge. There were still several hours to kill before I dared venture to go to the dance hall. Gazing vacantly at the opposite shore my thoughts drifted ceaselessly, like a ship without a rudder.

When finally I picked myself up and staggered off I was like a man under an anaesthetic who has managed to slip away from the operating table. Everything looked familiar yet made no sense; it took ages to coordinate a few simple impressions which by ordinary reflex calculus would mean table, chair, building, person. Buildings emptied of their automatons are even more desolate than tombs; when the machines are left idle they create a void deeper than death itself. I was a ghost moving about in a vacuum. To sit down, to stop and light a cigarette, not to sit down, not to smoke, to think, or not to think, breathe or stop breathing, it was all one and the same. Drop dead and the man behind you walks over you; fire a revolver and another man fires at you; yell and you wake the dead who, oddly enough, also have powerful lungs. Traffic is now going East and West; in a minute it will be going North and South. Everything is proceeding blindly according to rule and nobody is getting anywhere. Lurch and stagger in and out, up and down, some dropping out like flies, others swarming in like gnats. Eat standing up, with slots, levers, greasy nickels, greasy cellophane, greasy appetite. Wipe your mouth, belch, pick your teeth, cock your hat, tramp, slide, stagger, whistle, blow your brains out. In the next life I will be a vulture feeding on rich carrion: I will perch on top of the tall buildings and dive like a shot the moment I smell death. Now I am whistling a merry tune—the epigastric regions are at peace. *Hello, Mara, how are you?* And she will give me the enigmatic smile, throwing her arms about me in warm embrace. This will take place in a void under powerful

Klieg lights with three centimeters of privacy marking a mystic circle about us.

I mount the steps and enter the arena, the grand ballroom of the double-barrelled sex adepts, now flooded with a warm boudoir glow. The phantoms are waltzing in a sweet chewing gum haze, knees slightly crooked, haunches taut, ankles swimming in powdered sapphire. Between drum beats I hear the ambulance clanging down below, then fire engines, then police sirens. The waltz is perforated with anguish, little bullet holes slipping over the cogs of the mechanical piano which is drowned because it is blocks away in a burning building without fire escapes. She is not on the floor. She may be lying in bed reading a book, she may be making love with a prize-fighter, or she may be running like mad through a field of stubble, one shoe on, one shoe off, a man named Corn Cob pursuing her hotly. Wherever she is I am standing in complete darkness: her absence blots me out.

I inquire of one of the girls if she knows when Mara will arrive. *Mara?* Never heard of her. How should she know anything about anybody since she's only had the job an hour or so and is sweating like a mare wrapped in six suits of woolen underwear lined with fleece. Won't I offer her a dance—she'll ask one of the other girls about this Mara. We dance a few rounds of sweat and rose-water, the conversation running to corns and bunions and varicose veins, the musicians peering through the boudoir mist with jellied eyes, their faces spread in a frozen grin. The girl over there, Florrie, she might be able to tell me something about my friend. Florrie has a wide mouth and eyes of lapis lazuli; she's as cool as a geranium, having just come from an all-afternoon fucking fiesta. Does Florrie know if Mara will be coming soon? She doesn't think so . . . she doesn't think she'll come at all this evening. *Why?* She thinks she has a date with some one. Better ask the Greek—he knows everything.

The Greek says yes, Miss Mara will come . . . yes, just wait a while. I wait and wait. The girls are steaming, like sweating horses standing in a field of snow. Midnight. No sign of Mara. I move slowly, unwillingly, towards the door. A Porto Rican lad is buttoning his fly on the top step.

In the subway I test my eyesight reading the ads at the farther end of the car. I cross-examine my body to ascertain if I am exempt from any of the ailments which civilized man is heir to. Is my breath foul? Does my heart knock? Have I a fallen instep? Are my joints swollen with rheumatism? No sinus trouble? No pyorrhea? How about constipation? Or that tired feeling after lunch? No migraine, no acidosis, no intestinal catarrh, no lumbago, no floating bladder, no corns or bunions, no varicose veins? As far as I know I'm sound as a button, and yet. . . . Well, the truth is I lack something, something vital. . . .

I'm love-sick. Sick to death. A touch of dandruff and I'd succumb like a poisoned rat.

* * *

A few days passed without any sign of life from her. In the kitchen, after my wife had retired, I would sit and write voluminous letters to her. We were living then in a morbidly respectable neighborhood, occupying the parlor floor and basement of a lugubrious brown stone house. From time to time I had tried to write but the gloom which my wife created around her was too much for me. Only once did I succeed in breaking the spell which she had cast over the place; that was during a high fever which lasted for several days when I refused to see a doctor, refused to take any medicine, refused to take any nourishment. In a corner of the room upstairs I lay in a wide bed and fought off a delirium which threatened to end in death. I had never really been ill since childhood and the experience was delicious. To make my way to the toilet was like staggering through all the intricate passages of an ocean liner. I lived several lives in the few days that it lasted. That was my sole vacation in the sepulchre which is called home. The only other place I could tolerate was the kitchen. It was a sort of comfortable prison cell and, like a prisoner, here I often sat alone late into the night planning my escape. Here too my friend Stanley sometimes joined me, croaking over my misfortune and withering every hope with bitter and malicious barbs.

It was here I wrote the maddest letters ever penned. Any one who thinks he is defeated, hopeless, without resources, can take courage from me. I had a scratchy pen, a bottle of ink and paper—my sole weapons. I put down everything which came into my head, whether it made sense or not. After I had posted a letter I would go upstairs and lie down beside my wife and, with eyes wide open, stare into the darkness, as if trying to read my future. I said to myself over and over that if a man, a sincere and desperate man like myself, loves a woman with all his heart, if he is ready to cut off his ears and mail them to her, if he will take his heart's blood and pump it out on paper, saturate her with his need and longing, besiege her everlastingly, she cannot possibly refuse him. The homeliest man, the weakest man, the most undeserving man must triumph if he is willing to surrender his last drop of blood. No woman can hold out against the gift of absolute love.

I went again to the dance hall and found a message waiting for me. The sight of her handwriting made me tremble. It was brief and to the point. She would meet me at Times Square, in front of the drug store, at midnight the following day. I was to please stop writing her to her home.

I had a little less than three dollars in my pocket when we met. The greeting she gave me was cordial and brisk. No mention of my visit to the house or the letters or the gifts. Where would I like to go, she asked after a few words. I hadn't the slightest idea what to suggest. That she was standing there in the flesh, speaking to me, looking at me, was an event which I had not yet fully grasped. "Let's go to Jimmy Kelly's place," she said, coming to my rescue. She took me by the arm and walked me to the curb where a cab was waiting for us. I sank back into the seat, overwhelmed by her mere presence. I made no attempt to kiss her or even to hold her hand. She had come—that was the paramount thing. That was everything.

We remained until the early hours of the morning, eating, drinking, dancing. We talked freely and understandingly. I knew no more about her, about her real life, than I knew before, not because of any secrecy on her part but rather because the moment was too full and neither past nor future seemed important.

When the bill came I almost dropped dead.

In order to stall for time I ordered more drinks. When I confessed to her that I had only a couple of dollars on me she suggested that I give them a check, assuring me that since she was with me there would be no question about its acceptance. I had to explain that I owned no check book, that I possessed nothing but my salary. In short, I made a full clearance.

While confessing this sad state of affairs to her an idea had germinated in my crop. I excused myself and went to the telephone booth. I called the main office of the telegraph company and begged the night manager, who was a friend of mine, to send a messenger to me immediately with a fifty dollar bill. It was a lot of money for him to borrow from the till, and he knew I wasn't any too reliable, but I gave him a harrowing story, promising faithfully to return it before the day was out.

The messenger turned out to be another good friend of

mine, old man Creighton, an ex-minister of the gospel. He seemed indeed surprised to find me in such a place at that hour. As I was signing the sheet he asked me in a low voice if I was sure I would have enough with the fifty. "I can lend you something out of my own pocket," he added. "It would be a pleasure to be of assistance to you."

"How much can you spare?" I asked, thinking of the task ahead of me in the morning.

"I can give you another twenty-five," he said readily.

I took it and thanked him warmly. I paid the bill, gave the waiter a generous tip, shook hands with the manager, the assistant manager, the bouncer, the hat check girl, the door man, and with a beggar who had his mitt out. We got into a cab and, as it wheeled around, Mara impulsively climbed over me and straddled me. We went into a blind fuck, with the cab lurching and careening, our teeth knocking, tongue bitten, and the juice pouring from her like hot soup. As we passed an open plaza on the other side of the river, just at daybreak, I caught the astonished glance of a cop as we sped by. "It's dawn, Mara," I said, trying gently to disengage myself. "Wait, wait," she begged, panting and clutching at me furiously, and with that she went into a prolonged orgasm in which I thought she would rub my cock off. Finally she slid off and slumped back into her corner, her dress still up over her knees. I leaned over to embrace her again and as I did so I ran my hand up her wet cunt. She clung to me like a leech, wiggling her slippery ass around in a frenzy of abandon. I felt the hot juice trickling through my fingers. I had all four fingers up her crotch, stirring up the liquid moss which was tingling with electrical spasms. She had two or three orgasms and then sank back exhausted, smiling up at me weakly like a trapped doe.

After a time she got out her mirror and began powdering her face. Suddenly I observed a startled expression on her face, followed by a quick turn of her head. In another moment she was kneeling on the seat, staring out of the back window. "Some one's following us," she said. "Don't look!" I was too weak and happy to give a damn. "Just a bit of hysteria," I thought to myself, saying nothing but observing her attentively as she gave rapid, jerky orders to the driver to go this way and that, faster and faster. "*Please, please!*" she begged him, as though it were life and death. "Lady," I heard him say, as if from far off, from some other dream vehicle. "I can't give her any more . . . I've got a wife and kid . . . I'm sorry."

I took her hand and pressed it gently. She made an abortive gesture, as if to say—"You don't know . . . you don't know . . . this is terrible." It was not the moment to ask her questions. Suddenly I had the realization that we were in danger. Suddenly I put two and two together, in my own crazy fashion. I reflected quickly . . . nobody is following us . . . that's all coke and laudanum . . . but somebody's after her, that's definite . . . she's committed a crime, a serious one, and maybe more than one . . . nothing she says adds up . . . I'm in a web of lies . . . I'm in love with a monster, the most gorgeous monster imaginable . . . I should quit her now, immediately, without a word of explanation . . . otherwise I'm doomed . . . she's fathomless, impenetrable . . . I might have known that the one woman in the world whom I can't live without is marked with mystery . . . get out at once . . . jump . . . save yourself!

I felt her hand on my leg, rousing me stealthily. Her face was relaxed, her eyes wide open, full, shining with innocence. . . . "They've gone," she said, "it's all right now."

Nothing is right, I thought to myself. We're only beginning. Mara, Mara, where are you leading me? It's fateful, it's ominous, but I belong to you body and soul, and you will take me where you will, deliver me to my keeper, bruised, crushed, broken. For us there is no final understanding. I feel the ground slipping from under me. . . .

My thoughts she was never able to penetrate, neither then nor later. She probed deeper than thought: she read blindly, as if endowed with antennae. She knew that I was meant to destroy, that I would destroy her too in the end. She knew that whatever game she might pretend to play with me she had met her match. We were pulling up to the house. She drew close to me and, as though she had a switch inside her which she controlled at will, she turned on me the full incandescent radiance of her love. The driver had stopped the car. She told him to pull up the street a little farther and wait. We were facing one another, hands clasped, knees touching. A fire ran through our veins. We remained thus for several minutes, as in some ancient ceremony, the silence broken only by the purr of the motor.

"I'll call you to-morrow," she said, leaning forward impulsively for a last embrace. And then in my ear she murmured—"I'm falling in love with the strangest man on earth. You frighten me, you're so gentle. Hold me tight . . . believe in me always . . . I feel almost as if I were with a god."

* * *

She's on the floor, dancing with a dark-skinned fellow who is holding her close. As soon as the dance is out I rush over to her. "Where were you?" I ask. "What was the matter? Why didn't you come?"

She seemed surprised that I should be so upset over such a trivial thing. *What had kept her?* Oh, it was nothing at all. She had been out late, a rather wild party . . . not with Carruthers . . . he had left shortly after me. No, it was Florrie who had organized the party. Florrie and Hannah—did I remember them? (*Did I remember them?* Florrie the nymphomaniac and Hannah the drunken sot. How could I forget them?) Yes, there had been a lot to drink and somebody had asked her to do the split and she had tried . . . well, and she had hurt herself a bit. That was all. I should have realized that something had happened to her. She wasn't the sort who made dates and broke them—just like that.

"When did you get here?" I asked, remarking to myself that she seemed quite intact, unusually cool and collected, in fact.

She had come just a few minutes ago. What difference did it make? Her friend Jerry, an ex-pugilist who was now studying law, had taken her to dinner. He had been at the party last night and had been kind enough to see her home. She would see me Saturday afternoon in the Village—at the Pagoda Tea Room. Dr. Tao, who ran the place, was a good friend of hers. She would like me to meet him. He was a poet.

I said I would wait around for her and take her home, by subway this time if she didn't mind. She begged me not to bother—I would get home so late and so on. I insisted. I could see that she wasn't too pleased. In fact she was plainly annoyed. In a moment she excused herself to go to the dressing room. That meant a telephone call, I was certain. Again I wondered if she really lived at this place she called home.

She reappeared with a good-natured smile, saying that the manager had offered to let her off early. We might go at once, if we liked. First we were to have a bite somewhere. On the way to the restaurant, and all through the meal, she kept up a rapid-fire talk about the manager and his little kindnesses. He was a Greek with a tender heart. It was extraordinary what he had done for some of the girls. How did she mean? Like what? Well, like Florrie, for instance. The time Florrie had had an abortion—that was before she met her doctor friend. Nick had paid for everything; he had even sent her to the country for a few weeks. And Hannah, who had had all her teeth extracted. . . . Well, Nick had presented her with a lovely set of false teeth.

And Nick, what was he getting for all his trouble, I inquired blandly.

"Nobody knows anything about Nick," she continued. "He never makes any overtures to the girls. He's too busy with his affairs. He runs a gambling joint uptown, he plays the stock market, he owns a bath house at Coney Island, he has an interest in a restaurant somewhere . . . he's too busy to think about such things."

"You seem to be one of the favored ones," I said. "You come and go as you please."

"Nick thinks the world of me," she said. "Perhaps because I attract a different type of man than the other girls."

"Wouldn't you like to do something else for a living?" I asked abruptly. "You're not meant for this sort of thing—that's why you're such a success, I guess. Isn't there something else you'd rather do, tell me?"

Her smile indicated how naive my question was. "You don't think I do this because I like it, do you? I do it because I earn more money than I could elsewhere. I have a lot of responsibilities. It doesn't matter what I do—I must earn a certain amount of money each week. But don't let's talk about that, it's too painful. I know what you're thinking about, but you're wrong. Everybody treats me like a queen. The other girls are stupid. I use my intelligence. You notice that my admirers are mostly old men. . . ."

"Like Jerry, you mean?"

"Oh Jerry, he's an old friend. Jerry doesn't count."

I dropped the subject. Better not to inquire too deeply. There was one little thing that bothered me however, and I broached it as gently as I could. Why did she waste time on such trollops as Florrie and Hannah?

She laughed. Why, they were her best friends. They would do anything for her, they worshipped her. One has to have some one he can rely on in a pinch. Why, Hannah would hock her false teeth for her if she asked her to. Speaking of friends, there was a wonderful girl she would like to introduce me to some day—quite another type, almost aristocratic. Lola was her name. She had a little colored blood in her, but it was scarcely noticeable. Yes, Lola was a very dear friend. She was sure I would like her.

"Why not make a date?" I suggested promptly. "We could meet at my friend Ulric's studio. I've wanted you to meet him too."

She thought that would be excellent. Couldn't say when it would be, though, as Lola was always going off on trips. But she would try to make it soon. Lola was the mistress of some rich shoe manufacturer: she wasn't always free. But it would be good to have Lola—she had a racing car. Perhaps we could drive out into the country and stay the night somewhere. Lola had a way about her. She was just a little too haughty, in fact. But that was because of her colored blood. I mustn't let on that I knew anything about that. And as for my friend Ulric—I wasn't to breathe a word of that to him.

"But he likes colored girls. He'll be crazy about Lola."

"But Lola doesn't want to be liked for that reason," said Mara. "You'll see—she's very pale and very attractive. Nobody would suspect that she had a drop of colored blood in her."

"Well, I hope she's not *too* proper."

"You don't need to worry about that," said Mara promptly. "Once she forgets herself she's very gay. It won't be a dull evening, I assure you."

We had a bit of a walk from the subway station to her home. Along the way we stopped under a tree and started to mush it up. I had my hand up her dress and she was fumbling with my fly. We were leaning against the tree trunk. It was late and not a soul in sight. I could have laid her out on the sidewalk for all it mattered.

She had just got my pecker out and was opening her legs for me to ram it home when suddenly from the branches above a huge black cat pounced on us, screaming as if in heat. We nearly dropped dead with fright, but the cat was even more frightened since its claws had gotten caught in my coat. In my panic I beat the hell out of it and in return was badly clawed and bitten. Mara was trembling like a leaf. We walked into a vacant lot and lay on the grass. Mara was fearful I might get an infection. She would sneak home and come back with some iodine and what not. I was to lie there and wait for her.

It was a warm night and I lay back full length looking up at the stars. A woman passed but didn't notice me lying there. My cock was hanging out and beginning to stir again with the warm breeze. By the time Mara returned it was quivering and jumping. She kneeled beside me with the bandages and the iodine. My cock was staring her in the face. She bent over and gobbled it greedily. I pushed the things aside and pulled her over me. When I had shot my bolt she kept right on coming, one orgasm after another, until I thought it would never stop.

We lay back and rested awhile in the warm breeze. After a while she sat up and applied the iodine. We lit our cigarettes and sat there talking quietly. Finally we decided to go. I walked her to the door of her home and as we stood there embracing one another she grabbed me impulsively and whisked me off. "I can't let you go yet," she said. And with that she flung herself on me, kissing me passionately and reaching into my fly with murderous accuracy. This time we didn't bother to look for a vacant patch of ground, but collapsed right on the sidewalk under a big tree. The sidewalk wasn't too comfortable—I had to pull out and move over a few feet where there was a bit of soft earth. There was a little puddle near her elbow and I was for taking it out again and moving over another inch or so, but when I tried to draw it out she got frantic. "Don't ever take it out again," she begged, "it drives me crazy. Fuck me, fuck me!" I held out on her a long while. As before, she came again and again, squealing and grunting like a stuck pig. Her mouth seemed to have grown bigger, wider, utterly lascivious; her eyes were turning over, as if she were going into an epileptic fit. I took it out a moment to cool it off. She put her hand in the puddle beside her and sprinkled a few drops of water over it. That felt marvelous. The next moment she was on her hands and knees, begging me to give it to her assways. I got behind her on all fours; she reached her hand under and grabbing my cock she slipped it in. It went right in to the womb. She gave a little groan of pain and pleasure mixed. "It's gotten bigger," she said, squirming her ass around. "Put it in again all the way . . . go ahead, I don't care if it hurts," and with that she backed up on me with a wild lurch. I had such a cold-blooded erection that I thought I'd never be able to come. Besides, not worrying about losing it, I was able to watch the performance like a spectator. I would draw it almost out and roll the tip of it around the silky, soppy petals, then plunge it in and leave it there like a stopper. I had my two hands around her pelvis, pulling and pushing her at will. "Do it, do it," she begged, "or I'll go mad!" That got me. I began to work on her like a plunger, in and out full length without a let-up, she going Oh—Ah, Oh—Ah! and then bango! I went off like a whale.

We brushed ourselves off and started back towards the house once again. At the corner she stopped dead in her tracks and turning round to face me squarely, she said with a smile that was almost ugly—"*And now for the dirt!*"

I looked at her in amazement. "What do you mean? What are you talking about?"

"I mean," she said, never relinquishing that strange grimace, "that I need fifty dollars. I must have it to-morrow. *I must. I must.* . . . Now do you see why I didn't want you to take me home?"

"Why did you hesitate to ask me for it? Don't you think I can raise fifty dollars if you need it badly?"

"But I need it at once. Can you get a sum like that by noon? Don't ask me what it's for—it's urgent, very urgent. Do you think you can do it? Will you promise?"

"Why of course I can," I answered, wondering as I said so where in hell I would get it in such quick time.

"You're wonderful," she said, seizing my two hands and squeezing them warmly. "I do hate to ask you. I know you have no money. I'm always asking for money—that seems to be all I can do—get money for others. I hate it, but there's nothing else to do. You trust me, don't you? I'll give it back to you in a week."

"Don't talk that way, Mara. I don't want it back. If you're in need I want you to tell me. I may be poor but I can raise money too now and then. I wish I could do more. I wish I could take you out of that damned place—I don't like seeing you there."

"Don't talk about that now, please. Go home and get some sleep. Meet me at twelve-thirty to-morrow in front of the drug store at Times Square. That's where we met before, you remember? God, I didn't know then how much you would mean to me. I took you for a millionaire. You won't disappoint me to-morrow—you're sure?"

"I'm sure, Mara."

Money always has to be raised in jig time and paid back at regular stipulated intervals, either by promises or in cash. I think I could raise a million dollars if I were given enough time, and by that I don't mean sidereal time but the ordinary clock time of days, months, years. To raise money quickly, however, even carfare, is the most difficult task one can set me. From the time I left school I have begged and borrowed almost continuously. I've often spent a whole day trying to raise a dime; at other times I've had fat bills thrust into my hand without even opening my mouth. I don't know any more about the art of borrowing now than I did when I started. I know there are certain people whom you must never, not under any circumstances, ask for help. There are others again who will refuse you ninety-nine times and yield on the hundredth, and perhaps never again refuse you. There are some whom you reserve for the real emergency, knowing that you can rely on them, and when the emergency comes and you go to them you are cruelly deceived. There isn't a soul on earth who can be relied on absolutely. For a quick, generous touch the man you met only recently, the one who scarcely knows you, is usually a pretty safe bet. Old friends are the worst: they are heartless and incorrigible. Women, too, as a rule, are usually callous and indifferent. Now and then you think of some one you know who would come across, if you persisted, but the thought of the prying and prodding is so disagreeable that you wipe him out of your mind. The old are often like that, probably because of bitter experience.

To borrow successfully one has to be a mono-maniac on the subject, as with everything else. If you can give yourself up to it, as with Yoga exercises, that is to say, wholeheartedly, without squeamishness or reservations of any kind, you can live your whole life without earning an honest penny. Naturally the price is too great. In a pinch the best single quality is desperation. The best course is the unusual one. It is easier, for example, to borrow from one who is your inferior than from an equal or from one who is above you. It's also very important to be willing to compromise yourself, not to speak of lowering yourself, which is a *sine qua non*. The man who borrows is always a culprit, always a potential thief. Nobody ever gets back what he lent, even if the sum is paid with interest. The man who exacts his pound of flesh is always shortchanged, even if by nothing more than rancor or hatred. Borrowing is a positive thing, lending negative. To be a borrower may be uncomfortable, but it is also exhilarating, instructive, life-like. The borrower pities the lender, though he must often put up with his insults and injuries.

Fundamentally borrower and lender are one and the same. That is why no amount of philosophizing can eradicate the evil. They are made for one another, just as man and woman are made for each other. No matter how fantastic the need, no matter how crazy the terms, there will always be a man to lend an ear, to fork up the necessary. A good borrower goes about his task like a good criminal. His first principle is never to expect something for nothing. He doesn't want to know how to get the money on the least terms but exactly the contrary. When the right men meet there is a minimum of talk. They take each other at face value, as we say. The ideal lender is the realist who knows that to-morrow the situation may be reversed and the borrower become the lender.

There was only one person I knew who could see it in the right light and that was my father. He was the one I always held in reserve for the crucial moment. And he was the only one I never failed to pay back. Not only did he never refuse me but he inspired me to give to others in the same way. Every time I borrowed from him I became a better lender—or I should say giver, because I've never insisted on being repaid. There is only one way to repay kindnesses and that is to be kind in turn to those who come to you in distress. To repay a debt is utterly unnecessary, so far as the cosmic bookkeeping is concerned. (All other forms of bookkeeping are wasteful and anachronistic.) "Neither a borrower nor a lender be," said the good Shakespeare, voicing a wish-fulfillment out of his Utopian dream life. For men on earth, borrowing and lending is not only essential but should be increased to outlandish proportions. The fellow who is really practical is the fool who looks neither to the left nor the right, who gives without question and asks unblushingly.

To make it short, I went to my old man and without beating about the bush I asked him for fifty dollars. To my surprise he didn't have that much in the bank but he informed me quickly that he could borrow it from one of the other tailors. I asked him if he would be good enough to do that for me and he said sure, of course, just a minute.

"I'll give it back to you in a week or so," I said, as I was saying good-bye.

"Don't worry about that," he replied, "any time will do. I hope everything's all right with you otherwise."

At twelve-thirty sharp I handed Mara the money. She ran off at once, promising to meet me the next day in the garden of the Pagoda Tea Room.

* * *

A few days later I was sitting in Ulric's studio waiting for Mara to arrive with her friend Lola Jackson. Ulric had never met Mara.

"You think she's good stuff, eh?" he was saying, meaning Lola. "We won't have to stand on too much ceremony, what?"

These feelers which Ulric always put out amused me highly. He liked to be guaranteed that the evening would not be entirely wasted. He was never certain of me when it came to women or friends; in his humble opinion I was just a wee bit too reckless.

However, the moment he laid eyes on them he felt reassured. In fact, he was bowled over. He took me aside almost at once to congratulate me on my taste.

Lola Jackson was a queer girl. She had only one defect—the knowledge that she was not pure white. That made her rather difficult to handle, at least in the preliminary stages. A little too intent upon impressing us with her culture and breeding. After a couple of drinks she unlimbered enough to show us how supple her body was. Her dress was too long for some of the stunts she was eager to demonstrate. We suggested that she take it off, which she did, revealing a stunning figure which showed to advantage in a pair of sheer silk hose, a brassiere and pale blue panties. Mara decided to follow suit. Presently we urged them to dispense with the brassieres. There was a huge divan on which the four of us huddled in a promiscuous embrace. We turned the lights down and put on a record. Lola thought it too warm to keep anything on except the silk stockings.

We had about a square yard of space in which to dance flesh to flesh. Just as we had changed partners, just as the tip of my cock had buried itself in Lola's dark petals, the phone rang. It was Hymie Laubscher telling me in a grave and urgent voice that the messengers had declared a strike. "You'd better be on hand early to-morrow morning, H. M.," he said. "No telling what will happen. I wouldn't have bothered you if it hadn't been for Spivak. He's on your trail. He says you ought to have known that the boys were going on strike. He's hired a fleet of taxi cabs already. There's going to be hell to-morrow."

"Don't let him know you got in touch with me," I said. "I'll be there bright and early."

"*Are you having a good time?*" piped Hymie. "No chance of my horning in on the party, is there?"

"I'm afraid not, Hymie. If you're looking for something I can recommend you one up at I. Q. office—you know, the one with the big teats. She goes off duty at midnight."

Hymie was trying to tell me something about his wife's operation. I couldn't make it out because Lola had slipped up alongside me and was petting my cock. I hung up in the midst of it and pretended to explain to Lola what the message was about. I knew Mara would be on my heels in a moment.

I had just gotten it half way in, Lola's back bent almost in half, and still talking about the messenger boys, when I heard Ulric and Mara stirring. I pulled away and picking up the phone I called a number at random. To my astonishment a woman's voice answered sleepily—"Is that you, dear? I've just been dreaming about you." I said *Yes?* She went on, as if still half asleep: "Do hurry home, won't you dear? I've been waiting and waiting. Tell me you love me. . . ."

"I'll make it as quick as I can, *Maude,*" I said, in my own clear natural voice. "The messengers are on strike. I wish you'd call. . . ."

"*What's that?* What are you saying? What *is* this?" came the woman's startled voice.

"I said rush a few waybills* up to D.T. office and ask Costigan to. . . ." The phone clicked.

The three of them were lying on the divan. I could smell them in the dark. "I hope you don't have to go," said Ulric in a smothered voice. Lola was lying over him, her arms around his neck. I reached between her legs and caught hold of Ulric's pecker. I was on my knees, in a good position to tackle Lola from the rear should Mara suddenly decide to go to the lavatory. Lola raised herself a bit and sank down on Ulric's prick with a savage grunt. Mara was tugging at me. We lay

---

* Messengers, relayed from their own office to another to help out when there is a shortage.

down on the floor beside the divan and went to it. In the midst of it the hall door opened, the light was suddenly switched on, and there stood Ulric's brother with a woman. They were a bit drunk and had apparently returned at an early hour to do a bit of quiet fucking on their own.

"Don't let *us* stop you," said Ned, standing in the doorway inspecting the scene as if it were an every day affair. Suddenly he pointed to his brother and shouted—"Holy Smokes! What's happened? You're bleeding!"

We all looked at Ulric's bleeding cock: from the navel down to his knees he was a mass of blood. It was rather embarrassing for Lola.

"I'm sorry," she said, the blood dripping down her thighs, "I didn't think it would be so soon."

"That's all right," said Ulric, "what's a little blood between bouts?"

I went with him to the lavatory, pausing a moment on the way to be presented to his brother's girl. She was pretty far gone. I held out my mitt to shake hands and in reaching for it she accidentally made a pass for my prick. That made everybody feel a little easier.

"A great work-out," said Ulric, washing himself assiduously. "Do you think I might take another crack at it? I mean, there's no particular harm getting a little blood on the end of your cock, is there? I feel as though I'd like to have another go at it, what say?"

"It's good for the health," I said cheerily. "Wish I could swap places with you."

"I wouldn't be averse to that at all," said he, sliding his tongue lecherously over his lower lip. "Do you think you can manage it?"

"Not to-night," I said. "I'm going now. I've got to be fresh and spruce to-morrow."

"Are you going to take Mara with you?"

"I sure am. Tell her to come in here a minute, will you?"

When Mara opened the door I was powdering my cock. We fell into a clutch at once.

"What about trying it in the tub?"

I turned the warm water on and threw in a bar of soap. I soaped her crotch with tingling fingers. By this time my prick was like an electric eel. The warm water felt delicious. I was chewing her lips, her ears, her hair. Her eyes sparkled as if she had been struck by a fistful of stars. Every part of her was smooth and satiny and her breasts were ready to burst. We got out and, letting her straddle me, I sat on the edge of the tub. We were dripping wet. I reached for a towel with one hand and dried her a bit down the front. We lay down on the bath mat and she slung her legs around my neck. I moved her around like one of those legless toys which illustrate the principle of gravity.

Two nights later I was in a depressed mood. I was lying on the couch in the dark, my thoughts shifting rapidly from Mara to the bloody, futile telegraph life. Maude had come over to say something to me and I had made the mistake of running my hand carelessly up her dress as she stood there complaining about something or other. She had walked off insulted. I hadn't been thinking about fucking her—I just did it naturally, like you'd stroke a cat. When she was awake you couldn't touch her that way. She never took a fuck on the wing, as it were. She thought fucking had something to do with love: carnal love, perhaps. A lot of water had passed under the bridge since the days when I first knew her, when I used to twirl her around on the end of my cock sitting on the piano stool. Now she acted like a cook preparing a difficult menu. She would make up her mind deliberately, letting me know in her sly, repressed way that the time had come for it. Maybe that's what she had come for a moment ago, though it was certainly odd the way she begged for it. Anyway I didn't give a fuck whether she wanted it or not. Suddenly, though, thinking of Stanley's words, I began to have a yen for her. "Get in your last licks," I kept saying to myself. Well, maybe I'd go up and tackle her in her pseudo-sleep. Spivak came to mind. He was watching me like a hawk the last few days. My hatred for the telegraph life was concentrated in my hatred for him. He was the bloody cosmococcus in person. Must polish him off somehow before they fire me. I kept thinking how I could lure him to a dark wharf and have some obliging friend push him overboard. I thought of Stanley. Stanley would relish a job like that. . . .

How long was he going to keep me on tenterhooks? I wondered. And what form would it take, this abrupt deliverance? I could see Mara coming to meet me at the station. We'd start a new life together, righto! What sort of life I didn't dare think. Maybe Kronski would raise another three hundred dollars. And those millionaires she talked about, they ought to be good for something. I began thinking in thousands—a thousand for her old man, a thousand for travelling expenses, a thousand to tide us over for a few months. Once in Texas, or some God-forsaken place like that, I'd have more confidence. I'd stop off at newspaper offices with her—she always made a good impression—and I'd ask permission to write a little sketch. I'd walk in on business men and show them how to write their ads. In hotel lobbies I'd be sure to meet up with a friendly soul, some one who would give me a break. The country was so big, so many lonely people, so many generous souls ready to give, if only they met the right individual. I would be sincere and forthright. Say we get to Mississippi, some old ramshackle hotel. A man walks up to me out of the darkness and asks me how I feel. A guy just aching for a little chat. I'd introduce him to Mara. We'd saunter out arm in arm and stroll about in the moonlight, the trees strangled with lianas, the magnolias rotting on the floor of the earth, the air humid, sultry, making things rot—and men too. To him I'd be a fresh breeze from the North. I'd be honest, sincere, almost humble. Would put my cards on the table immediately. There you are, man, there's the situation. I love this place. I want to stay here all my life. That would scare him off a little, because you don't start talking that way to a Southerner straight off. *What's your game?* Then I'd speak up again, soft and distant, like a clarinet with a wet sponge plugging the bell. I'd give him a little melody out of the cold North, a sort of chill factory whistle on a frosty morning. Mister man, I don't like the cold. No sir! I want to do some honest work, anything to keep alive. *Can I talk straight?* You won't think I'm cracked, will you? It's lonely up there in the North. Yes sir, we go blue with fright and loneliness. Live in little rooms, eat with knives and forks, carry watches, liver pills, bread crumbs, sausages. Don't know where we're at up there, *honest*, Mister. We're frightened to death we'll say something, something real. Don't sleep . . . not really. Thrash around all night praying for the world to end. We don't believe in anything: we hate everybody, we poison one another. Everything so tight and solid, everything riveted with cruel hot irons. Don't make a thing with our hands. Sell. Buy and sell. Buy and sell, that's all, Mister. . . .

I could visualize the old gentleman distinctly as he stood under a droopy tree mopping his feverish brow. He wouldn't run away from me, like others had. I wouldn't let him! I'd hold him spellbound—the whole night long, if I felt like it. Make him give us a cool wing in the big house near the bayou. The darkie would appear with a tray, serving mint juleps. We would be adopted. "*This is your home, son; stay as long as you like.*" No desire to play tricks on a man like that. No, if a man treated me that way I'd be faithful to him, to the bitter end. . . .

It was all so real I felt I had to tell Mara about it right

away. I went to the kitchen and began a letter. "Dear Mara—All our problems are solved. . . ." I went on as though it were all clear and definitive. Mara looked different to me now. I saw myself standing under the big trees talking to her in a way that surprised me. We were walking arm in arm through the thick growths, conversing like human beings. There was a big yellow moon out and the dogs were yapping at our heels. It seemed to me we were married and the blood ran deep and still between us. She would be craving a pair of swans for the little lake in back of the house. No money talk, no Neon lights, no chop suey. How wonderful just to breathe naturally, to never hurry, never get anywhere, never do anything important—except live! She thought so too. She had changed, Mara. Her body had grown fuller, heavier; she moved slowly, talked calmly, became silent for long periods, all so real and natural like. Should she wander off by herself I felt certain she would come back unchanged, smelling sweeter, moving more sure-footedly. . . .

"Do you get it, Mara? Do you see how it will be?"

There I was, putting it all down so honestly, almost weeping with the sheer wonder of it, when I heard Maude paddling slip-slop through the hall. I gathered the sheets together and folded them. I put my fist over them and waited for her to say something.

"Who are you writing to?" she asked—just as direct and sure as that.

"To some one I know," I answered calmly.

"A woman, I suppose?"

"Yes, a woman. A girl, to be more exact." I said it heavily, solemnly, still thick with the trance, the image of her under the big trees, the two swans floating aimlessly on the unruffled lake. If you want to know, I thought to myself, I will tell you. I don't see why I should lie any more. I don't hate you, as I once did. I wish you could love as I do—it would make it so much easier. I don't want to hurt you. I just want you to let me be.

"You're in love with her. You don't need to answer—I know it's so."

"Yes, that's true—I am in love. I found some one I really love."

"Maybe you'll treat her better than you did me."

"I hope so," I said, still calm, still hoping she'd hear me through to the end. "We never really loved each other, Maude, that's the truth, isn't it?"

"You never had any respect for me—as a human being," she replied. "You insult me in front of your friends; you run around with other women; you don't even show any interest in your child."

"Maude, I wish just for once that you wouldn't talk that way. I wish we could talk about it without bitterness."

"*You* can—because you're happy. You've found a new toy."

"It isn't that, Maude. Listen, supposing all the things you say are true—what difference does it make *now*? Supposing we were on a boat and it was sinking . . ."

"I don't see why we have to suppose things. You're going to take up with some one else and I'm going to be left with all the drudgery, all the responsibilities."

"I know," I said, looking at her with genuine tenderness. "I want you to try to forgive me for that—can you? What good would it do to stay? We wouldn't ever learn to love each other. Can't we part friends? I don't mean to leave you in the lurch. I'm going to try to do my share—I mean it."

"That's easy to say. You're always promising things you can't fulfill. You'll forget us the moment you walk out of this house. *I know you.* I can't afford to be generous with you. You deceived me bitterly, from the very beginning. You've been selfish, utterly selfish. I never thought it possible for a human being to become so cruel, so callous, so thoroughly inhuman. Why, I hardly recognize you now. It's the first time you've acted like a. . . ."

"Maude, it's cruel what I'm going to say, but I have to say it. I want you to understand something. Maybe I had to go through this with you in order to learn how to treat a woman. It isn't altogether my fault—fate had something to do with it too. You see, the moment I set eyes on her I knew. . . ."

"Where did you meet her?" said Maude, her feminine curiosity suddenly getting the better of her.

"In a dance hall. She's a taxi girl. Sounds bad, I know. But if you saw her. . . ."

"I don't want to see her. I don't want to hear anything more about her. I just wondered." She gave me a quick pitying look. "And you think she's the woman who will make you happy?"

"You call her a woman—she's not, she's just a young girl."

"So much the worse. Oh, what a fool you are!"

"Maude, it's not like you think, not at all. You musn't judge, really. How can you pretend to know? And in any case I don't care. I've made up my mind."

At this she hung her head. She looked indescribably sad and weary, like a human wreck hanging from a meat hook. I looked down at the floor, unable to bear the sight of her face.

We sat like that a full few minutes, neither of us daring to look up. I heard a sniffle and as I looked up I saw her face quivering with pain. She put her arms forward on the table and, weeping and sobbing, she flung her head down, pressing her face against the table. I had watched her weep many times but this was the most ghastly, unresisting sort of surrender. It unnerved me. I stood over her and put my hand on her shoulder. I tried to say something but the words stuck in my throat. Not knowing what to do I rubbed my hand over her hair, caressed it sadly, and distantly too, as though it were the head of a strange, wounded animal I had come upon in the dark.

"Come, come," I managed to gurgle, "this won't do any good."

Her sobs redoubled. I knew I had said the wrong thing. I couldn't help myself. No matter what she were to do—even if she were to kill herself—I couldn't change the situation. I had expected tears. I had also half expected to do this very thing—stroke her hair as she wept and say the wrong thing. My mind was on the goal. If she would get through with it and go to bed I could sit down and finish the letter. I could add a postscript about cauterizing the wound. I could say with honest joy and sorrow mixed—"It's over."

That's what was going on in my mind as I stroked her hair. I was never further from her. While I felt the quivering gasps of her body I also felt pleasure at thinking how serene she would be a week hence when I had gone. "You will be feeling like a new woman," I thought to myself. "And now you are going through all this anguish—it's right and natural, of course, and I don't blame you for it—only get done with it!" I must have given her a shake to punctuate the thought, for at that instant she suddenly sat erect and, looking at me with wild, hopeless, tear-stained eyes, she flung her arms around me and pulled me to her in a frantic, maudlin embrace. "You won't leave me yet, will you?" she sobbed, kissing me with salty, hungry lips. "Put your arms around me, please. Hold me tight. God, I feel so lost!" She was kissing me with a passion I had never felt in her before. She was putting body and soul into it—and all the sorrow that stood between us. I slid my hands under her arm-pits and raised her gently to her feet. We were as close as lovers could be, swaying as only the human animal can sway when he is given utterly to another. Her kimono slipped open and she was naked underneath. I slid my hand down the small of her back, over her plump buttocks, wedged my fingers deep into the big crack, pressing her against me, chewing her lips, biting her ear lobes, her neck, licking her eyes, the roots of her hair. She got limp and heavy, closing her eyes, closing her mind. She sagged as though she were going to drop to the floor. I caught her up and carried her through the hall, up the flight of stairs, threw her on the bed. I fell over her, as if stupefied, and let her rip my things off. I lay on my back like a dead man, the only thing alive being my prick. I felt her mouth closing over it and the sock on my left foot slowly slipping off. I ran my fingers through her long hair, slid them round under her breast, moulded her bread basket which was soft and rubbery like. She was making some sort of wheeling motion in the dark. Her legs came down over my shoulders and her crotch was up against my lips. I slid her ass over my head, like you'd raise a pail of milk to slake a lazy thirst, and I drank and chewed and guzzled like a buzzard. She was so deep in heat that her teeth were clamped dangerously around the head of my cock. In that frantic, teary passion she had worked herself up to I had a fear that she might sink her teeth in deep, bite the end of it clean off. I had to tickle her to make her relax her jaws. It was fast, clean work after that—no tears, no love business, no promise me this and that. *Put me on the fucking block and fuck!* that's what she was asking for. I went at it with cold-blooded fury. This might be the very last fuck. Already she was a stranger to me. We were committing adultery, the passionate, incestuous kind which the Bible loves to talk about. Abraham went into Sarah or Leander and he *knew* her. (Strange italicizations in the English Bible.) But the way those horny old patriarchs tackled their young and old wives, sisters, cows and sheep was very knowing. They must have gone in head first, with all the cunning and skill of aged lechers. I felt like Isaac fornicating with a rabbit in the temple. She was a white rabbit with long ears. She had Easter eggs inside her and she would drop them one by one in a basket. I took a long think inside her, studying every crevice, every slit and tear, every soft, round bump that had swollen to the size of a shrivelled oyster. She moved over and took a rest, reading it like Braille (New York Point) with her inquisitive fingers. She crouched on all fours like a she animal, quivering and whinnying with undisguised pleasure. Not a human word out of her, not a sign that she knew any language except this block-and-tackle-subgum-one-ton-blow-the-whistle sort. The gentleman from Mississippi had completely faded out: he had slipped back into the swampy limbo which forms the permanent floor of the continents. One swan remained, an octaroon with ruby duck lips fastened to a pale blue head. Soon we'd be in clover, the blow-off, with plums and apricots falling from the sky. The last push, the drag of choked, white-hot ashes, and then two logs lying side by side waiting for the axe. Fine finish. Royal flush. I *knew* her and she *knew* me. Spring will come again and Summer and Winter. She will sway in somebody else's arms, go into a blind fuck, whinny, blow off, do the crouch and sag—but not with me. I've done my duty, given her the last rites. I closed my eyes and played dead to the world. Yes, we would learn to live a new life, Mara and I. I must get up early and hide the letter in my coat pocket. It's strange sometimes how you wind up affairs. You always think you're going to put the last word in the ledger with a broad flourish; you never think of the automaton who closes the account while you sleep. It's all the strictest kind of double-entry. It gives you the creeps, it's all so nicely calculated.

The axe is falling. Last ruminations. Honeymoon Express and all aboard: Memphis, Chattanooga, Nashville, Chickamauga. Past snowy fields of cotton . . . alligators yawning in the mud . . . the last apricot is rotting on the lawn . . . the moon is full, the ditch is deep, the earth is black, black, black.

* * *

The next morning it was like after a storm—breakfast as usual, a touch for carfare, a dash for the subway, a promise to take her to the movies after dinner. For her it was probably just a bad dream which she would do her best to forget during the course of the day. For me it was a step towards deliverance. No mention of the subject was ever made again. But it was there all the time and it made things easier between us. What she thought I don't know, but what I thought was very clear and definite. Every time I assented to one of her requests or demands I said to myself: "Fine, is that all you want of me? I'll do anything you like except give you the illusion that I am going to live the rest of my life with you."

She was inclined now to be more lenient with herself when it came to satisfying her bestial nature. I often wondered what she told herself in making excuses to herself for these extra-nuptial, pre- or post-morganatic bouts. Certainly she put her heart and soul into them. She was a better fucker now than in the early days when she used to put a pillow under her ass and try to kiss the ceiling. She was fucking with desperation, I guess. Fuck for fuck's sake and the devil take the hindmost.

A week had passed and I hadn't seen Mara. Maude had asked me to take her to a theatre in New York, a theatre just opposite the dance hall. I sat throughout the performance thinking of Mara so close and yet so far away. I thought of her so insistently and unremittingly that as we were leaving the theatre I gave voice to an impulse which I was powerless to quelch. "How would you like to go up there?" I said, pointing to the dance hall, "and meet her?" It was a cruel thing to say and I felt sorry for her the moment it left my mouth. She looked at me, Maude, as if I had struck her with my fist. I apologized at once and, taking her by the arm, I led her quickly away in the opposite direction, saying as I did so—"It was just an idea. I didn't mean to hurt you. I thought you might be curious, that's all." She made no answer. I made no further efforts to smooth the thing over. In the subway she slipped her arm in mine and let it rest there, as if to say—"I understand, you were just tactless and thoughtless, as usual." On the way home we stopped off at her favorite ice cream parlor and there, over a plate of French ice cream which she doted on, she unlimbered sufficiently to eke out a thin conversation about domestic trifles, a sign that she had dismissed the incident from her mind. The French ice cream, which she regarded as a luxury, combined with the opening of a fresh wound, had the effect of making her amorous. Instead of undressing upstairs in the bedroom, as she did ordinarily, she went to the bathroom which adjoined the kitchen and, leaving the door open, she took off her things one by one, leisurely, studiedly, almost like a strip-teaser, calling me in finally as she was combing out her hair to show me a blue mark on her thigh. She was standing there naked except for her shoes and stockings, her hair flowing luxuriantly down her back.

I examined the mark carefully, as I knew she wanted me to, touching her lightly here and there to see if there were any other tender spots which she might have overlooked; at the same time I kept up a running fire of solicitous queries in a calm, matter of fact voice which enabled her to prime herself for a cold-blooded fuck without admitting to herself that that was what she was doing. If I said to her, as I did, in the calm, dull, professional voice of the M.D.—"I think you'd better lie on the table in the kitchen where I can examine you better"—she would do so without the least coaxing, spreading her legs wide apart and letting me insert a finger without a qualm, because now by this time she remembered that since a fall which she had had some time ago there was a little bump inside her, at least so she thought; it worried her, this bump; perhaps if I would put my fingers in ever so gently she could track it down, and so on and so forth. Nor did it appear to disturb her in the least when I suggested that she lie there a moment on the table, while I removed my clothes because it was getting too warm for me in the kitchen, next to the red hot stove, *and so on* and *so forth.* And so I removed my things, all but my socks and shoes, and with an erection fit to break a plate I stepped blandly forth and resumed operations. Or rather, I in turn had now become aware of things past, such as bumps, bruises, spots, warts, birthmarks et cetera, and would she kindly give *me* the once over while we were at it, and then we would go to bed because it was getting late and I didn't want to tire her out.

Strangely enough she wasn't tired at all, she confessed, getting down from the table and solicitously squeezing my cock and then my balls and then the root of my cock, all with such firm, discreet and delicate manipulations that I almost gave her a squirt in the eye. After that she was curious to see how much taller I was than she, so first we stood back to back and then front to front; even then, when it was jumping between her legs like a firecracker, she pretended to be thinking of feet and inches, saying that she ought to take her shoes off because her heels were high, *and so on and so forth.* And so I made her sit down on the kitchen chair and slowly I pulled off her shoes and stockings, and she, as I politely rendered her service, thoughtfully stroked my cock, which was difficult to do being in the position she was, but I graciously abetted her strategy by moving in closer and hoisting her legs up in the air at a right angle; then, without any more ado I lifted her up by the hind quarters, shoved it in to the hilt and carried her into the next room where I tumbled her on to the couch, sank it in again and went at it with sound and fury, she doing the same and begging me in the most candid, non-professional, non-casual language to hold it, to make it last, to keep it in forever, and then as an after-thought to wait a minute while she slipped out and turned over, raising herself on her knees, her head sunk low, her ass wriggling frantically, her thick gurgling voice saying in the English language openly and admittedly to herself for her own ears to hear and to recognize: "Get it in all the way . . . please, do . . . *I'm horny.*"

Yes, on occasion she could trot out a word like that, a vulgar word that would have made her curl up with horror and indignation if she were in her right senses, but now after the little pleasantries, after the vaginal exploration by finger, after the weight lifting and measuring contest, after the comparison of bruises, marks, bumps and what not, after the delicately casual manipulation of prick and scrotum, after the delicious French ice cream and the thoughtless faux pas outside the theatre, to say nothing of all that had transpired in her imagination since the cruel avowal a few nights ago, a word like "horny" was just the right and proper word to indicate the temperature of the Bessemer steel furnace which she had made of her inflamed cunt. It was the signal to give her the works and spare nothing. It meant something like this:—"No matter what I was this afternoon or yesterday, no matter what I think I am or how I detest you, no matter what you do with that thing to-morrow or the day after, now I want it and I want everything that goes with it: I wish it were bigger and fatter and longer and juicier: I wish you would break it off and leave it in there: I don't care how many women you've fucked, I want you to fuck *me*, fuck my cunt, fuck my ass off, fuck and fuck and fuck. *I'm horny*, do you hear? I'm so horny I could bite it off. Shove it in all the way, harder, harder, break your big prick off and leave it in there. *I'm horny*, I tell you . . ."

Usually after these bouts I awoke depressed. Looking at her with her clothes on and that grim, tight, caustic, everyday expression about her mouth, studying her at the breakfast table, indifferently, not having anything else to look at, I wondered sometimes why I didn't take her for a walk some evening and just push her off the end of a pier. I began to look forward like a drowning man to that solution which Stanley had promised and of which as yet there was not the least sign. To cap it all I had written a letter to Mara saying that we had to find a way out soon or I would commit suicide. It must have been a maudlin letter because when she telephoned me she said it was imperative to see me immediately. This shortly after lunch on one of those hectic days when everything seemed to go wrong. The office was jammed with applicants and even if I had had five tongues and five pairs of arms and twenty-five telephones instead of three at my elbow, I could never have hired as many applicants as were needed to fill the sudden and inexplicable vacuum which had come about overnight. I tried to put Mara off until the evening but she would not be put off. I agreed to meet her for a few minutes at an address which she gave me, the apartment of a friend of hers, she said, where we would be undisturbed. It was in the Village.

I left a mob of applicants hanging at the rail, promising Hymie who was frantically telephoning for "waybills" that I'd be back in a few minutes. I jumped into a cab at the corner and got out in front of a doll's house with a miniature garden in front. Mara came to the door in a light mauve dress under which she was nude. She flung her arms around me and kissed me passionately.

"A wonderful little nest, this," I said, holding her off to take a better look at the place.

"Yes, isn't it?" she said. "It belongs to Carruthers. He lives down the street with his wife; this is just a little den which he uses now and then. I sleep here sometimes when it's too late to go home."

I said nothing. I turned to look at the books—the walls were solidly lined with them. Out of the corner of my eye I saw Mara snatch something from the wall—seemed like a sheet of wrapping paper.

"What's that?" I said, not really curious but pretending to be.

"It's nothing," she answered. "Just a sketch of his which he asked me to destroy."

"Let's see it!"

"You don't want to look at it—it's worthless"—and she started to crumple it up.

"Let's see it anyway," I said, grasping her arm and snatching the paper from her hand. I opened it up and saw to my amazement that it was a caricature of myself with a dagger through the heart.

"I told you he was jealous," she said. "It doesn't mean anything—he was drunk when he did it. He's been drinking a great deal lately. I have to watch him like a hawk. He's just a big child, you know. You mustn't think he hates you—he acts that way with everybody who shows the least sign of interest in me."

"He's married, you said. What's the matter—doesn't he get along with his wife?"

"She's an invalid," said Mara, almost solemnly.

"In a wheel chair?"

"No-o-o, not exactly," she replied, a faint irrepressible smile suffusing her lips. "Oh, why talk about that now? What difference does it make? You know I'm not in love with him. I told you once that he had been very kind to me; now it's my turn to look after *him*—he needs some one to steady him."

"So you sleep here now and then—while he stays with his invalid wife, is that it?"

"He sleeps here too sometimes: there are two cots, if you notice. Oh, please," she begged, "don't let's talk about *him*. There's nothing for you to worry about, can't you see, can't you believe me?" She came close to me, put her arms around me. Without ado I lifted her up and carried her over to the couch. I pulled her dress up and, opening wide her legs, I slipped my tongue into her crack. In a moment she had me over her. When she had gotten my cock out she took her two hands and opened her cunt for me to slip it in. Almost at once she had an orgasm, then another, and another. She got up and washed herself quickly. As soon as she had finished I followed suit. When I came out of the bathroom she was lying on the couch with a cigarette to her lips. I sat there a few minutes with my hand between her legs, talking quietly to her.

"I've got to get back to the office," I said, "and we haven't had a chance to talk."

"Don't go yet," she begged, sitting upright and putting her hand affectionately over my prick. I put my arm around her and kissed her long and passionately. She had her fingers in my fly again and was reaching for my prick when suddenly we heard someone fumbling at the door knob.

"It's him," she said, jumping quickly to her feet and making for the door. "Stay where you are, it's all right," she threw out quickly as she glided forward to meet him. I hadn't time to button my fly. I stood up and casually straightened it out as she flew into his arms with some silly joyous exclamation.

"I've got a visitor," she said. "I asked him to come. He's leaving in a few minutes."

"Hello," he said, coming forward to greet me with hand out and an amiable smile on his lips. He showed no unusual surprise. In fact, he seemed much more affable than he did the night I first met him at the dance hall.

"You don't have to go this instant, do you?" said he, undoing a bundle which he had brought with him. "You might have a little drink first, won't you? Which do you prefer—Scotch or Rye?"

Before I could say yes or no Mara had slipped out to get some ice. I stood with my back partially turned to him as he busied himself with the bottles and, pretending to be interested in a book on the shelf before me, I stealthily buttoned my fly.

"I hope you don't mind the looks of the place," he said. "This is just a little retreat, a hide-out, where I can meet Mara and her little friends. She looks cute in that dress, don't you think?"

"Yes," I said, "it is rather attractive."

"Nothing much there," he said, nodding towards the book shelves. "The good ones are all over at the house."

"Seems like quite a fine collection," I said, glad to be able to divert the conversation to this ground.

"You're a writer, I understand—or so Mara tells me."

"Not really," I replied. "I'd like to be. You're probably one yourself, aren't you?"

He laughed. "Oh," he said deprecatingly, as he measured out the drinks, "we all begin that way, I guess. I've scribbled a few things in my time—poems mostly. I don't seem to be able to do anything any more, except drink."

Mara returned with the ice. "Come here," he said putting the ice on the table and throwing an arm around her waist, "you haven't kissed me yet." She held her head up and coolly received the slobbery kiss which he planted on her lips.

"I couldn't stand it at the office any longer," he said, squirting the fizz water into the glasses. "I don't know why I go to the damned place—there's nothing for me to do except look important and sign my name to silly papers." He took a long swallow. Then, motioning to me to take a seat, he flung himself into the big Morris chair. "Ah, that's better," he grunted, like a tired business man, though obviously he hadn't done a stroke of work. He beckoned to Mara. "Sit here a minute," he said, patting the arm of the chair. "I want to talk to you. I've got good news for you."

It was a highly interesting scene to witness after what had taken place just a few minutes ago. I wondered for a moment whether he were putting on an act for my benefit. He tried to pull her head down to give her another slobbery kiss but she resisted, saying—"Oh come, you're acting silly. Put that drink down, *please*. You'll be drunk in a moment and then there'll be no talking to you."

She put her arm over his shoulder and ran her fingers through his hair.

"You see what a tyrant she is," he said, turning to me. "God help the poor sap who marries her! Here I rush home to give her a piece of good news and. . . ."

"Well, what is it?" Mara interrupted. "Why don't you come out with it?"

"Give me a chance and I'll tell you," said Carruthers, patting her rump affectionately. "By the way," turning to me, "won't you pour yourself another drink? Pour me one too—that is, if you can get her permission. I have nothing to say around here. I'm just a general nuisance."

This sort of banter and cross-fire promised to continue indefinitely. I had made up my mind that it was too late to go back to the office—the afternoon was shot. The second drink had put me in the mood to stay and see it through.

Mara wasn't drinking, I noticed. I felt that she wanted me to leave. The good news got sidetracked, then forgotten. Or perhaps he had told her on the sly—he seemed to have dismissed the subject too abruptly. Perhaps while she was begging him to spill the news she had pinched his arm warningly. (Yes, what is the good news? And that pinch telling him not to dare blurt it out in front of me.) I was all at sea. I sat on the other couch and discreetly turned up the cover to see if there were any sheets on it. There weren't. Later I would hear the truth about the matter. We had a long way to go yet.

Carruthers was indeed a drunkard—a pleasant, sociable one too. One of those who drink and sober up at intervals. One of those who never think of food. One of those who have an uncanny memory, who observe everything with an eagle's eye and yet seem to be unconscious, sunk, dead to the world.

"Where's that drawing of mine?" he asked suddenly, out of the blue, looking steadily at the spot on the wall where it had been hung.

"I took it down," said Mara.

"So I see," he snarled, but not too disagreeably. "I wanted to show it to your friend here."

"He's already seen it," said Mara.

"Oh, he has? Well then, it's all right. Then we're not concealing anything from him, are we? I don't want him to have any illusions about me. You know that if *I* can't have you I won't let anybody else have you, isn't that so? Otherwise everything's fine. Oh, by the way, I saw your friend Valerie yesterday. She wants to move in here—just for a week or two. I told her I'd have to speak to you about it—you're running the place."

"It's your place," said Mara testily, "you can do as you please. Only, if she comes in I move out. I have a place of my own to live in; I only come here to look after you, to prevent you from drinking yourself to death."

"It's funny," he said, turning to me, "how those two girls detest each other. On my word, Valerie is an adorable creature. She hasn't an ounce of brains, it's true, but then that's no great drawback; she has everything else a man wants. You know, I kept her for a year or more; we got along splendidly too—until this one came along," and he nodded his head in Mara's direction. "Between you and me I think she's jealous of Valerie. You should meet her—you will if you stick around long enough. I have a hunch she's going to drop in before the day's over."

Mara laughed in a way I had never heard her laugh before. It was a mean, ugly laugh. "That nit-wit," she said scornfully, "why she can't even look at a man without getting into trouble. She's a walking abortion. . . ."

"You mean your friend Florrie," said Carruthers with a stupid fixed grin.

"I wish you'd leave her name out of this," said Mara angrily.

"You've met Florrie, haven't you?" asked Carruthers, ignoring the remark. "Did you ever see a more lascivious little bitch than that? And Mara is trying to make a lady of her. . . ." He burst out laughing. "It's strange, the trollops she picks up. Roberta—that was another wild one for you. Always had to ride around in limousines. Had a floating kidney, she said, but what it really was . . . well, between ourselves, she was just a lazy bum. But Mara had to take her under her wing, after I kicked her out, and nurse her. Really, Mara, for an intelligent girl, as you pretend you are, you do behave like a fool sometimes. Unless"—and he looked up at the ceiling meditatively—"there's something else to it. You never know"—still gazing at the ceiling—"what makes two women stick together. Birds of a feather flock together, that's the old saying. Still, it's strange. I know Valerie, I know Florrie, I know this one, I know them all—and yet, if you were to press me, I don't know anything about them, not a thing. It's another generation than the one I was brought up with; they're like another species of animal. To begin with, they have no moral sense, none of them. They refuse to be house-broken; it's like living in a menagerie. You come home and find a stranger lying in your bed—and you excuse yourself for intruding. Or they'll ask you for money in order to take a boy friend to a hotel for the night. And if they get into trouble you have to find a doctor for them. It's exciting but some times it's a damned nuisance too. It would be easier to keep rabbits, *what!*"

"That's the way he talks when he's drunk," said Mara, trying to laugh it off. "Go on, tell him some more about us. I'm sure he enjoys it."

I wasn't so sure that he was drunk. He was one of those men who talk loosely drunk or sober, who say even more fantastic things, in fact, when they are sober. Embittered, disillusioned men, usually, who act as if nothing could surprise them any more; at bottom, however, thoroughly sentimental, soaking their bruised emotional system in alcohol in order not to burst into tears at some unexpected moment. Women find them particularly charming because they never make any demands, never show any real jealousy, though outwardly they may go through all the motions. Often, as with Carruthers, they are saddled with crippled, thwarted wives, creatures whom out of weakness (which they call pity or loyalty) they allow themselves to be burdened with for life. To judge from his talk, Carruthers had no difficulty in finding attractive young women to share his love-nest. Sometimes there were two or three living with him at the same time. He probably had to make a show of jealousy, of possessiveness, in order not to be made an utter fool of. As for his wife, as I found out later, she was an invalid only to this extent—that her hymen was still intact. For years Carruthers had endured it like a martyr. But suddenly, when he realized that he was getting on in years, he had begun tearing around like a college boy. And then he had taken to drink. Why? Had he found that he was already too old to satisfy a healthy young girl? Had he suddenly regretted his years of abstinence? Mara, who had vouchsafed this information, was of course purposely vague and clinical about the subject. She did admit, however, that she had often slept with him on the same couch, leaving me to infer that obviously he never dreamed of molesting her. And then in the next breath adding that of course the other girls were only too pleased to sleep with him; the implication was, of course, that he only "molested" those who liked to be molested. That there was any particular reason why Mara should not want to be molested I couldn't see. Or was I supposed to think that he wouldn't molest a girl who had his welfare so much at heart? We had quite a ticklish wrangle about it as I was taking leave of her. It had been a crazy day and night. I had gotten tight and had fallen asleep on the floor. This was before dinner, and the reason for it was that I was famished. According to Mara, Carruthers had grown quite incensed over my conduct; she had had quite a time dissuading him from breaking a bottle over my head. In order to mollify him she had lain down with him on the couch for a while. She didn't say whether he had tried to "molest" her or not. Anyway he had only taken a cat nap; when he awoke he was hungry, wanted to eat right away. During his sleep he had forgotten that he had a visitor; seeing me lying on the floor sound asleep he had become angry again. Then they had gone out together and had a good meal; on the way home she had induced him to buy a few sandwiches for me and some coffee. I remembered the sandwiches and the coffee—it was like an interlude during a blackout. Carruthers had forgotten about me with Valerie's arrival. That I remembered too, though dimly. I remembered seeing a beautiful young girl enter and fling her arms about Carruthers. I remembered being handed a drink and falling back again into a torpor. And then? Well then, as Mara explained it, there had been a little tiff between herself and Valerie. And Carruthers had gotten blind drunk, had staggered out into the street and disappeared.

"But you were sitting on his lap when I woke up!" I said.

Yes, that was so, she admitted, but only after she had been out searching for him, wandering all through the Village, and finally picking him up on the steps of a church and bringing him home in a taxi.

"You must certainly think a lot of him to go to all that trouble."

She didn't deny it. She was tired of going all over that ground again with me.

So that was how the evening had passed. And Valerie? Valerie had left in a huff, after smashing an expensive vase. And what was that bread knife doing alongside me, I wanted to know. *That?* Oh, that was some more of Carruthers' tomfoolery. Pretending that he was going to cut my heart out. She hadn't even bothered to take the knife out of his hand. He was harmless, Carruthers. Wouldn't hurt a fly. Just the same, I thought to myself, it would have been wiser to wake me up. What else had happened, I wondered. Christ only knows what went on during the blackout. If she could let me put the blocks to her, knowing that Carruthers was apt to walk in at any moment, surely, she could let him "molest" her a few minutes (if only to pacify him), seeing that I was in a deep trance and would never be any the wiser.

However, it was now four in the morning and Carruthers was sound asleep on the couch. We were standing in a doorway on Sixth Avenue trying to come to some understanding. I was insisting that she let me take her home; she was trying to make me understand that it was too late.

"But I've taken you home before at an even later hour." I was determined not to let her return to Carruthers' den.

"You don't understand," she pleaded. "I haven't been home for several weeks. All my things are there."

"Then you're living with him. Why didn't you say that in the first place?"

"I'm *not* living with him. I'm only staying there temporarily until I find a place to live. I'm not going back home any more. I had a bad quarrel with my mother. I walked out. Told them I'd never come back again."

"And your father—what did he say?"

"He wasn't there when it happened. I know he must be heartbroken, but I couldn't stand it any longer."

"I'm sorry," I said, "if that's how it is. I suppose you're broke too. Let me walk you back—you must be fagged out."

We started walking through the empty streets. She stopped suddenly and threw her arms around me. "You trust me, don't you?" she said, looking at me with tears in her eyes.

"Of course I do. But I wish you would find another place to stay. I can always dig up the price of a room. Why don't you let *me* help you?"

"Oh, I won't be needing any help now," she said brightly. "Why, I almost forgot to tell you the good news! Yes, I'm going away for a few weeks—to the country. Carruthers is sending me to his cabin up in the North woods. The three of us are going—Florrie, Hannah Bell and myself. It'll be a real vacation. Maybe you can join us? You'll try, won't you? *Aren't you glad?*" She stopped to give me a kiss. "You see, he's not a bad sort," she added. "He's not coming up himself. He wants to give us a treat. Now if he were in love with me, as you seem to think, wouldn't he want to go up there with me alone? He doesn't like *you*, that I admit. He's afraid of you—you're too serious. After all, you've got to expect him to have some feelings. If his wife were dead he'd undoubtedly ask me to marry him—not because he's in love with me but because he wants to protect me. *Do you see now?*"

"No," I said, "I don't see. But it's all right. You certainly need a vacation; I hope you'll enjoy yourself there. As for Carruthers, no matter what you say about him, I don't like him and I don't trust him. And I'm not at all sure that he's acting from such generous motives as you describe. I hope he croaks, that's all, and if I could give him a drop of poison I'd do it—without a qualm."

"I'm going to write you every day," she said, as we stood at the door saying farewell.

"Mara, listen," I said, drawing her close to me and murmuring the words in her ear. "I had a lot to tell you today and it's all gone up in smoke."

"I know, I know," she said feverishly.

"Maybe things will change when you're gone," I continued. "Something's got to happen soon—we can't go on this way forever."

"That's what I'm thinking too," she said softly, snuggling against me affectionately. "I hate this life. I want to think it out when I'm up there and alone. I don't know how I ever got into this mess."

"Good," I said, "maybe we'll get somewhere then. You'll write, that's a promise?"

"Of course I will . . . *every day*," she said, as she turned to go.

I stood there a moment after she had turned in, wondering whether I was a fool to let her go, wondering if it wouldn't be better to drag her out and just smash a way through, wife or no wife, job or no job. I walked off, still debating it in my mind, but my feet dragging me towards home.

* * *

Well, she was off to the North woods. Just arrived, in fact. Those two pole cats had accompanied her and everything was just ducky. There were two wonderful backwoodsmen who looked after them, cooked their meals, showed them how to shoot the rapids, played the guitar and the harmonica for them on the back porch at night when the stars came out, and so on—all crammed on the back of a picture postcard showing the wonderful pine cones which drop from the pine trees up in Maine.

I immediately went around to Carruthers' den to see if he were still in town. He was there all right and quite surprised, and not any too pleased, to see me. I pretended that I had come to borrow a book which had caught my fancy the other evening. He informed me dryly that he had given up the practice of lending out books long ago. He was thoroughly sober and obviously determined to freeze me out as quickly as possible. I noticed, as I was taking leave, that he had tacked up the picture of me with the dagger through the heart. He noticed that I had noticed it but made no reference to it.

I felt somewhat humiliated but vastly relieved just the same. For once she had told me the truth! I was so overjoyed that I rushed to the public library, buying a pad and an envelope on the way, and sat there till closing time writing her a huge letter. I told her to telegraph me—couldn't wait to receive word by mail. After mailing the letter I wrote out a long telegram and dispatched it to her. Two days later, not having heard from her, I sent another telegram, a longer one, and after I had dispatched it I sat down in the lobby of the McAlpin Hotel and wrote her an even more voluminous letter than the first one. The next day I received a short letter, warm, affectionate, almost childish. No mention of the first telegram. That made me quite frantic. Perhaps she had given me a phoney address. But why would she do that? Anyway, better telegraph again! Demand full address and nearest telephone. Had she received the second telegram and both letters? "Keep a sharp lookout for mail and future telegrams. Write often. Telegraph when possible. Advise when returning. I love you. I'm mad about you. The Cabinet Minister speaking."

The "Cabinet Minister" must have done the trick. Soon there came a telegram for Glahn the Hunter, followed by a letter signed Victoria.* God was looking over her shoulder as she wrote. She had seen a deer and she had followed it through the woods and had lost her way. The backwoodsmen had found her and carried her home. They were wonderfully simple fellows, and Hannah and Florrie had fallen in love with them. That is, they went canoeing with them and sometimes slept in the woods with them all night. She was coming back in a week or ten days. She couldn't bear staying away from me longer than that. Then this: "I am coming back to you, I want to be your wife." Just as simple as that, the way she put it. I thought it marvelous. I loved her all the more for being so direct, so simple, so frank and honest. I wrote her three letters in a row, moving from place to place, as I shuffled about in a delirium of ecstasy.

On fever hooks waiting for her return. She had said she'd be back Friday night. Would telephone me at Ulric's studio soon as she hit town. Friday night came and I sat there until two in the morning waiting for her phone call. Ulric, always skeptical, said maybe she meant the following Friday. I went home thoroughly dejected but certain I would hear from

---

* All characters from Knut Hamsun's books.

her in the morning. Next day I telephoned Ulric several times to inquire if he had had any word from her.

* * *

Back in town I found a note on Ulric's bell, from Mara. She had arrived shortly after we left. Had been sitting on the steps waiting for me, waiting for hours, if I were to believe her words. A postscript informed me that she was off to Rockaway with her two friends. I was to call her there as soon as I could.

I arrived at dusk and found her waiting for me at the station; she was in a bathing suit over which she had thrown a mackintosh. Florrie and Hannah were sleeping it off again at the hotel; Hannah had lost her beautiful new set of false teeth and was in a state of nervous prostration. Florrie, she said, was going back to the woods again; she had fallen hard for Bill, one of the backwoodsmen. But first she had to have an abortion performed. It was nothing—not for Florrie anyway. The only thing that bothered her was that she seemed to grow larger down there with each abortion; soon she wouldn't be able to take on anything but niggers.

She led me to another hotel where we were to pass the night together. We sat talking awhile in the lugubrious dining room over a glass of beer. She looked queer in that mackintosh—like a person who's been driven out of the house by fire in the middle of the night. We were itching to get to bed but in order not to arouse suspicion we had to pretend to be in no great hurry. I had lost all sense of place: it seemed as if we had made a rendezvous in a dark room by the Atlantic Ocean in the wake of an exodus. Two or three other couples slipped in noiselessly, sipped their drinks, and chatted furtively in subdued whispers. A man walked through with a bloody meat cleaver, holding a decapitated chicken by the legs; the blood dripped on to the floor, leaving a zigzag trail—like the passage of a drunken whore who is menstruating freely.

Finally we were shown to a cell at the end of a long corridor. It was like the terminus of a bad dream, or the missing half of a Chirico painting. The corridor formed the axis of two wholly unrelated worlds; if you were to go left instead of right you might never find your way back again. We undressed and fell on the iron cot in a sexual sweat. We went at it like a pair of wrestlers who have been left to untangle themselves in an empty arena after the lights are out and the crowd dispersed. Mara was struggling frantically to bring on an orgasm. She had somehow become detached from her sexual apparatus; it was night and she was lost in the dark; her movements were those of a dreamer desperately struggling to re-enter the body which had begun the act of surrender. I got up to wash myself, to cool it off with a little cold water. There was no sink in the room. In the yellow light of an almost extinct bulb I saw myself in a cracked mirror; I had the expression of a Jack the Ripper looking for a straw hat in a pisspot. Mara lay prone on the bed, panting and sweating; she had the appearance of a battered odalisque made of jagged pieces of mica. I slipped into my trousers and staggered through the funnel-like corridor in search of the wash-room. A bald-headed man, stripped to the waist, stood before a marble basin washing his trunk and arm-pits. I waited patiently until he had finished. He snorted like a walrus in performing his ablutions; when he had done he opened a can of talcum powder and sprinkled it generously over his torso which was creased and caked like an elephant's hide.

When I returned I found Mara smoking a cigarette and playing with herself. She was burning up with desire. We went at it again, trying it dog-fashion this time, but still it was no go. The room began to heave and bulge, the walls were sweating, the mattress which was made of straw was almost touching the floor. The performance began to take on all the aspects and proportions of a bad dream. From the end of the corridor came the broken wheeze of an asthmatic; it sounded like the tail end of a gale whizzing through a corrugated rat hole.

Just as she was about to come we heard some one fumbling at the door. I slid off her and poked my head out. It was a drunk trying to find his room. A few minutes later, when I went to the wash-room to give my cock another cool spritz-bath, he was still looking for his room. The transoms were all open and from them came a stertorous cacophony which resembled the Epiphany of John the locust-eater. When I returned to resume the ordeal my cock felt as if it were made of old rubber bands. I had absolutely no more feeling at that end; it was like pushing a piece of stiff suet down a drain-pipe. What's more, there wasn't another charge left in the battery; if anything was to happen now it would be in the nature of gall and leathery worms or a drop of pus in a solution of thin pot cheese. What surprised me was that it continued to stand up like a hammer; it had lost all the appearance of a sexual implement; it looked disgustingly like a cheap gadget from the five and ten cent store, like a bright-colored piece of fishing tackle minus the bait. And on this bright and slippery gadget Mara twisted like an eel. She wasn't any longer a woman in heat, she wasn't even a woman; she was just a mass of undefinable contours wriggling and squirming like a piece of fresh bait seen upside down through a convex mirror in a rough sea.

I had long ceased to be interested in her contortions; except for the part of me that was in her I was as cool as a cucumber and remote as the dog star. It was like a long distance death message concerning some one whom you had forgotten long ago. All I was waiting for was to feel that incredibly aborted explosion of wet stars which drop back to the floor of the womb like dead snails.

Towards dawn, Eastern Standard Time, I saw by that frozen condensed milk expression about the jaw that it was happening. Her face went through all the metamorphoses of early uterine life, only in reverse. With the last dying spark it collapsed like a punctured bag, the eyes and nostrils smoking like toasted acorns in a slightly wrinkled lake of pale skin. I fell off her and dove straight into a coma which ended towards evening with a knock on the door and fresh towels. I looked out the window and saw a collection of tar-covered roofs spotted here and there with doves of taupe. From the ocean front came the boom of surf followed by a frying pan symphony of exasperated sheet metal cooling off in a drizzle at 139 degrees Centigrade. The hotel was droning and purring like a fat and moribund swamp fly in the solitude of a pine forest. Along the axis of the corridor there had been a further sag and recess during the interim. The Grade A world to the left was all sealed and boarded, like those colossal bath houses along the boardwalk which, in the off season, curl up on themselves and expire in gasps through endless chinks and slats. The other nameless world to the right had already been chewed off by a triphammer, the work doubtless of some maniac who had endeavored to justify his existence as a day laborer. Underfoot it was slimy and slippery, as if an army of zippered seals had been weaving it back and forth to the wash-room all day long. Here and there an open door revealed the presence of grotesquely plastic water nymphs who had managed to squeeze their mammiferous trundles of avoirdupois into sylph-like fish nets made of spun glass and ribbons of wet clay. The last roses of Summer were fading away into goiterous udders with arms and legs. Soon the epidemic would be over and the ocean would resume its air of gelatinous grandeur, of mucilaginous dignity, of sullen and spiteful solitude.

We stretched ourselves out in the hollow of a suppurating sand dune next to a bed of waving stink weed on the lee side of a macadamized road over which the emissaries of progress and enlightenment were rolling along with that familiar and soothing clatter which accompanies the smooth locomotion of spitting and farting contraptions of tin woven together by steel knitting needles. The sun was setting in the West as usual, not in splendor and radiance however but in disgust, like a gorgeous omelette engulfed by clouds of snot and phlegm. It was the ideal setting for love, such as the drug stores sell or rent between the covers of a handy pocket edition. I took off my shoes and leisurely deposited my big toe in the first notch of Mara's crotch. Her head was pointed south, mine north; we pillowed them on folded hands, our bodies relaxed and floating effortlessly in the magnetic drift, like two enormous twigs suspended on the surface of a gasoline lake. A visitor from the Renaissance, coming upon us unexpectedly, might well have assumed that we had become dislodged from a painting depicting the violent end of the mangy retinue of a sybaritic Doge. We were lying at the edge of a world in ruins, the composition being a rather precipitate study of perspective and foreshortening in which our prostrated figures served as a picaresque detail.

The conversation was thoroughly desultory, spluttering out with a dull thud like a bullet encountering muscle and sinew. We weren't talking, we were simply parking our sexual implements in the free parking void of anthropoid chewing gum machines on the edge of a gasoline oasis. Night would fall poetically over the scene, like a shot of ptomaine poison wrapped in a rotten tomato. Hannah would find her false teeth behind the mechanical piano; Florrie would appropriate a rusty can-opener with which to start the blood flowing.

The wet sand clung to our bodies with the tenacity of fresh-laid wall-paper. From the factories and hospitals nearby came the ingratiating aroma of exhausted chemicals, of hair soaked in pipi, of useless organs plucked out alive and left to rot slowly through an eternity in sealed vessels labelled with great care and veneration. A brief twilight sleep in the arms of Morpheus the Danubian dachshund.

When I got back to town Maude inquired in her polite fish-like way if I had had a pleasant holiday. She remarked that I looked rather haggard. She added that she was thinking of taking a little vacation herself; she had received an invitation from an old convent friend to pass a few days at her home in the country. I thought it an excellent idea.

Two days later I accompanied her and the child to the station. She asked me if I wouldn't care to ride part of the way with them. I saw no reason why I shouldn't. Besides I thought maybe she had something of importance to tell me. I boarded the train and rode some distance into the country, talking about things of no consequence and wondering all the time when she would come out with it. Nothing happened. I finally got off the train and waved good-bye. "Say good-bye to daddy," she urged the child. "You won't see him again for several weeks." Bye bye! Bye bye! I waved good-naturedly, like any suburban papa seeing his wife and child off. Several weeks, she had said. That would be excellent. I walked up and down the platform waiting for the train and pondering on all the things I would do in her absence. Mara would be delighted. It would be like having a private honeymoon: we could do a million wonderful things in a stretch of several weeks.

* * *

"The thing to happen now," I said, as I downed a glassful, "is for Maude to come back and surprise us."

"She wouldn't do that, would she?"

"Christ only knows what she might do."

"I think we'd better sleep down here," said Mara. "I wouldn't like to sleep in her bed."

We finished the wine and got undressed. Mara came out of the bathroom in Maude's silk kimono. It gave me a start to see her in Maude's outfit. "I'm your wife, am I not?" she said, putting her arms around me. It gave me a thrill to hear her say that. She walked about the room examining the things.

"Where do you write?" she asked. "At that little table?"

I nodded.

"You ought to have a big table and a room of your own. How can you write here?"

"I have a big desk upstairs."

"Where? In the bedroom?"

"No, in the parlor. It's wonderfully lugubrious up there—would you like to see it?"

"No," she said quickly, "I'd rather not go up there. I'll always think of you as sitting here in this corner by the window. . . . Is this where you wrote me all those letters?"

"No," I said, "I wrote you from the kitchen."

"Show me," she said. "Show me just where you sat. I want to see how you looked."

I took her by the hand and led her back to the kitchen. I sat down and pretended I was writing her a letter. She bent over me and putting her lips to the table she kissed the spot encircled by my arms.

"I never dreamt I would see your home," she said. "It's strange to see the place which is to have such an effect upon your life. It's a holy place. I wish we could take this table with us and this chair—everything—even the stove. I wish we could move the whole room and build it into our own home. It belongs to us, this room."

We went to bed on the divan in the basement. It was a

warm night and we went to sleep in the raw. About seven in the morning, as we lay entwined in each other's arms, the rolling doors were violently pushed open and there stood my darling wife, the landlord who lived upstairs, and his daughter. In flagrant delectation we were caught. I sprang out of bed stark naked. Holding a towel which was on the chair beside the couch I flung it around me and waited for the verdict. Maude motioned to her witness to step in and take a look at Mara who was lying there holding a sheet over her bosom.

"I'll ask you to please get this woman out of here as quickly as possible," said Maude, and with that she turned on her heel and went upstairs with her witnesses.

Had she been sleeping upstairs in our own bed all night? If so, why had she waited until morning?

"Take it easy, Mara. The goose is cooked now. We may as well stay and have breakfast."

I dressed hurriedly and ran out to get some bacon and eggs.

"God, I don't see how you can take it so calmly," she said, sitting at the table with a cigarette to her lips, watching me prepare the breakfast. "Haven't you any feelings?"

"Sure I have. My feeling is that everything has worked out splendidly. *I'm free*, do you realize that?"

"What are you going to do now?"

"I'm going to work, for one thing. This evening I'll go to Ulric's place—you might meet me there. I have an idea my friend Stanley is behind all this. We'll see."

At the office I sent a telegram to Stanley to meet me at Ulric's that evening. During the day I had a telephone call from Maude suggesting that I find myself a room. She said she would get the divorce as soon as possible. No comments upon the situation, just a pure business-like statement. I was to let her know when I wished to call for my things.

Ulric took it rather gravely. It meant a change of life and

all changes were serious to him. Mara on the other hand was thoroughly in possession of herself and already looking forward to the new life. It remained to see how Stanley would take it.

Presently the bell rang and there he was, sinister-looking as usual and drunk as a pope. I hadn't seen him that way for years. He had decided that it was an event of the first importance and that it should be celebrated. As far as getting any details from him was concerned it was absolutely impossible. "I told you I'd fix it for you," he said. "You walked into it like a fly into a web. I had it figured out to a T. I didn't ask you any questions, did I? I knew just what you'd do."

He took a swig from a flask which he was carrying in his inside coat pocket. He didn't even bother to remove his hat. I could see him now as he must have looked when at Fort Oglethorpe. He was the sort of fellow I would have given a wide berth, seeing him in that state.

The telephone rang. It was Dr. Kronski asking for *Mister* Miller. "Congratulations!" he shouted. "I'm coming over there to see you in a few minutes. I have something to tell you."

"By the way," I said, "do you know anybody who has an extra room to let?"

"That's just what I was going to talk to you about. I've got a place all picked out for you—up in the Bronx. It's a friend of mine—he's a doctor. You can have a whole wing of the house to yourself. Why don't you take Mara with you? You'll like it there. He's got a billiard room on the ground floor, and a good library, and. . . ."

"Is he Jewish?" I asked.

"*Is he?* He's a Zionist, an anarchist, a Talmudist and an abortionist. A damned fine chap—and if you're in need of help he'll give you his shirt. I was just around to your house—that's how I found out. Your wife seems to be tickled to death.

She'll live pretty comfortably on the alimony you'll have to pay her."

I told Mara what he had said. We decided to have a look at the place immediately. Stanley had disappeared. Ulric thought he might have gone to the bathroom.

I went to the bathroom and knocked. No answer. I pushed the door open. Stanley was lying in the tub fully dressed, his hat over his eye, the empty bottle in his hand. I left him lying there.

"He's gone, I guess," I shouted to Ulric as we sailed out.

* * *

The Bronx! We had been promised a whole wing of the house—a turkey wing, with feathers and goose pimples thrown in. Kronski's idea of a haven.

It was a suicidal period which began with cockroaches and hot pastrami sandwiches and ended à la Newberg in a cubby-hole on Riverside Drive where Mrs. Kronski the Second began her thankless task of illustrating a vast cycloramic appendix to the insanities.

It was under Kronski's influence that Mara decided to change her name again—from Mara to Mona. There were other, more significant changes which also had their origin here in the purlieus of the Bronx.

We had come in the night to Dr. Onirifick's hideout. A light snow had fallen and the colored panes of glass in the front door were covered with a mantle of pure white. It was just the sort of place I had imagined Kronski *would* select for our "honeymoon." Even the cockroaches, which began scurrying up and down the walls as soon as we turned on the lights, seemed familiar—and ordained. The billiard table which stood in a corner of the room was at first disconcerting, but when

Dr. Onirifick's little boy casually opened his fly and began to make pipi against the leg of the table everything seemed quite as it should be.

The front door opened directly on to our room which was equipped with a billiard table, as I say, a large brass bedstead with eiderdown quilts, a writing desk, a grand piano, a hobby horse, a fire place, a cracked mirror covered with flyspecks, two cuspidors and a settee. There were in all no less than eight windows in our room. Two of them had shades which could be pulled down about two-thirds of the way; the others were absolutely bare and festooned with cobwebs. It was very jolly. No one ever rang the bell or knocked first; every one walked in unannounced and found his way about as best he could. It was "a room with a view" both inside and out.

Here we began our life together. A most auspicious début! The only thing lacking was a sink in which we could urinate to the sound of running water.

* * *

Mona will be there waiting for me. She will embrace me warmly, as if we had never embraced before. We will have only a couple of hours together and then she will leave—to go to the dance hall where she still works as a taxi girl. I will be sound asleep when she returns at three or four in the morning. She will pout and fret if I don't awaken, if I don't throw my arms around her passionately and tell her I love her. She has so much to tell me each night and there is no time to tell it. Mornings, when I leave, she is sound asleep. We come and go like railroad trains. This is the beginning of our life together.

I love her, heart and soul. She is everything to me. And

yet she is nothing like the women I dreamed of, like those ideal creatures whom I worshipped as a boy. She corresponds to nothing I had conceived out of my own depths. She is a totally new image, something foreign, something which Fate whirled across my path from some unknown sphere. As I look at her, as I get to love her morsel by morsel, I find that the totality of her escapes me. My love adds up like a sum, but she, the one I am seeking with desperate, hungry love, escapes like an elixir. She is completely mine, almost slavishly so, but I do not possess her. It is I who am possessed. I am possessed by a love such as was never offered me before—an engulfing love, a total love, a love of my very toe-nails and the dirt beneath them—and yet my hands are forever fluttering, forever grasping and clutching, seizing nothing.

* * *

I was not aware, when I first knew Mona, how much she needed me. Nor did I realize how great a transformation she had made of her life, her habits, her background, her antecedents, in order to offer me that ideal image of herself which she all too quickly suspected that I had created. She had changed everything—her name, her birthplace, her mother, her upbringing, her friends, her tastes, even her desires. It was characteristic of her that she should want to change my name too, which she did. I was now Val, the diminutive of Valentine which I had always been ashamed of—it seemed like a sissy's name—but now that it issued from her lips it sounded like the name which suited me. Nobody else called me Val, though they heard Mona repeat it endlessly. To my friends I was what I always had been; they were not hypnotized by a mere change of name.

Of transformations. . . . I remember vividly the first

night we passed at Dr. Onirifick's place. We had taken a shower together, shuddering at the sight of the myriads of roaches which infested the bathroom. We got into bed beneath the eiderdown quilt. We had had an ecstatic fuck in this strange public room filled with bizarre objects. We were drawn very close together that night. I had separated from my wife and she had separated from her parents. We hardly knew why we had accepted to live in this outlandish house; in our proper senses neither of us would have dreamed of choosing such a setting. But we were not in our right senses. We were feverish to begin a new life, and we felt guilty, both of us, for the crimes we had committed in order to embark on the great adventure. Mona felt it more than I, in the beginning. She felt that she had been responsible for the break. It was the child which I had left behind, not my wife, whom she felt sorry for. It preyed on her mind. With it was the fear, no doubt, that I would wake up one day and realize that I had made a mistake. She struggled to make herself indispensable, to love me with such devotion, such complete self-sacrifice, that the past would be annihilated. She didn't do it deliberately. She wasn't even aware of what she was doing. But she clung to me desperately, so desperately that when I think of it now the tears come to my eyes. Because it was unnecessary: I needed her even more than she needed me.

And so, as we were falling off to sleep that night, as she rolled over to turn her back on me, the cover slipped off and I became aware, from the animal-like crouch she had assumed, of the massive quality of her back. I ran my two hands over her flesh, caressed her back as one would caress the flanks of a lioness. It was curious that I had never been aware of her superb back. We had slept together many times and we had fallen asleep in all sorts of postures, but I had noticed nothing. Now, in this huge bed which seemed to float in the wan light of the big room, her back became engraved in my memory. I had no definite thoughts about it—just vague pleasure sensations of the strength and the vitality that was in her. *One who could support the world on her back!* I didn't formulate anything so definite as that, but it was there, the thought, in some vague, obscure region of my consciousness. In my fingertips more likely.

Under the shower I had teased her about her tummy, which was growing rather generous, and I realized at once that she was extremely sensitive about her figure. But I was not critical of her opulent flesh—I was delighted to discover it. It carried a promise, I thought. And then, under my very eyes, this body which had been so generously endowed began to shrink. The inner torture was beginning to take its toll. At the same time the fire that was in her began to burn more brightly. Her flesh was consumed by the passion that ravaged her. Her strong, columnar neck, the part of her body which I most admired, grew slenderer and slenderer, until the head seemed like a giant peony swaying on its fragile stem.

"You're not ill?" I would ask, alarmed by this swift transformation.

"Of course not!" she would say. "I'm reducing."

"But you're carrying it too far, Mona."

"I was like this as a girl," she would answer. "It's natural for me to be thin."

"But I don't want you to grow thin. I don't want you to change. Look at your neck—do you want to have a scrawny neck?"

"My neck isn't scrawny," she would say, jumping up to look at herself in the mirror.

"I didn't say it was, Mona . . . but it may get that way if you keep on in this reckless fashion."

"Please Val, don't talk about it. You don't understand. . . ."

"Mona, don't talk that way. I'm not criticizing you. I only want to protect you."

"You don't like me this way . . . is that it?"

"Mona, I like you *any* way. I love you. I adore you. But please be reasonable. I'm afraid you're going to fade away, evaporate in thin air. I don't want you to get ill. . . ."

"Don't be silly, Val. I never felt better in my life."

"By the way," she added, "are you going to see the little one this Saturday?" She would never mention either my wife or the child by name. Also, she preferred to think I was visiting only the child on these weekly excursions to Brooklyn.

I said I thought I would go . . . why, was there any reason not to?

"No, no!" she said, jerking her head strangely and turning away to look for something in the bureau drawer.

I stood behind her, as she was leaning over, and clasped my arms around her waist.

"Mona, tell me something. . . . Does it hurt you very much when I go over there? Tell me honestly. Because if it does, I'll stop going. It has to come to an end some day anyway."

"You know I don't want you to stop. Have I ever said anything against it?"

"No-o-o," I said, lowering my head and gazing intently at the carpet. "No-o-o, you never say anything. But sometimes I wish you would. . . ."

"Why do you say that?" she cried sharply. She looked almost indignant. "Haven't you a right to see your own daughter? I would do it, if I were in your place." She paused a moment and then, unable to control herself, she blurted out: "I would never have left her if she had been mine. I wouldn't have given her up, not for anything!"

"Mona! What are you saying. What does this mean?"

"Just that. I don't know how you can do it. I'm not worth such a sacrifice. Nobody is."

"Let's drop it," I said. "We're going to say things we don't mean. I tell you, I don't regret anything. It was no sacrifice, understand that. I wanted you and I got you. I'm happy. I could forget everybody if it were necessary. You're the whole world to me, and you know it."

I seized her and pulled her to me. A tear rolled down her cheek.

"Listen, Val, I don't ask you to give up anything, but. . . ."

"But what?"

"Couldn't you meet me once in a while at night when I quit work?"

"At two in the morning?"

"I know . . . it *is* an ungodly hour . . . but I feel terribly lonely when I leave the dance hall. Especially after dancing with all those men, all those stupid, horrible creatures who mean nothing to me. I come home and you're asleep. What have I got?"

"Don't say that, *please*. Yes, of course I'll meet you—now and then."

"Couldn't you take a nap after dinner and. . . ."

"Sure I could. Why didn't you tell me sooner? It was selfish of me not to think of that."

"You're not selfish, Val."

"I am too. . . . Listen, supposing I ride down with you this evening? I'll come back, take a snooze, and meet you at closing time."

"You're sure it won't be too tiring?"

"No, Mona, it'll be wonderful."

On the way home, however, I began to realize what it would mean to arrange my hours thus. At two o'clock we would catch a bite somewhere. An hour's ride on the elevated.

In bed Mona would chat a while before going to sleep. It would be almost five o'clock by that time and by seven I would have to be up again ready for work.

* * *

Saturdays I usually quit work at noon, lunching either with Hymie Laubscher and Romero or with O'Rourke and O'Mara. Sometimes Curley joined us, or George Miltiades, a Greek poet and scholar, who was one of the messenger force. Now and then O'Mara would invite Irma and Dolores to join us; they had worked their way up from humble secretaries in the Cosmococcic employment bureau to buyers in a big department store on Fifth Avenue. The meal usually stretched out until three or four in the afternoon. Then, with dragging feet, I would wend my way over to Brooklyn to pay my weekly visit to Maude and the little one.

As the snow was still on the ground we were no longer able to take our walks through the park. Maude was generally attired in a negligee and bathrobe; her long hair hung loosely, almost to her waist. The rooms were super-heated and encumbered with furniture. She usually kept a box of candy near the couch where she reclined.

The greetings we exchanged would make one think we were old friends. Sometimes the child was not there when I arrived, having gone to a neighbor's house to play with one of her little friends.

"She waited for you until three o'clock," Maude would say, with an air of mild reproach, but secretly thrilled that it had turned out thus.

I would explain that my work had detained me at the office. To this she would give me a look which signified—"I know your excuses. Why don't you think up something different?"

"How is your friend Dolores?" she would ask abruptly. "Or," giving me a sharp look, "isn't she your friend any more?"

A question like this was meant as a gentle insinuation that she hoped I was not deceiving the other woman (Mona) as I had her. She would never mention Mona's name, of course, nor would I. She would say "she" or "her" in a way that was unmistakably clear as to whom she meant.

There was also, in these questions, an overtone of deeper implications. Since the divorce proceedings were only in the preliminary stages, since the rupture had not yet been definitely created by law, there was no telling what might happen in the meantime. We were no longer enemies, at least. There was always the child between us—a strong bond. And, until she could arrange her life differently, they were both dependent on me. She would like to have known more about my life with Mona, whether it was going as smoothly as we had expected or not, but pride prevented her from inquiring too openly. She doubtless reasoned to herself that the seven years we had lived together constituted a not altogether negligible factor in this now seemingly tenuous situation. One false move on Mona's part and I would fall back into the old pattern. It behooved her to make the most of this strange new friendship which we had established. It might prepare the ground for another and deeper relationship.

I felt sorry for her sometimes when this unexpressed hope manifested itself only too clearly. There was never the slightest fear on my part that I would sink back into the old pattern of conjugal life. Should anything happen to Mona—the only threat of separation I could think of was death—I would certainly never resume a life with Maude. It was much more plausible that I should turn to someone like Irma or Dolores, or even Monica, the little waitress from the Greek restaurant.

"Why don't you come over here and sit beside me—I won't bite you."

Her voice seemed to come from far away. Often it happened that when we were left alone, Maude and I, my mind would wander off. As now, for example, I would often respond in a semi-trance, the body obedient to her wishes but the rest of me absent. A brief struggle of wills always ensued, a struggle rather between her will and my absence of will. I had no desire to tickle her erotic fancies; I was there to kill a few hours and be off without opening any fresh wounds. Usually, however, my hand would absent-mindedly stray over her voluptuous form. There was nothing more to it at first than the involuntary caress that one would give a pet. But little by little she would make me aware that she was responding with concealed pleasure; then, just when she had succeeded in riveting my attention upon her body, she would make some abrupt move to break the connection.

"*Remember, I'm not your wife any more!*"

She loved to hurl that at me, knowing that it would incite me to renewed efforts, knowing that it would focus my mind, as well as my fingers, upon the forbidden object: *herself*. These taunts served another purpose too—they roused an awareness of her power to offer or deny. She always seemed to be saying with her body: "To have this you can't ignore *me*." The idea that I could be satisfied with her body only was a most humiliating one for her. "I'd give you more than any woman could offer," she seemed to say, "if only you *looked* at me, if only you saw *me*, the real me." She knew only too well that I looked beyond her, that the dislocation between our centers was far more real, far more dangerous, now than it had ever been. She knew too that there was no other way of reaching me than through the body.

It's a curious fact that a body, however familiar it may be to sight and touch, can become eloquently mysterious once we feel that the owner of it has become elusive or evasive. I remember the renewed zest with which I explored Maude's body after I learned that she had been to see a doctor for a vaginal examination. What gave spice to the situation was that the doctor in question had been an old suitor of hers, one of those suitors whom she had never mentioned. Out of the blue one day she announced that she had been to his office, that she had had a fall one day which she had told me nothing about, and, having lately run into her old sweetheart, whom she knew she could trust (!), she had decided to let him examine her.

"You just walked in on him and asked to be examined?"

"No, not quite like that." She had to laugh herself at this.

"Well, what did happen exactly?"

I was curious to know whether he had found her improved or otherwise in the interval of five or six years which had elapsed. Hadn't he made any advances? He was married, of course, she had already informed me of that. But he was also extremely handsome, a magnetic personality, she had taken pains to let me know.

"Well, how did it feel to get on the table and spread your legs open—before your old sweetheart?"

She tried to make me understand that she had grown absolutely frigid, that Dr. Hilary, or whatever the devil his name was, had urged her to relax, that he had reminded her that he was acting as a physician, and so on and so forth.

"Did you succeed in relaxing—finally?"

Again she laughed, one of those tantalizing laughs which she always produced when she had to speak of "shameful" things.

"Well, what did he do?" I pressed.

"Oh, nothing much, really. He just explored the vagina (she wouldn't say *my* vagina!) with his finger. He had a rubber over his finger of course." She added this as though to absolve herself of any suspicion that the procedure might have been anything more than a perfunctory one.

"He thought I had filled out beautifully," she volunteered, to my surprise.

"Oh, he did, did he? He gave you a thorough examination, then?"

The recollection of this little incident had been stirred by a remark she had just dropped. She said she had been worried about the old pain which had reappeared recently. She redescribed the fall which she had years ago when she believed, mistakenly, that she had injured her pelvis. She spoke with such seriousness that when she took my hand and placed it above her cunt, just at the ridge of the Mons Venus, I thought the gesture one of complete innocence. She had a thick growth of hair there, a genuine rose bush which, if the fingers strayed within striking distance of it, immediately stood on end, stiffened like a brush. It was one of those bushy things which are maddening to touch through a film of silk or velvet. Often, in the early days, when she wore attractive flimsy things, when she acted coquettish and seductive, I used to make a grab for it and hold on to it while standing in some public place, the lobby of a theatre, or an elevated station. She used to get furious with me. But, standing close to her, blocking the sight of my groping hand, I would continue to hold on to it, saying: "Nobody can see what I'm doing. Don't move!" And I would continue talking to her, my hand buried in her muff, she hypnotized with fear. In the theatre, as soon as the lights were lowered, she would always spread her legs apart and let me fool with her. She thought nothing of it then to open my fly and play with my cock throughout the performance.

Her cunt still held a thrill. I was conscious of it now, my hand resting warmly on the edge of her thick sporran. She kept up a continuous flow of talk in order to postpone that embarrassing moment of silence when there would be nothing but the pressure of my hand and the tacit admission that she wished it to remain there.

As though vitally interested in what she was relating, I suddenly reminded her of the step-father whom she had lost. As I anticipated, she thrilled immediately to the suggestion. Excited by the very mention of the name, she placed her hand over mine and pressed it warmly. That my own hand slipped a little farther down, that the fingers became entangled in the thick hairs, she seemed not to mind at all—for the moment. She carried on about him gushingly, quite like a school-girl. As my fingers twined and untwined I felt a double passion stirring in me. Years ago, when I first used to call on her, I was violently jealous of this step-father. She was then a woman of twenty-two or three, her figure full-blown, mature in every sense of the word; to see her sitting on his lap before the window, at dusk, talking to him in a low, caressing voice, used to infuriate me. "I love him," she would say, as though that excused her behavior, for with her the word love always meant something pure, something divorced from carnal pleasure. It was in Summer that these scenes occurred, and I, who was only waiting for the old duffer to release her, was all too conscious of the warm naked flesh beneath the filmy, gauze-like dress she wore. She might just as well have sat naked in his arms, it seemed to me. I was always conscious of the weight of her in his arms, of the way she settled down on him, her thighs rippling, her generous crack anchored firmly over his fly. I was certain that, however pure the old man's love for her was, he must have been aware of the luscious fruit he was holding in his arms. Only a corpse could have been impervious to the sap and the heat generated by that warm body. Moreover, the better I knew her, the more I thought it natural for her to offer her body in this furtive, libidinous way. An incestuous relationship was not beyond her; if she had to be "violated" she would prefer that it be done by the father she loved; the fact that he was not her real father, but the one she had chosen, simplified the situation, if indeed she ever permitted herself to think about such things openly. It was this damned, perverted relationship which had made it so difficult for me to bring her out into any clear, open sexual relationship in those days. She expected of me a love which I was unable to give her. She wanted me to fondle her like a child, whisper sweet nothings in her ear, pet her, pamper her, humor her. She wanted me to embrace and caress her in some absurd, incestuous way. She didn't want to admit that she had a cunt and I a prick. She wanted love talk and silent, furtive pressures, explorations with the hands. I was too forthright, too brutal, for her liking.

After she had had a taste of the real thing she was nearly beside herself—with passion, rage, shame, humiliation, and what not. She evidently had never thought it would be so enjoyable, nor so disgusting. What was disgusting—to her—was the abandonment. To think that there was something hanging between a man's legs which could make her forget herself completely was exasperating to her. She did so want to be independent—when not just a child. She didn't want the in-between realm, the surrender, the fusion, the exchange. She wanted to keep that little tight core of self which was hidden away in her breast and only allow herself the legitimate pleasure of surrendering the body. That body and soul could not be separated, especially in the sex act, was a source of the most profound irritation. She always behaved as if, having abandoned her cunt to the exploration of the penis, she had lost something, some little particle of her abysmal self, some element which could never be replaced. The more she fought against it the more complete was her abandon. No woman can fuck as savagely as the hysterical woman who has made her mind frigid.

Playing now with the stiff, wiry hairs of that brush of hers, letting a finger stray down occasionally to the tip of her cunt, my thoughts roamed vagrantly deep into the past. I had almost the feeling that I was her chosen father, that I was playing with this lascivious daughter in the hypnotic dusk of an overheated room. Everything was false and deep and real at the same time. If I were to act as she wished, act the part of the tender, understanding lover, there would be no doubt of the reward. She would devour me in passionate surrender. Only keep up the pretenses and she would open those thighs of hers with a volcanic ardor.

"Let me see if it hurts inside," I whispered, withdrawing my hand and deftly slipping it under the filmy shift and up her cunt. The juices were oozing from her; her legs slipped farther apart, responsive to the slightest pressure of my hand.

"There . . . does it hurt *there?*" I asked, piercing deep within her.

Her eyes were half closed. She gave a meaningless nod, signifying neither yes nor no. I slipped two more fingers inside her cunt and quietly stretched my length beside her. I put an arm under her head and drew her gently to me, my fingers still deftly churning the juices that were seeping from her.

She lay still, absolutely passive, her mind thoroughly absorbed in the play of my fingers. I took her hand and slid it into my fly which came unbuttoned magically. She grasped my prick firmly and gently, caressing it with a practiced touch. I stole a quick glance at her and saw an expression almost of bliss on her countenance. This was what she loved, this blind, tactile exchange of emotions. If she could only really fall asleep now and let herself be fucked, pretend that she had no watchful, waking part in it . . . just give herself completely and yet be innocent . . . what bliss that would be! She liked to fuck with the inner cunt, lying absolutely still, as in a trance. With semaphores erect, distended, jubilant, twitching, tickling, sucking, clinging, she could fuck to her heart's content, fuck till the last drop of juice was exhausted.

It was imperative now not to make a false move, not to puncture the thin skin which she was still spinning, like a cocoon, about her naked, carnal self. To make the transfer from finger to prick required the adroitness of a mesmerist. The deadly pleasure had to be increased most gradually, as though it were a poison to which the body became only gradually accustomed. She would have to be fucked through the veil of the cocoon, just as years ago, in order to take her, I had to violate her through her nightgown. . . . A devilish thought came to my mind, as my cock twitched with delight under her skillful caresses. I thought of her sitting on her stepfather's lap, in the gloaming, her crack glued to his fly as always. I wondered what the expression on her face would have been had she suddenly felt that glow-worm of his penetrating her dreamy cunt; if, while murmuring her perverse litany of adolescent love in his ears, if, unconscious of the fact her gauze-like dress no longer covered her fleshy buttocks, this unmentionable thing which was hidden between his legs suddenly stood bolt upright and climbed inside her, exploding like a water pistol. I looked at her to see if she could read my thoughts, exploring the folds and crevices of her inflamed cunt meanwhile with bold, aggressive palps. Her eyes were tightly closed, her lips parted lasciviously; the lower part of her body began to squirm and twist, as if trying to free itself from a net. Gently I removed her hand from my cock, at the same time gingerly lifting a leg and slinging it over me. For a few moments I let my cock jump and quiver at the mouth of her crack, letting it slide from front to rear and back again, as if it were a flexible rubber toy. An idiotic refrain was repeating itself in my head: "What is this I hold over thy head—*fine or super-fine?*" I continued this little game for a tantalizing spell, now and then nosing the head of my prick in an inch or so, then running it up against the tip of her cunt and letting it nestle down in her dewy bush. All of a sudden she gave a gasp and with eyes wide open she swung full round; balanced on hands and knees, she strove frantically to catch my prick with her slimy trap. I put my two hands around her buttocks, the fingers doing a glissando along the inner edge of her swollen cunt, and opening it like you would a torn rubber ball, I placed my cock at the vulnerable point and waited for her to bear down. For a moment I thought she had suddenly changed her mind. Her head, which had been hanging loosely, the eyes helplessly following the frantic movements of her cunt, now thrust itself up taut, the gaze suddenly shifted to some point above my head. An expression of utter selfish pleasure filled the full, roving orbs, and as she began to rotate her ass, my prick only half inside her, she began to chew her underlip. With that I slid a trifle lower and pulling her down with all my force I jabbed it in up to the hilt, so deep that she gave a groan and her head fell forward on the pillow. At this moment, when I could have taken a carrot and shoved it around inside her for all the difference it would have made, there came a loud knock at the door. We were both so startled that our hearts almost stopped beating. As usual, she recovered first. Tearing herself from me, she ran to the door.

"Who's there?" she asked.

"It's only me," came the timid, quaking voice which I recognized immediately.

"Oh, it's *you!* Why didn't you say so? What is it?"

"I only wanted to know," came the faint, dragging voice with a slowness which was exasperating, "if Henry was there?"

"Yes, of course he's here," snapped Maude, pulling herself together ."Oh, Melanie," she said, as if the latter were torturing her, "is that all you wanted to know? Couldn't you . . . ?"

"There's a telephone call for Henry," said poor old Melanie. And then even more slowly, as if she were just able to get that much more out of her system: "I . . . think . . . it's important."

"All right," I yelled, getting up from the couch and buttoning my fly, "I'll be right there!"

When I picked up the receiver I got quite a shock. It was Curley telephoning from Cockroach Hall. He couldn't tell me what it was, he said, but I was to get home as fast as I could.

"Don't talk that way," I said, "tell me the truth. What happened? Is it Mona?"

"Yes," he said, "but she'll be all right in a little while."

"She's not dead then?"

"No, but it was a close call. Hurry up . . . ," and with that he hung up.

In the hall I ran into Melanie, her bosom half exposed, limping along with melancholy satisfaction. She gave me an understanding look, one of pity, envy and reproach combined.

"I wouldn't have disturbed you, you know"—her voice drawled painfully upward—"if they hadn't said it was important. Dear me," and she started dragging her body towards the stairs, "there's so much to do. When you're young. . . ."

I didn't wait to hear her out. I ran downstairs and almost into Maude's arms.

"What is it?" she asked solicitously. Then, since I didn't answer immediately, she added: "Did something happen . . . to . . . to *her*?"

"Nothing serious, I hope," said I, fumbling about for my coat and hat.

"Must you go right away? I mean. . . ."

There was more than anxiety in Maude's voice; there was a hint of disappointment, a faint suggestion of disapproval.

"I didn't turn the light on," she continued, moving towards the lamp as if to switch it on, "because I was afraid Melanie might come down with you." She fussed a little with her bathrobe, as if to bring my mind back to the subject which was uppermost in her mind.

I suddenly realized that it was cruel to run off without a little show of tenderness.

"I've really got to run," I said, dropping my hat and coat and moving swiftly to her side. "I hate to leave you now . . . like this," and taking the hand which was about to light the lamp, I drew her to me and embraced her. She offered no resistance. On the contrary, she put her head back and offered her lips. In a moment my tongue was in her mouth and her body, limp and warm, was pressing convulsively against mine. ("Hurry, hurry!" came Curley's words.) "I'll make it quick," I said to myself, not caring now whether I made a rash move or not. I slipped my hand under her gown and plunged the fingers into her crotch. To my surprise she reached for my fly, opened it, and took out my prick. I backed her against the wall and let her place my prick against her cunt. She was all aflame now, conscious of every move she made, deliberate and imperious. She handled my prick as if it were her own private property.

It was awkward trying to get at it bolt upright. "Let's lie here," she whispered, sinking to her knees and dragging me down likewise.

"You'll catch cold," I said, as she feverishly attempted to slide out of her things.

"I don't care," she said, pulling my pants down and pulling me to her recklessly. "Oh God," she groaned, chewing her lips again and squeezing my balls as I slowly inserted my prick. "Oh God, give it to me . . . put it all the way in!" and she gasped and groaned with pleasure.

Not wishing to jump up immediately and make a grab

for my hat and coat I rested there on top of her, my prick still inside her and stiff as a ramrod. She was like a ripe fruit inside and the pulp seemed to be breathing. Soon I felt the two little flags fluttering; it was like a flower swaying, and the caress of the petals was tantalizing. They were moving uncontrollably, not with hard, convulsive jerks, but like silken flags responding to a breeze. And then it was as though she suddenly assumed the control: with the walls of her cunt she became a soft lemon squeezer inside, plucking and clutching at will, almost as if she had grown an invisible hand.

Lying absolutely still, I surrendered myself to these artful manipulations. ("Hurry, hurry!" But I recalled very clearly now that he had said she wasn't dead.) I could always summon a taxi; a few minutes more or less wouldn't matter. Nobody would ever imagine that I had stayed behind for this.

(Take your pleasure while it lasts. . . . Take your pleasure. . . .)

She knew now that I wouldn't run. She knew that she could draw it out as long as she pleased, especially lying quiet this way, fucking only with that inner cunt, fucking with a mindless mind.

I put my mouth to hers and began to fuck with my tongue. She could do the most amazing things with her tongue, things I had forgotten she knew. Sometimes she slid it into my throat as though to let me swallow it, then withdrew it tantalizingly to concentrate on the signalling below. Once I pulled my prick out all the way, to give it a breath of air, but she reached for it greedily and slipped it back in again, thrusting herself forward so that it would touch bottom. Now I drew it out just to the tip of her cunt and, like a dog with a moist nose, I sniffed at it with the tip of my pecker. This little game was too much for her; she began to come, a long drawn-out orgasm that exploded softly like a five-pointed star. I was in such a cold-blooded state of control that as she went through her spasms I poked it around inside her like a demon, up, sideways, down, in, out again, plunging, rearing, jabbing, snorting, and absolutely certain that I wouldn't come until I was damned good and ready.

And now she did something she had never done before. Moving with furious abandon, biting my lips, my throat, my ears, repeating like a crazed automaton, "Go on, give it to me, go on, give it, go on, Oh God, give it, give to me!" she went from one orgasm to another, pushing, thrusting, raising herself, rolling her ass, lifting her legs and twining them round my neck, groaning, grunting, squealing like a pig, and then suddenly, thoroughly exhausted, begging me to finish her off, begging me to shoot. "Shoot it, shoot it . . . I'll go mad." Lying there like a sack of oats, panting, sweating, utterly helpless, utterly played out that she was, I slowly and deliberately rammed my cock back and forth, and when I had enjoyed the chopped sirloin, the mashed potatoes, the gravy and all the spices, I shot a wad into the mouth of her womb that jolted her like an electric charge.

In the subway I tried to prepare myself for the ordeal ahead. Somehow I felt certain that Mona was not in danger. To tell the truth, the news was not altogether a shock; I had been expecting an outburst of some sort for weeks. A woman can't go on pretending that she is indifferent when her whole future is in jeopardy. Particularly a woman who feels guilty. While I didn't doubt that she had made an effort to do something desperate, I knew also that her instincts would prevent her from accomplishing her end. What I feared more than anything was that she might have bungled the job. My curiosity was aroused. What had she done? How had she gone about it? Had she planned it knowing that Curley would come to the rescue? I hoped, in some strange, perverted way, that her story would sound convincing; I didn't want to hear some preposterous, outlandish tale which in my unsettled condition would cause me to burst out into hysterical laughter. I wanted to be able to listen with a straight face—to look sorrowful and sympathetic because I *felt* sorrowful and sympathetic.

*   *   *

. . . It's a devil of a long ride to the Bronx, and if you let your mind go you can write a book between Borough Hall and Tremont. Besides, despite the exhaustive bout with Maude, one of those slow, creepy erections was coming on. It's a commonplace observation but true just the same—the more you fuck, the more you want to fuck, and the better you do fuck! When you overdo it your cock seems to get more flexible: it hangs limp, but on the alert, as it were. You only have to brush your hand over your fly and it responds. For days you can walk around with a rubber truncheon dangling between your legs. Women seem to sense it, too.

Now and then I tried to fix my mind on Mona, to set my face in plastic sorrow, but it wouldn't last. I felt too damned good, too relaxed, too carefree. Horrible as it sounds, I thought more of the fuck I anticipated pulling off once I soothed her down. I smelled my fingers to make sure I had scoured them properly. In doing so a rather comical image of Maude assailed me. I had left her lying on the floor, exhausted, and had rushed to the bathroom to tidy myself up. As I was scrubbing my cock she opens the door. Wants to take a douche immediately, always fearful of getting caught. I tell her to go ahead, not to mind me. She peels off her things, fastens the hose to the gas jet, and lies on the bath mat, her legs running up the wall.

"Can I help you?" says I, drying my cock and sprinkling some of her excellent sachet powder over it.

"Do you mind?" says she, wiggling her ass so that her legs will stand up straighter.

"Open it up a bit," I urge, taking the nozzle in readiness to insert it.

She did as I told her, pulling her gash open with all her fingers. I bent over and examined it leisurely. It was a dark, liverish color and the lips were rather exaggerated. I took them between my fingers and rubbed them gently together, like you would two velvety petals. She looked so helpless lying with her ass propped against the wall and her legs sticking up straight, like the hands of a compass, that I had to chuckle.

"Please don't fool now," she begged, as if the delay of a few seconds might mean an abortion. "I thought you were in such a hurry."

"I am," I replied, "but Jesus, when I look at this thing I get horny again."

I inserted the nozzle. The water began running out of her, over the floor. I threw some towels down to soak it up. When she stood up I took the soap and wash rag and scrubbed her cunt for her. I soaped her well, inside and out—a delicious tactile sensation which was mutual.

It felt silkier than ever now, her cunt, and I whooshed my fingers in and out, like you'd strum a banjo. I had one of those half-hearted, swollen erections which makes a cock look even more murderous than when full blown. It was hanging out of my fly, brushing her thigh. She was still naked. I began to dry her off. To do so comfortably I sat on the edge of the tub, my cock gradually stiffening and making spasmodic leaps at her. As I pulled her close, to dry her flanks, she looked down at it with a hungry, despairing look, fascinated and yet half-ashamed of herself for acting the glutton. Finally she could stand it no longer. She got to her knees impulsively and took it in her mouth. I ran my fingers through her hair, caressed the shell of her ears, the nape of her neck, caught her teats and massaged them gently, lingering over the nipples until they stood out taut. She had unfastened her mouth and was licking it now as if it were a stick of candy. "Listen," said I, murmuring the words in her ear, "we won't go through it again but just let me put it in a few moments and then I'll go. It's too good to stop all of a sudden. I won't come, I promise. . . ." She looked at me imploringly, as if to say "Can I believe you? Yes, I do want it. Yes, yes, only don't knock me up, will you?"

I pulled her to her feet, turned her around like a dummy, placed her hands on the edge of the tub, and raised her bum just a trifle. "Let's do it this way for a change," I murmured, not inserting my cock immediately, but rubbing it up and down her crack from behind.

"You won't come, will you?" she begged, craning her neck around and giving me a wild, imploring look through the mirror over the washstand. "I'm wide open. . . ."

That "wide open" brought out all the lust in me. "You bloody bitch," says I to myself, "that's just what I want. I'm going to piss in your palatial womb!" And with that I let it slip in slowly, little by little, moving it from right to left, grazing the pockets and lining of her wide-open cunt until I felt the mouth of her womb; there I wedged it good and solid, soldering it to her as if I intended to leave it in for good. "Oh, oh!" she groaned. "Don't move, please . . . just hold it!" I held it all right, even when that rear end began revolving like a pin-wheel.

"Can you still hold it?" she murmured huskily, trying again to look around and catching her reflection in the mirror.

"I can hold it," I said, not making the slightest movement, knowing that that would encourage her to unleash all her tricks.

"It feels wonderful," she said, her head falling limp, as if it had become unhinged. "You're bigger now, do you know it? Is it tight enough for you? I'm terribly opened up."

"It's all right," I said. "It fits marvelously. Listen, don't move any more . . . just clutch it . . . you know how. . . ."

She tried but somehow it wouldn't perform, her little lemon squeezer. I withdrew abruptly, without warning. "Let's lie down . . . *here*," I said, pulling her away and placing a dry towel under her. My cock was glistening with juice and hard as a pole. It hardly seemed to be a prick any more: it was like an instrument I had attached, an erection made flesh. She lay prone, looking at it with terror and joy, wondering what next it might think to do—yes, quite as if *it* were deciding things and not me or her.

"It's cruel of me to keep you," she said, as I socked it in swiftly. The suction created a smacking sound, like wet farts.

"Jesus, now I'm going to fuck you good and proper. Don't worry, I won't come . . . I haven't got a drop left. Move all you want . . . jerk it up and down . . . that's it, rub it around, go on, do it . . . fuck your guts out!"

"Shhh!" she whispered, putting her hand to my mouth. I bent forward and bit into her neck, long and deep; I bit her ears, her lips. I pulled out again for one tantalizing second, and bit the hair over her cunt, caught the two little lips up and slid them between my teeth.

"Put it in, put it in!" she begged, her lips slavering, her hand reaching for my prick and placing it back in again. "Oh God, I'm going to come . . . I can't hold it any more. Oh, oh. . . ." and she went into a spasm, slapping it up against me with such fury, such abandon, that she looked like a crazed animal. I pulled out without coming, my prick shiny, glistening, straight as a ramrod. Slowly she rose to her feet. Insisted on washing it for me, patted it admiringly, tenderly, as if it had been found tried and true. "You must run," she said, holding my prick between her two hands, the towel wrapped around it. And then, dropping the towel and looking away—"I hope she's all right. Tell her so, will you?"

Yes, I had to smile thinking of this last minute scene. "*Tell her so. . . .*" That extra fuck had softened her up. I thought of a book I had read which told of rather strange experiments with carnivorous animals—lions, tigers, panthers. Seems that when these ferocious beasts were kept well-fed—over-fed, indeed—one could put gentle creatures in the same cage with them and they would never molest them. The lion attacked only out of hunger. He was not perpetually murderous. That was the gist of it. . . .

And Maude. . . . Having satisfied herself to her heart's content, she had probably realized for the first time that it was useless to harbor a grudge against the other woman. If, she may have told herself, if it were possible to be fucked like that whenever she wished, it wouldn't matter what claims the other one had on me. Perhaps it entered her mind for the first time that possession is nothing if you can't surrender yourself. Perhaps she even went so far as to think that it might be better this way—having me protect her and fuck her and not having to get angry with me because of jealous fears. If the other one could hold on to me, if the other one could keep me from running around with every little slut that came across my path, if together they could share me, tacitly of course and without embarrassment and confusion, perhaps after all it might be better than the old arrangement. Yes, to be fucked that way, fucked without fear of being betrayed, to be fucking your own husband who is now your friend (and perhaps a lover again), to be taking what you want of him, calling him when you need him, sharing a warm, passionate secret with him, reliving the old fucks, learning new ones, stealing and yet not stealing, but giving oneself with pleasure and abandon, growing younger again, losing nothing except a conventional tie . . . yes, it might be ever so much better.

I'm sure something of this sort had been running through her head, had spread its aureole about her. I could see her, in my mind's eye, languorously brushing her hair, feeling her breasts, examining the marks of my teeth on her neck, hoping Melanie would not notice them but not caring too deeply whether she did or not. Not caring greatly any more whether Melanie overheard things or not. Asking herself wistfully perhaps how it had ever come about that she had lost me. Knowing now that if she had to live her life all over again she would never act as she had, never worry about useless things. So foolish to worry about what the other woman may be doing! What matter if a man did let his feet stray now and then? She had locked herself up, put a cage around herself; she had pretended she had no desires, pretended she dare not fuck—because we weren't man and wife any longer. What a terrible humiliation! Wanting it dreadfully, longing for it, almost begging for it like a dog—and there it was all the time, waiting for her. Who cared whether it was right or not? Wasn't this wonderful stolen hour better than anything she had ever known? *Guilt?* She had never felt less guilty in her life. Even if the "other one" had died meanwhile she couldn't feel bad about it.

I was so certain of what had been going on in her mind that I made a mental note to ask her about it next time we met. Of course next time she might be her old self again—that was only too possible with Maude. Besides, it wouldn't do to let her see that I was too interested—that might only stir up the poison. The thing to do would be to keep it on an impersonal level. No sense in letting her relapse into her old ways. Just walk in with a cheery greeting, ask a few questions, send the kid out to play, move in close, quietly, firmly take out my prick and put it in her hand. Make sure the room was not too bright. No nonsense! Just walk up to her and, while asking how things are going, slip a hand up her dress and start the juice flowing.

That extra last minute fuck had done wonders for me too. Always, when one digs down into the reservoir, when one summons the last ounce, so to speak, one is amazed to discover that there is a boundless source of energy to be drawn on. It had happened to me before, but I had never given it serious attention. Staying up all night and going to work without sleep had a similar effect upon me; or the converse, staying in bed long past the period of recuperation, forcing myself to rest when I no longer needed rest. To break a habit, establish a new rhythm—simple devices, long known to the ancients. It never failed. Break down the old pattern, the worn-out connections, and the spirit breaks loose, establishes new polarities, creates new tensions, bequeaths new vitality.

Yes, I observed with the keenest pleasure now how my mind was sparking, how it radiated in every direction.

* * *

"*She tried to poison herself!*"

Those were the words that greeted me on opening the door of Dr. Onirifick's establishment. It was Curley who made the announcement, smothering his words under the rattle of the door-knob.

A glance over his shoulder told me that she was asleep. Kronski had taken care of her. He had requested that nothing be said to Dr. Onirifick about it.

"I smelled the chloroform as soon as I came in," Curley explained. "She was seated in the chair, huddled up, as if she had had a stroke."

"I thought maybe it was an abortion . . . ," he added, looking a little sheepish.

"Why did she do it, did she say?"

Curley hemmed and hawed.

"Come on, don't be silly. What was it—jealousy?"

He wasn't sure. All he knew was what she blabbed on coming to. She had repeated over and over that she couldn't stand it any longer.

"Stand what?" I asked.

"Your seeing your wife, I suppose. She said she had picked the receiver up to telephone you. She felt that something was wrong."

"How did she put it exactly, do you remember?"

"Yes, she talked a lot of nonsense about being betrayed. She said it wasn't the child you went to see but your wife. She said you were weak, that when she was not with you you were capable of doing anything. . . ."

I looked at him in astonishment. "She really said that? You're not putting it on, are you?"

Curley pretended not to hear. He went on to speak of Kronski, how well he had behaved.

"I didn't think he could lie so cleverly," said Curley.

"Lie? How do you mean?"

"The way he talked about you. You should have heard it. God, it was almost as if he were making love to her. He said such wonderful things about you that she began to weep and sob like a child."

"Imagine," he continued, "telling her that you were the most loyal, faithful fellow in the world! Saying that you had changed completely since you knew her—that no woman could tempt you!"

Here Curley couldn't restrain a sickly grin.

"Well, it's true," I said, almost angrily. "Kronski was telling the truth."

"That you love her so much you. . . ."

"And what makes you think I don't?"

"Because I know you. You'll never change."

I sat down near the bed and looked at her. Curley moved about restlessly. I could feel the anger in him smoldering. I knew what was at the bottom of it.

"She's quite all right now, I suppose?" I inquired after a time.

"How do I know, she's not *my* wife." The words flashed back like the gleam of a knife.

"What's the matter with you, Curley? Are you jealous of Kronski? Or are you jealous of *me?* You can hold her hand and pet her when she wakes up. You know me . . ."

"Damned right I do!" came Curley's sullen reply. "You should have been here holding her hand yourself. You're never there when any one wants you. I suppose you were holding Maude's hand—now that she doesn't want you any more. I remember how you treated her. I thought it funny then—I was too young to know better."

* * *

Kronski had told the truth! That's what I kept repeating to myself as I sat beside the bed and waited for her to return to life. She was not dead, thank God. Merely asleep. She looked as though she were floating in luminol.

It was so unusual for me to play the role of the bereaved one that I became fascinated by the thought of how I would act if she were actually to die now before my eyes. Supposing she were never to open her eyes again? Supposing she passed from this deep trance into death? I tried to concentrate on that thought. I wanted desperately to know how I would feel if she were to die. I tried to imagine that I was a fresh widower, that I had not even called the undertaker.

First of all, however, I got up to put my ear to her mouth. Yes, she was still breathing. I pulled the chair close to the foot of the bed and concentrated as best I could on death—*her death*. No extraordinary emotions manifested themselves. To be truthful, I forgot about my supposed personal loss and became absorbed in a rather blissful contemplation of the desirability of death. I began to think about my own death, and how I would enjoy it. The prone figure lying there, hardly breathing, floating in the wake of a drug like a small boat attached to the stern of a vessel, was myself. I had wanted to die and now I was dying. I was no longer aware of this world but not yet in the other one. I was passing slowly out to sea, drowning without pain of suffocation. My thoughts were neither of the world I was leaving nor of the one I was approaching. In fact, there was nothing comparable to thought going on. Nor was it dreaming. I was more like a diaspora; the knot was unravelling, the self was dribbling away. There wasn't even a self any more: I was the smoke from a good cigar, and like smoke I was vanishing in thin air, and what was left of the cigar was crumbling to dust and dissolution.

I gave a start. The wrong tack. I relaxed and gazed at her less fixedly. Why should I think about her death?

Then it came to me: only if she were dead could I love her the way I imagined I loved her!

"Still the actor! You did love her once, but you were so pleased with yourself to think that you could love another beside yourself that you forgot about her almost immediately. You've been watching yourself make love. You drove her to this in order to feel again. To lose her would be to find her again."

I pinched myself, as if to convince myself that I was capable of feeling.

"Yes, you are not made of wood. You have feelings—but they're misdirected. Your heart works spasmodically. You're grateful to those who make your heart bleed; you don't suffer for them, you suffer in order to enjoy the luxury of suffering. You haven't begun to suffer yet; you're only suffering vicariously."

There was some truth in what I was telling myself. Ever since I had entered the room I had been preoccupied with how I should act, how I should express my feelings. As for that last minute business with Maude—that was excusable. My feelings had switched, that was all. Fate had tricked me. Maude, pfui! I didn't give a fuck about her. I couldn't remember when she had ever stirred any real feeling in me. What a cruel piece of irony it would be if Mona were to discover the truth! How could I ever explain such a dilemma? At the very moment I am betraying her, as she divined, Kronski is telling her how faithful and devoted I am. And Kronski was right! But Kronski must have suspected, when he was telling her the truth, that it was built on a lie. He was affirming his faith in me because he himself wanted to believe in me. Kronski was no fool. And he was probably a far better friend than I had ever estimated him to be. If only he didn't show such eagerness to reach into my guts! If only he would quit driving me into the open.

Curley's remark returned to plague me. Kronski had behaved so wonderfully—as if he were making love to her! Why was it that I always got a thrill when I thought of some one making love to her? Jealous? I was quite willing to be made jealous if only I could witness this power she had of making others love her. My ideal—it gave me quite a shock to formulate it!—was that of a woman who had the world at her feet. If I thought there were men impervious to her charms I would deliberately aid her to ensnare them. The more lovers she garnered the greater my own personal triumph. Because she did love *me*, that there was no doubt about. Had she not singled me out from all the others, I who had so little to offer her?

I was weak, she had told Curley. Yes, but so was she. I was weak as regards women in general; she was weak as regards the one she loved. She wanted my love to be focused on her exclusively, even in thought.

Oddly enough, I *was* beginning to focus on her exclusively, in my own weak way. If she had not brought her weakness to my attention I would have discovered for myself, with each new adventure, that there was only one person in the world for me—and that it was her. But now, having placed it before my mind dramatically, I would always be haunted by the thought of the power I exercised over her. I might be tempted to prove it, even against the grain.

I dismissed this train of thought—violently. That wasn't at all how I wanted things to be. I did love her exclusively, only her, and nothing on earth would make me swerve.

I began to review the evolution of this love. *Evolution?* There had been no evolution. It had been instantaneous. Why, and I was amazed to think that I should adduce this proof, why, even the fact my first gesture had been one of rejection was proof of the fact that I recognized the attraction. I had said no to her instinctively, because of fear. I went all over that scene in the dance hall the evening I walked out on my old life. She was coming towards me, from the center of the floor. I had cast a quick glance to either side of me, hardly believing it possible that she had singled *me* out. And then a panic, though I was dying to throw myself into her arms. Had I not shaken my head vigorously? No! No! Almost insultingly. At the same time I was shaken by the fear that even if I were to stand there forever she would never again cast an eye in my direction. Then I knew I wanted her, that I would pursue her relentlessly even if she had no use for me. I left the rail and went over to the corner to smoke. Trembling from head to foot. I kept my back to the dance floor, not daring to look at her. Jealous already, jealous of whomever it might be that she would choose for the next partner. . . .

(It was wonderful to recapture those moments. Now, by God, I was feeling again. . . .)

Yes, after a time I had picked myself up and returned to the rail, pressed on all sides by a pack of hungry wolves. She was dancing. She danced several dances in succession, with the same man. Not close, like the other girls, but airily, looking up into the man's face, smiling, laughing, talking. It was plain that he meant nothing to her.

Then came my turn. She *had* deigned to notice me after all! She seemed not at all displeased with me; on the contrary, she behaved as though she were going out of her way to be pleasant. And so, in a swoon, I had let her carry me round the floor. And then again, and again, and again. And even before I ventured to draw her into conversation I knew I would never leave the place without her.

We danced and danced, and when we were tired of dancing we sat in a corner and talked, and for every minute I talked or danced a clock ticked off the dollars and cents. How rich I was that night! What a delicious sensation it was to peel off dollar after dollar recklessly! I acted like a millionaire because I *was* a millionaire. For the first time in my life I knew what it was to be wealthy, to be a Mogul, a Rajah, a Maharajah. I was giving my soul away—not bartering it, as did Faust, but pissing it away.

There had been that strange conversation about Strindberg, which was to run through our life like a silver thread. I was always going to reread *Miss Julie*, because of what she said that night, but I never did—and probably never would.

Then I waited for her in the street, on Broadway, and as she came towards me this second time she took complete possession of me. In the booth, at Chin Lee's, she became still another person. She became—and this was really the secret of her irresistible charm—*she became vague.*

I didn't frame it thus to myself, but as I sat blindly groping through the smoke of her words, I knew that I would fling myself like a madman into every gap in her story. She was spinning a web too delicate, too tenuous, to support the weight of my prying thoughts. Another woman acting thus would have aroused my suspicions. I would have branded her a skilful liar. This one was not lying. She was embroidering. She was stitching—and now and then she dropped a stitch.

Here a thought flitted through my head which had never formulated itself before. It was one of those larval thoughts which scud through the mind like a thin moon through mutton chops. *She has been doing this always!* Yes, it had probably occurred to me at the time, but I had dismissed it instantly. The way she leaned over, the weight of her resting on one arm, the hand, the right hand, moving like a needle—yes, at that moment, and again several times later, an image had flashed through my mind, but I had had no time, or rather she had given me no time, to track it down. But now it was clear. Who was it that "had been doing it always"? *Fate.* There were three of them, and there was something sinister about them. They lived in a twilight and they spun a web: one of them had assumed this posture, had shifted her weight, had looked into the camera with hand poised, then resumed that endless stitching, spinning, weaving, that silent talk which weaves in and out of the spoken web of words.

A shuttle moving back and forth, a bobbin ceaselessly bobbing. Now and then a dropped stitch. . . . Like the man who lifted her dress. He was standing on the stoop saying good-night. Silence. He blows his brains out. . . . Or the father flying his kites on the roof. He comes flying down out of the sky, like a violet angel of Chagall's. He walks between his race horses, holding one on either side, by the bridle. Silence. The Stradivarius is missing. . . .

We are on the beach and the moon is scudding through the clouds. But before that we were sitting close together in the motorman's box in the elevated train. I had been telling her the story of Tony and Joey. I had just written it—perhaps because of her, because of the effect of certain vaguenesses. She had thrown me back suddenly on myself, made loneliness seem delectable. She had stirred those grape-like bunches of emotion which were strung like a garland on the skeleton of my ego. She had revived the boy, the boy who ran through the fields to greet his little friends. There was never any actor then! That boy ran alone. That boy ran to throw himself into the arms of Joey and Tony. . . . Why did she look at me so intently when I told her the story of Joey and Tony? There was a terrible brightness in her face that I can never forget. Now I think I know what it was. I think I had stopped her—stopped that incessant spinning and weaving. There was gratitude in her eyes, as well as love and admiration. I had stopped the machine and she had risen like a vapor, for just a few minutes. That terribly bright look was the nimbus of her liberated self.

Then sexual plunges. Submerging that cloud of vapor. Like trying to hold smoke under water. Peeling off layer after layer of darkness in the dark. Another kind of gratitude. A bit horrible, though. As if I had taught her the prescribed way to commit hari-kiri. . . . That utterly inexplicable night at Rockaway Beach—in the Doctor Caligari hotel and bathing establishment. Running back and forth to the lavatory. Swooping down on her, scooping it out, piercing her . . . plunging, plunging, as if I had become a gorilla with knife in hand and were slashing the Sleeping Beauty to life. The next—morning—or was it afternoon? Lying on the beach with our toes in one another's crotch. Like two Surrealist objects demonstrating a hazardous *rencontre.*

And then Dr. Tao, his poem printed on fire-cracker paper. Encysted in the mind, because she had failed to meet me in the garden as she promised. I was holding it in my hand while talking to her over the telephone. Some of the gold had rubbed off and clung to my fingers. She was still in bed—with that slut Florrie. They had drunk too much the night before. Yes, she had stood on a table—*where?* somewhere!—and had tried to do the split. And she had hurt herself. But I was too furious to care whether she had hurt herself or not. She was alive, wasn't she, and she had failed to show up. And perhaps Florrie was lying there beside her, as she pretended, and perhaps it wasn't Florrie but that guy Carruthers. Yes, that old fool who was so kind and thoughtful, but who had still enough gumption in him to stick daggers in people's portraits.

A desolating thought suddenly assailed me. The danger from Carruthers was past. Carruthers had helped her. Others had helped her before him no doubt. . . . But this was the thought: if I had not come that night to the dance hall with a wad in my pocket, if I had had just enough for a few dances, what then? And putting aside that first grand occasion, what about that other time in the empty lot? ("*And now for the dirt . . . !*") Supposing I had failed her then? But I couldn't have failed her, that was just it. She must have realized that or she would never have risked it. . . .

In cold-blooded honesty I was forced, nevertheless, to concede that those few miraculous sums I had managed to produce at the right moment had been an important factor. They had helped her to believe that she could rely on me.

I wiped the slate clean. Damn it, if one were to interrogate Fate that way everything could be explained by what you had to eat for breakfast. Providence puts opportunities in your path: they can be translated as money, luck, youth, vitality, a thousand different things. If the attraction isn't there nothing can be made of even the most golden opportunity. It was because I would do anything for her that so many opportunities were afforded me. *Money,* shit! Money had nothing to do with it. So much anfractuosity, or defectuosity, or impecuniosity! It was like the definition of hysteria in Dr. Onirifick's library: "an undue permeability of the psychical diaphragm."

No, I wasn't going to get off into these complicated eddies. I closed my eyes to sink back into that other clear stream which ran on and on like a silver thread. In some quiet part of me there was a legend which she had nourished. It was of a tree, just as in the Bible, and beneath it stood the woman called Eve with an apple in her hand. Here it ran like a clear stream, all that really constituted my life. Here there was feeling, from bank to bank.

What was I getting at—*here where the subterranean stream ran clear?* Why that image of the Tree of Life? Why was it so exhilarating to retaste the poisonous apple, to kneel in supplication at the feet of a woman in the Bible? Why was the Mona Lisa's smile the most mysterious of all human expressions? And why should I transpose this smile of the Renaissance to the lips of an Eve whom I had known only as an engraving?

There was something which hung on the fringe of memory, some enigmatic smile which expressed serenity, beatitude, beneficence. But there was also a poison, a distillation which exuded from that mystifying smile. And this poison I had quaffed and it had blurred the memory. There had been a day when I had accepted something in exchange for something; on that day a strange bifurcation had taken place.

In vain I ransacked my brain. However, I was able to recall this much. On a certain day in Spring I met her in the

Rose Room of a large hotel. She had arranged to meet me there in order to show me a dress she had bought. I had come ahead of time and after a few restless moments I had fallen into a trance. It was her voice which brought me to. She had spoken my name and the voice had passed through me, like smoke through gauze. She *was* ravishing, appearing suddenly like that before my eyes. I was still coming out of the mist. As she sat down I rose slowly, still moving through a fog, and knelt at her feet, mumbling something about the radiance of her beauty. For a full few minutes she made no effort to rouse me. She held my two hands in hers and smiled down at me, that effulgent, luminous smile which spreads like a halo and then vanishes, never to reappear again. It was the seraphic smile of peace and benediction. It was given in a public place wherein we found ourselves alone. It was a sacrament, and the hour, the day, the place were recorded in letters of gold in the book of the legend which lay at the foot of the Tree of Life. Thenceforth we who had united were joined by an invisible being. Never again were we to be alone. Never again would come that hush, that finality—until death perhaps. Something had been given, something received. For a few timeless moments we had stood at the gates of Paradise—then we were driven forth and that starry effulgence was shattered. Like tongues of lightning it vanished in a thousand different directions.

* * *

It was only a short time after we were installed in the Palace of Time and the River that I discovered one morning, while taking a shower, that the head of my cock was ringed with bleeding sores. It gave me quite a fright, needless to say. Immediately I thought that I had contracted the "syph." And since I had been faithful in my way I could only suppose that Mona had given it to me.

However, it isn't in my nature to run to the doctor at once. With us the doctor has always been looked upon as a mountebank if not a downright criminal. We usually wait for the surgeon who of course is in league with the undertaker. We always pay handsomely for the perpetual care of the grave.

"It will go away of itself," I told myself, taking my prick out twenty or thirty times a day.

It could have been the back-fire from one of those menstrual pea-soup fucks too. Often, in fatuous masculine pride, one mistakes the tomato juice flow of the period for a precoital flow. Many a proud dick is sunk in this Scapa Flow . . .

The simplest thing, of course, was to question Mona, which I promptly proceeded to do.

"Now listen," I said, still in good humor, "if you've got a dose you'd better tell me. I'm not going to ask you how you came by it . . . I want the truth, that's all."

The directness of this made her burst out laughing. She laughed a little too heartily, I thought.

"You could get a dose from sitting on the toilet," I said.

This made her laugh even more heartily—almost hysterically.

"Or it could be a throw-back from an old dose. I don't care when or where it happened . . . *have you got it, that's what I want to know.*"

The answer was No. Emphatically No! She was sobering up now and with the change came a little show of anger. How could I think up such an accusation? What did I take her for—a trollop?

"Well, if that's the case," said I, putting a good face on it, "there's no need to worry. You don't get a clap out of thin air. I'll forget about it. . . ."

But then it wasn't so easy to forget—just like that. In the first place the fucking was taboo. A week had passed, and a week is a long time when you're used to fucking every night and in between a piece now and then—on the wing, as it were.

Every night it stood up like a pole. I even went to the absurd length of using a condom—just once—because it hurt like hell. The only other thing to do was to play stink-finger or suck her off. I was a little leery about the latter, despite her prophylactic protestations.

Masturbation was the best substitute. In fact, it opened up a new area of exploration. Psychologically, I mean. Lying there, with my arm around her and my fingers up her crotch, she became strangely confidential. It was as though the erogenous zone of her mind were being tickled by my fingers. The juice began to spill out . . . "*the dirt*," as she had once called it.

Interesting how women dish up the truth! Often they begin with a lie, a harmless little lie, which is just a feeler. Just to see how the wind blows, don't you know. Should they sense that you're not too hurt, not too offended, they risk a morsel of truth, a few crumbs cleverly wrapped in a tissue of lies.

That wild automobile ride, for instance, which she's rehearsing under her breath. One wasn't to think for one moment that she enjoyed going out with three strange men—and two dopey fluffs from the dance hall. She had only consented because at the last minute there was no other girl to be found. And then, of course, she may have been hoping, though she didn't know it at the time, that one of the men might be human, might listen to her story and help her out—with a fifty dollar bill perhaps. (She always had her mother to fall back on: mother, the prime cause and motivator of all crime. . . .)

And then, as always happens on automobile rides, they began to get fresh. If the other girls hadn't been along it might have turned out differently; they had their dresses up over their knees before the car had hardly started. They had to drink too—that was the worst of it. Of course she only pretended to drink . . . swallowed just a few drops . . . enough to wet her whistle . . . the others gulped it down. She didn't mind so much kissing the men either—that was nothing—but the way they grabbed her right away . . . pulling her teats out and running their hands up her legs . . . the two of them at once. They must have been Italians, she thought. Lecherous brutes.

Then she confessed to something which I knew was a god-damned lie, but it was interesting just the same. One of those "deformations" or "displacements," as in dreams. Yes, you see, oddly enough the other two girls felt sorry for her . . . sorry that they had got her into such a pickle. They knew she wasn't in the habit of sleeping with every Tom, Dick and Harry. So they stopped the car and changed seats, letting her sit up front with the hairy guy who had seemed decent and quiet thus far. They sat on the men's laps in the back, their dresses raised, facing forward, and while smoking their cigarettes and laughing and drinking, they let the men in the rear have their fill of pleasure.

"And what did the other guy do while this was going on?" I finally felt impelled to ask.

"He didn't do anything," she said. "I let him hold my hand and I talked to him as fast as I could so as to keep his mind off it."

"Come on," I said, "don't tell me that. Now what *did* he do—*out with it!*"

Well, anyway, he did hold her hand for a long time, believe it or not. Besides, what could he do—wasn't he driving the car?

"You mean to say he never thought of stopping the car?"

Of course he did. He tried several times, but she talked him out of it. . . . That was the line. She was thinking desperately how to get round to the truth.

"And after a while?" I said, just to ease her over the rough spots.

"Well, all of a sudden he dropped my hand. . . ." She paused.

"Go on!"

"And then he grabbed it again and placed it in his lap. His fly was open and it was standing up . . . and twitching. It was a tremendous thing. I got terribly frightened. But he wouldn't let me take my hand away. I had to jerk him off. Then he stopped the car and tried to push me out. I begged him not to throw me out. 'Drive on slowly,' I said, 'I'll do it . . . later. I'm frightened.' He wiped himself with a handkerchief and started going again. Then he began talking the vilest filth. . . ."

"Like what? Just what did he say, do you remember?"

"Oh, I don't want to talk about it . . . it was disgusting."

"Since you've told me this much I don't see why you hesitate over words," I said. "What's the difference . . . you might as well. . . ."

"All right, if you want it. . . . 'You're just the kind I like to fuck,' he said. 'I've been meaning to fuck you for a long time. I like the turn of your ass. I like your teats. You're no virgin—what the hell are you so delicate about? You've been fucked all over the lot—you're cunt right up to the eyes'—and things like that."

"You're making me horny," I said. "Go on, tell me everything."

I could see now that she was only too delighted to get it off her chest. We didn't have to pretend anything any more—we were both enjoying it.

The men in the rear seat wanted to swap, it seems. That really frightened her. "The only thing I could do was to pretend that I wanted to be fucked by the other one first. He wanted to stop at once and get out. 'Drive slowly,' I coaxed, 'I'll give it to you afterwards . . . I don't want them all on me at once.' I grabbed his prick and began to massage it. It was stiff in a minute . . . even bigger than before. Jesus, I tell you, Val, I never felt a tool like that before. He must have been an animal. He made me grab his balls too—they were heavy and swollen. I jerked it fast, hoping to make him come quick. . . ."

"Listen," I interrupted, getting excited by the tale of the big horse cock, "let's talk straight. You must have wanted a fuck bad, with that thing in your hand. . . ."

"Wait," she said, her eyes glittering. She was as wet as a goose now from the massaging I was giving her all the while. . . .

"Don't make me come now," she begged, "or I won't be able to finish the story. Jesus, I never thought you'd want to hear all this." She closed her legs on my hand, so as not to get too excited. "Listen, kiss me . . ." and she ran her tongue down my throat. "Oh God, I wish we could fuck now. This is torture. You've got to get that tended to soon . . . I'll go crazy. . . ."

"Don't get off the track. . . . Now what next? What did he do?"

"He grabbed me by the neck and forced my head down into his lap. 'I'm going to drive slow like you said,' he mumbled, 'and I want you to suck that off. After that I'll be ready to give you a fuck, a good one.' It was so enormous I thought I'd choke. I felt like biting it. Honest, Val, I never saw anything like it. He made me do everything. 'You know what I want,' he said. 'Use your tongue. You've had a prick in your mouth before.' Finally he began to move up and down, to slide it in and out. All the time he held me by the neck. I was nearly crazy. Then he came—ugh! it was filthy! I thought he'd never stop coming. I pulled my head away quickly and he shot a stream of it into my face—like a bull."

By this time I was on the verge of coming myself. My prick was dancing like a wet candle. "Clap or no clap, I'm going to fuck tonight," thought I to myself.

She went on with the story after a lull. How he made her huddle in the corner of the car with her legs up and poked around inside of her while driving with one hand, the car zigzagging back and forth across the road. How he made her open her cunt with her two hands and then turned the flashlight on it. How he put his cigarette inside her and made her try to inhale with her cunt. And the two in the rear leaning over and pawing her. How one of them tried to stand up and shove his prick in her mouth, but too drunk to do anything. And the girls—by this time stark naked and singing filthy songs. Not knowing where he was driving or what was coming next. "No," she said, "I was too scared to be passionate. They were capable of anything. They were thugs. All I could think of was how to escape. I was terrified. And all he kept saying was: 'You wait, you lovely bitch . . . I'll fuck the ass off you. How old are you? You wait. . . .' And then he'd grab himself and swing it like a club. 'When you get this inside your cute little twat you're going to feel something. I'll make it come out of your mouth. How many times do you think I can do it? Guess!' I had to answer him. 'Twice . . . three times?' I guess you ain't ever had a real fuck. *Feel it!*' and he made me hold it again while he jerked back and forth. It was slimy and slippery . . . he must have been coming all the time. '*How does it feel, sister?* I can put another inch or two on that when I ram it up that hole of yours. By the way, how would you like it up the other end? Listen, when I get through with you you won't be able to say fuck for a month.' That's the way he talked. . . ."

"For Christ's sake, don't stop there," I said. "What next?"

Well, he stopped the car, beside a field. No more shilly-shallying. The girls in the back were trying to put on their clothes, but the men shoved them out without a stitch on. They were screaming. One of them got a clout in the jaw for her pains and fell like a log beside the road. The other one started to clasp her hands, as if she were praying, but she couldn't make a sound, so paralyzed with fright she was.

"I waited for him to open the door on his side," said Mona. "Then I jumped out quickly and started running across the field. My shoes came off, my feet were cut by the thick stubble. I ran like mad and him after me. He caught up with me and pulled the dress off me—tore it off with one yank. Then I saw him raise his hand and the next moment I saw stars. There were needles in my back and needles in the sky. He was on top of me and going at it like an animal. It hurt terribly. I wanted to scream but I knew he would only strike me again. I lay there stiff with fright and let him maul me. He bit me all over—my lips and ears, my neck, my shoulders, my breasts—and never once did he stop moving—just fucking away like some crazed animal. I thought everything had broken inside me. When he pulled away I thought he had finished. I began to cry. 'Stop that,' he said, 'or I'll kick you in the jaw.' My back felt as though I had been rolling in glass. He lay down flat on his back and told me to suck him off. It was still big and slimy. I think he must have had a perpetual erection. I had to obey. 'Use your tongue,' he said. 'Lick it up!' He lay there breathing heavily, his eyes rolling, his mouth wide open. Then he pulled me on top of him, bouncing me up and down like a feather, turning and twisting me as if I were made of rubber. 'That's better, eh?' he said. 'You work now, you bitch!' and he held me lightly by the waist with his two hands while I fucked with all my might. I swear Val, I didn't have a bit of feeling left—except a burning pain as though a red-hot sword had been thrust inside me. 'That's enough of that,' he said. 'Now get down on all fours—and lift your ass up high.' Then he did everything . . . taking it out of one place and putting it in the other. He had my head buried in the ground, right in the dirt, and he made me hold his balls with my two hands. 'Squeeze them,' he said, 'but not too hard or I'll lay you cold!' The dirt was getting in my eyes . . . it stung horribly. Suddenly I felt him push with all his might . . . he was coming again . . . it was hot and thick. I couldn't stand it another moment. I sank down flat on my face and I felt the stuff pour over my back. I heard him say '*God damn you!*' and then he must have struck me again because I don't remember anything until I woke up shivering with cold and found myself covered with cuts and bruises. The ground was wet and I was alone. . . ."

At this point the story went into another groove. And then another and another. In my eagerness to keep up with her flights I almost overlooked the point of the story, which was that she had contracted a disease. She didn't realize at first what it was, because it had announced itself in the beginning as a bad case of haemorrhoids. Lying on the wet ground had done that, she averred. At least that had been the doctor's opinion. Then came the other thing—but she had gone to the doctor in time and he had cured her.

To me, interesting as this might have been, considering that I was still concerned about the ringworms, another fact had emerged which transcended it in importance. Somehow I hadn't paid such close attention to the details of the aftermath—how she had picked herself up, begged a ride to New York, borrowed some clothes from Florrie, and so on. I remember having interrupted her to ask how long ago it was that the rape had occurred and my impression is that her answer was rather vague. But suddenly, while trying to put two and two together, I realized that she was talking about Carruthers, about living at his place and cooking for him and so on. How had that happened?

"But I just told you," she said. "I went to his place because I didn't dare to go home looking as I did. He was terribly kind. He treated me as if I were his own daughter. It was his doctor I went to—he took me there himself."

I supposed from this that living with Carruthers meant that she had been living with him at the place where she had once given me the rendezvous, where Carruthers had walked in on us unexpectedly and where he had made a jealous scene. But I was mistaken.

"It was long before that," she said. "He was living uptown then," and she mentioned the name of some famous American humorist with whom Carruthers then shared a flat.

"Why you were almost a child then—unless you're lying about your age."

"I was seventeen. I had run away from home during the war. I went to New Jersey and took a job in a munitions plant. Carruthers made me leave the job and go back to college."

"So you did finish your studies?" I said, a bit confused by all the contradictions.

"Of course I did! I wish you'd stop insin. . . ."

"And you met Carruthers in the munitions plant?"

"Not *in* the plant. He was working in a dye factory nearby. He used to take me into New York now and then. He was the vice-president, I think. Anyway, he could do as he pleased. He used to take me to the theatre and to night clubs. . . . He liked to dance."

"And you weren't living with him then?"

"No, that was later. Even uptown, after the rape, I didn't

live with him. I did the cooking and the housework to show him that I was grateful for all he had done. He never asked me to be his mistress. He wanted to marry me . . . but he didn't have the heart to leave his wife. She was an invalid. . . ."

"You mean sexually?"

"I told you all about *her*. What difference does it make?"

"I'm all balled up," I said.

"But I'm telling you the truth. You asked me to tell you everything. Now you don't believe me."

At this moment the horrible suspicion flashed through my mind that the "rape" (and perhaps it hadn't been a rape!) had occurred in a past all too recent. Perhaps the "Italian" with the insatiable prick had been nothing more than an amorous lumberman in the North woods. No doubt there had been more than one "rape" pulled off on these midnight automobile rides which hot-blooded young girls indulge in after hitting up the flask. The image of her standing alone and naked in a wet field at dawn, her body covered with cuts and bruises, the uterine wall broken down, the rectum mutilated, her shoes gone, her eyes black and blue . . . well, that was the sort of thing a romantic young lady might cook up to cover a careless lapse that ends with gonorrhea and haemorrhoids, though the haemorrhoids did seem a bit *gratuit*.

"I think we'd better go to the doctor tomorrow, the both of us, and have a blood test taken," I said quietly.

"Of course I'll go with you," she replied.

We embraced one another silently and then we slid into a long fuck.

* * *

Well, we visited the doctor Kronski had elected, we had blood tests taken, and we even had dinner with the doctor. He was a young man and not overly sure of himself, I thought. He didn't know what to make of my cock. Wanted to know if I had ever had a dose—or the "syph." I told him I had had the clap twice. Had it ever come back? Not that I knew of. And so on. He thought it best to wait a few days before doing anything. In the meantime he'd have analyzed our blood. He thought we both looked healthy, though looks were often deceptive. In short, he talked around and about, as young doctors often do—and old ones too—leaving us none the wiser.

Between the first and second visits I had to visit Maude. I told her all about it. She of course was convinced that Mona was responsible. She had expected as much. It was laughable, really, what an interest she took in my sick dick. As though it were still her private property. I had to take it out and show it to her, b'Jesus. She handled it gingerly at first, but then, her professional interest aroused and the thing growing heavier in her hand all the while, she became less and less cautious. I had to be careful not to get too excited or I might have thrown caution to the winds. At any rate, before permitting me to shove it back in my fly she begged me to let her bathe it gently in a solution. She was sure that could do no harm. So I went to the bathroom with her, my prick stiff as a rod, and I watched her pet it and pamper it.

When we visited the doctor again we learned that the signs were all negative. However, he explained, even that didn't constitute a final proof.

"You know," he said—evidently he had been thinking it over before our arrival—"I've been thinking that you'd be much better off if you were circumcised. When the foreskin is removed that stuff will come off too. You've got an uncommonly long foreskin—hasn't it bothered you?"

I confessed I had never given it a thought before. One is born with a foreskin and one dies with it. Nobody thinks about his appendix until it's time to have it cut out.

"Yes," he went on, "you'd be lots better off without that foreskin. You'd have to go to the hospital, of course . . . it might take about a week or so."

"And what would that cost?" I inquired, picking up the scent.

He couldn't say exactly—perhaps a hundred dollars.

I told him I'd think it over. I wasn't too keen about losing my precious foreskin, even if there were hygienic advantages attached to it. A funny thought then entered my head—that thereafter the head of my cock would be insensitive. I didn't like that idea at all.

However, before I left his office he had persuaded me to make a date with his surgeon for a week hence. "If it should clear up in the meantime you won't need to go through with the operation—if you don't like the idea."

"*But,*" he added, "if I were you I'd have it done whether I liked it or not. It's much cleaner."

In the interval the nightly confessions proceeded apace. Mona had not been working at the dance hall for several weeks now and we had the evenings together. She wasn't sure what she would do next—it was always the money question which disturbed her—but she was certain she would never return to the dance hall. She seemed just as relieved as I to know that her blood test had come out all right.

"But you didn't think there was anything wrong with you, did you?"

"One never knows," she said. "That was such a horrible place . . . the girls were filthy."

"The *girls?*"

"And the men too. . . . Don't let's talk about it." After a short silence she laughed and said: "How would you like it if I went on the stage?"

"It would be fine," I said. "Do you think you can act?"

"I know I can. You wait, Val, I'll show you . . ."

That evening we came home late and sneaked quietly into bed. Holding on to my cock she began another string of confessions. She had been wanting to tell me something . . . I wasn't to get angry . . . I wasn't to interrupt her. I had to promise.

I lay there and listened tensely. The money question again. It was always there, like a bad sore. "You didn't want me to go on staying at the dance hall, did you?" Of course I didn't. What next? I wondered.

Well naturally she had to find some way of raising the necessary funds. Go on! I thought to myself. Get it over with! I gave myself an anaesthetic and listened to her without opening my trap. It was all quite painless, strange to relate. She was talking about old men, nice old men whom she had become acquainted with at the dance hall. What they wanted was to have the company of a beautiful young girl—some one they could eat with and take to the theatre. They didn't really care about dancing—or even going to bed with a girl. They wanted to be *seen* with young women—it made them feel younger, gayer, more hopeful. They were all successful old bastards—with false teeth and varicose veins and all that sort of thing. They didn't know what to do with their money. One of them, the one she was talking about, owned a big steam laundry. He was over eighty, brittle, blue-veined, glassy-eyed. He was almost a child. Surely I couldn't be jealous of *him!* All he asked of her was permission to spend his money on her. She didn't say how much he had already forked out, but she inferred it was a tidy sum. And now there was another one—he lived at the Ritz Carlton. A shoe manufacturer. She sometimes ate in his room, because it gave him pleasure. He was a multi-millionaire—and a little gaga, to believe her words. At the most he had only courage enough to kiss her hand. . . . Yes, she had been meaning to tell me about these things for weeks, but she had been afraid I might take it badly. "You don't, do you?" she said, bending over me. I didn't answer immediately. I was thinking, wondering, puzzling over it all. "Why don't you say something?" she said, nudging me. "You said you wouldn't be angry. You promised."

"I'm not angry," I said. And then I grew silent again.

"But you are! You're hurt. . . . O Val, you're so foolish. Do you think I would tell you these things if I thought you would be hurt?"

"I don't think anything," I said. "It's all right, believe me. Do whatever you think best. I'm only sorry that it has to be this way."

"But it won't always be this way! It's just for a little while. . . . That's why I want to get in the theatre. I hate it just as much as you do."

"O. K." I said. "Let's forget about it."

The morning that I was to report to the hospital I woke up early. As I was taking my shower I looked at my prick and by crikey there wasn't a sign of irritation. I could hardly believe my eyes. I woke Mona and showed it to her. She kissed it. I got in bed again and tore off a quick one—to test it out. Then I went to the telephone and called the doctor. "It's all better," I said, "I'm not going to have my foreskin cut off." I hung up quickly in order to forestall any further persuasions on his part.

As I was leaving the phone booth I suddenly took it into my head to phone Maude.

"I can't believe it," she said.

"Well, it's a fact," I said, "and if you don't believe it I'll prove it to you when I come over next week."

She seemed to want to hang on to the phone. Kept talking about a lot of irrelevant things. "I've got to go," I said, getting annoyed with her.

"Just a moment," she begged. "I was going to ask you

if you couldn't come over sooner, say Sunday, and take us out to the country. We might have a little picnic, the three of us. I'd do up a lunch. . . ."

Her voice sounded very tender.

"All right," I said, "I'll come. I'll come early . . . about eight o'clock."

"You're sure you're all right?" she said.

"I'm absolutely sure. I'll show it to you—Sunday."

She gave a short, dirty little laugh. I hung up before she had closed her trap.

* * *

The divorce trial was impending. That made me even more savage and bitter, for some inexplicable reason. I hated the farce which has to be gone through in the name of justice. I loathed and despised the lawyer whom Maude had retained to protect her interests. He looked like a corn-fed Romain Rolland, a chauve-souris without a crumb of humor or imagination. He seemed to be charged with moral indignation; he was a prick through and through, a coward, a sneak, a hypocrite. He gave me the creeps.

We had it out about him the day of the outing. Lying in the grass somewhere near Mineola. The child running about gathering flowers. It was warm, very warm, and there was a hot dry wind blowing which made one nervous and rooty. I had taken my prick out and put it in her hand. She examined it shyly, not wishing to be too clinical about it and yet dying to convince herself that there was nothing wrong. After a while she dropped it and rolled over on her back, her knees up, and the warm wind licking her bottom. I jockeyed her into a favorable position, made her pull her panties off. She was in one of her protesting moods again. Didn't like being mauled like that in an open field. But there's not a soul around, I insisted. I made her spread her legs farther apart; I ran my hand up her cunt. It was gooey.

I pulled her to me and tried to get it in. She balked. She was worried about the child. I looked around. "She's all right," I said, "she's having a good time. She's not thinking about us."

"But supposing she comes back . . . and finds us. . . ."

"She'll think we're sleeping. She won't know what we're doing. . . ."

With this she pushed me away violently. It was outrageous. "You'd take me in front of your own child! It's horrible."

"It's not horrible at all. You're the one who's horrible. I tell you, it's innocent. Even if she should remember it—when she's grown up—she'll be a woman then and she'll understand. There's nothing dirty about it. It's your dirty mind, that's all."

By this time she was slipping her panties on. I hadn't bothered to shove my prick back in my trousers. It was getting limp now; it fell on the grass, dejected.

"Well, let's have something to eat then," I said. "If we can't fuck we can always eat."

"Yes, *eat!* You can eat any time. That's all you care about, eating and sleeping."

"*Fucking,*" I said, "not sleeping."

"I wish you'd stop talking to me that way." She began to undo the lunch. "You have to spoil everything. I thought we might have a peaceful day, just once. You always said you wanted to take us out on a picnic. You never did. Not once. You thought of nothing but yourself, your friends, your women. I was a fool to think you might change. You don't care about your child—you've hardly noticed her. You can't even restrain yourself in her presence. You'd take me in front of her and pretend that it was innocent. You're vile. . . . I'm glad it's all over. By this time next week I'll be free . . . I'll be rid of you forever. You've poisoned me. You've made me bitter and hateful. You make me despise myself. Since I know you I don't recognize myself any more. I've become what you wanted me to become. You never loved me . . . *never.* All you wanted was to satisfy your desires. You've treated me like an animal. You take what you want and you go. You go from me to the next woman—any woman—just so long as she'll open her legs for you. You haven't an ounce of loyalty or tenderness or consideration in you. . . . Here, take it!" she said, shoving a sandwich in my fist. "I hope you choke on it!"

As I brought the sandwich to my mouth I smelled the odor of her cunt on my fingers. I sniffed my fingers while looking up at her with a grin.

"You're disgusting!" she said.

"Not so very, my lady. It smells good to me, even if you are a hateful sour-puss. I like it. It's the only thing about you I like."

She was furious now. She began to weep.

"Weeping because I said I liked your cunt! What a woman! Jesus, I'm the one who ought to do the despising. What sort of woman are you?"

Her tears became more copious. Just then the child came running up. What was the matter? Why was mother crying?

"It's nothing," said Maude, drying her tears. "I turned my ankle." A few dry sobs belched from her despite her efforts to restrain herself. She bent over the basket and selected a sandwich for the child.

"Why don't you do something, Henry?" said the child. She sat there looking from one to the other with a grave, puzzled look.

I got to my knees and rubbed Maude's ankle.

"Don't touch me!" she said harshly.

"But he wants to make it better," said the child.

"Yes, daddy'll make it better," I said, rubbing the ankle gently, and then patting the calf of her leg.

"Kiss her," said the child. "Kiss her and make the tears go away."

I bent forward and kissed Maude on the cheek. To my astonishment she flung her arms around me and kissed me violently on the mouth. The child also put her arms around us and kissed us.

Suddenly Maude had a fresh spasm of weeping. This time it was really pitiful to behold. I felt sorry for her. I put my arms around her tenderly and comforted her.

"God," she sobbed, "what a farce!"

"But it isn't," I said. "I mean it sincerely. I'm sorry, sorry for everything."

"Don't cry any more," begged the child. "I want to eat. I want Henry to take me over there," and she pointed with her little hand to a copse of wood at the edge of the field. "I want you to come too."

"To think this is the only time . . . and it had to be like this." She was sniffling now.

"Don't say that, Maude. The day isn't over yet. Let's forget about all that. Come on, let's eat."

Reluctantly, wearily, it seemed, she picked up a sandwich and held it to her mouth. "I can't eat," she murmured, dropping the sandwich.

"Come on, yes you can!" I urged, putting my arm around her again.

"You act this way now . . . and later you'll do something to spoil it."

"No I won't . . . I promise you."

"Kiss her again," said the child.

I leaned over and kissed her softly and gently on the lips. She seemed really placated now. A soft light came into her eyes.

"Why can't you be like this always?" she said, after a brief pause.

"I am," I said, "when I'm given a chance. I don't like to fight with you. Why should I? We're not man and wife any longer."

"Then why do you treat me the way you do? Why do you always make love to me? Why don't you leave me alone?"

"I'm not making love to you," I answered. "It's not love, it's passion. That's not a crime, is it? For God's sake, let's not start that all over again. I'm going to treat you the way you want to be treated—*today*. I won't touch you again."

"I don't ask that. I don't say you shouldn't touch me. But it's the *way* you do it . . . you don't show any respect for me . . . for my person. That's what I dislike. I know you don't love me any more, but you can behave decently towards me, even if you don't care any more. I'm not the prude you pretend I am. I have feelings too . . . maybe deeper, stronger than yours. I can find some one else to replace you, don't think that I can't. I just want a little time. . . ."

She was munching her sandwich half-heartedly. Suddenly there was a gleam in her eye. She put on a coy, roguish expression.

"I could get married tomorrow, if I wanted to," she continued. "You never thought that, did you? I've had three proposals already, as a matter of fact. The last one was from . . ." and here she mentioned the lawyer's name.

"*Him?*" I said, unable to repress a disdainful smile.

"Yes, *him*," she said. "And he's not what you think he is. I like him very much."

"Well, that explains things. Now I know why he's taken such a passionate interest in the case."

I knew she didn't care for him, this Rocambolesque, any more than she cared for the doctor who explored her vagina with a rubber finger. She didn't care for anybody really; all she wanted was peace, surcease from pain. She wanted a lap to sit on in the dark, a prick to enter her mysteriously, a babble of words to drown her unmentionable desires. Lawyer what's-his-name would do of course. Why not? He would be as faithful as a fountain pen, as discreet as a rat trap, as provident as an insurance policy. He was a walking briefcase with pigeon holes in his belfry; he was a salamander with a heart of pastrami. He was shocked, was he, to learn that I had brought another woman to my own home? Shocked to learn that I had left the used condoms on the edge of the sink? Shocked that I had stayed for breakfast with my paramour? A snail is shocked when a drop of rain hits its shell. A general is shocked when he learns that his garrison has been massacred in his absence. God himself is shocked doubtless when He sees how revoltingly stupid and insensitive the human beast really is. But I doubt if angels are ever shocked—not even by the presence of the insane.

I was trying to give her the dialectics of the moral dynamism. I twisted my tongue in the endeavour to make her understand the marriage of the animal and the divine. She understood about as well as a layman understands when you explain the fourth dimension. She talked about delicacy and respect as if they were pieces of angel cake. Sex was an animal locked up in a zoo which one visited now and then in order to study evolution.

Towards evening we rode back to the city, the last stretch in the elevated train, the child asleep in my arms. Mamma and Papa returning from the picnic grounds. Below, the city spread out with senseless geometrical rigidity, an evil dream rearing itself architecturally. A dream from which it is impossible to awaken. Mr. and Mrs. Megalopolitan with their offspring. Hobbled and fettered. Suspended in the sky like so much venison. A pair of every kind hanging by the hocks. At one end of the line starvation; at the other end bankruptcy.

Between stations the pawnbroker, with three golden balls to signify the triune God of birth, buggery and blight. Happy days. A fog rolling in from Rockaway. Nature folding up like a dead leaf—at Mineola. Every now and then the doors open and shut: fresh batches of meat for the slaughterhouse. Little scraps of conversation, like the twittering of titmice. Who would think that the chubby little youngster beside you will in ten or fifteen years be shitting his brains out with fright on a foreign field? All day long you make innocent little gadgets; at night you sit in a dark hall and watch phantoms move across a silver screen. Maybe the realest moments you know are when you sit alone in the toilet and make caca. That doesn't cost anything or commit you in any way. Not like eating or fucking, or making works of art. You leave the toilet and you step into the big shit-house. Whatever you touch is shitty. Even when it's wrapped in cellophane the smell is there. *Caca!* The philosopher's stone of the industrial age. Death and transfiguration—into shit! The department store life—with filmy silks on one counter and bombs on the other counter. No matter what interpretation you put on it, every thought, every deed, is cash registered. You're fucked from the moment you draw your first breath. One grand international business machine corporation. *Logistics*, as they say.

Mamma and Papa are now as peaceful as blutwurst. Not an ounce of fight left in them. How glorious to spend a day in the open, with the worms and other creatures of God. What a delightful entr'acte! Life glides by like a dream. If you were to cut the bodies open while still warm you would find nothing resembling this idyll. If you were to scrape the bodies out and fill them with stones they would sink to the bottom of the sea, like dead ducks.

It begins to rain. It pours. Hailstones big as bob-o'-links bounce from the pavement. The city looks like an ant pile smeared with salvarsan. The sewers rise and disgorge their vomit. The sky is as sullen and lurid as the bottom of a test tube.

I feel murderously gay all of a sudden. I hope to Christ it will rain like this for forty days and nights. I'd like to see the city swimming in its own shit; I'd like to see mannikins floating into the river and cash registers ground under the wheels of trucks; I'd like to see the insane pouring out of the asylums with cleavers and hacking right and left. The water cure! Like they gave it to the Filipinos in '98! But where is our Aguinaldo? Where is the rat who can breast the flood with a machete between his lips?

I bring them home in a cab, deposit them safely just as a bolt of lightning strikes the steeple of the bloody Catholic church on the corner. The broken bells make a hell of a din as they hit the pavement. Inside the church a plaster Virgin is smashed to smithereens. The priest is so taken by surprise that he hasn't time to button up his pants. His balls swell up like rocks.

Melanie flutters about like a demented albatross. "Dry your things!" she wails. A grand undressing, with gasps and shrieks and objurgations. I get into Maude's dressing sack, the one with the maribou feathers. Look like a fairy about to give an impersonation of Loulou Hurluburlu. All flub and foozle now. I'm getting a hard-on, "a personal hard-on," if you know what I mean.

Maude is upstairs putting the child to bed. I walk around in my bare feet, the dressing sack wide open. A lovely feeling. Melanie peeks in, just to see if I'm all right. She's walking around in her drawers with the parrot perched on her wrist. Afraid of the lightning she is. I'm talking to her with my hands folded over my prick. Could be a scene out of the "Wizard of Oz" by Memling. Time: *dreiviertel takt*. Now and then the lightning strikes afresh. It leaves the taste of burning rubber in the mouth.

I'm standing in front of the big mirror admiring my quivering cock when Maude trips in. She's as frisky as a hare and all decked out in tulle and mousseline. She seems not at all frightened by what she sees in the mirror. She comes over and stands beside me. "Open it up!" I urge. "Are you hungry?" she says, undoing herself leisurely. I turn her around and press her to me. She raises a leg to let me get it in. We look at each other in the mirror. She's fascinated. I pull the wrap up over her ass so that she can have a better look. I lift her up and she twines her legs around me. "Yes, do it," she begs. "Fuck me! Fuck me!" Suddenly she untwines her legs, unhitches. She grabs the big arm chair and turns it around, resting her hands on the back of it. Her ass is stuck out invitingly. She doesn't wait for me to put it in—she grabs it and places it herself, watching all the time through the mirror. I push it back and forth slowly, holding my skirts up like a bedraggled hussy. She likes to see it coming out—how far will it come before it falls out. She reaches under with one hand and plays with my balls. She's completely unleashed now, as brazen as a pot. I withdraw as far as I can without letting it slip out and she rolls her ass around, sinking down on it now and then and clutching it with a feathery beak. Finally she's had enough of that. She wants to lie down on the floor and put her legs around my neck. "Get it in all the way," she begs. "Don't be afraid of hurting me . . . I want it. I want you to do everything." I got it in so deep it felt as though I were buried in a bed of mussels. She was quivering and slithering in every ream. I bent over and sucked her breasts; the nipples were taut as nails. Suddenly she pulled my head down and began to bite me wildly—lips, ears, cheeks, neck. "You want it, don't you?" she hissed. "You want it, you want it. . . ." Her lips twisted obscenely. "You want it . . . you want it!" And she fairly lifted herself off the floor in her abandon. Then a groan, a spasm, a wild, tortured look as if her face were under a mirror pounded by a hammer. "Don't take it out yet," she grunted. She lay there, her legs still slung around my neck, and the little flag inside her began twitching and fluttering. "God," she said, "I can't stop it!" My prick was still firm. It hung obedient on her wet lips, as though receiving the sacrament from a lascivious angel. She came again, like an accordion collapsing in a bag of milk. I got hornier and hornier. I pulled her legs down and lay them flat alongside my own. "Now don't move, damn you," I said. "I'm going to give it to you straight." Slowly and furiously I moved in and out. "Ah, ah. . . . Oh!" she hissed, sucking her breath in. I kept it up like a Juggernaut. Moloch fucking a piece of bombazine. Organza Friganza. The bolero in straight jabs. Her eyes were going wild; she looked like an elephant walking the ball. All she needed was a trunk to trumpet with. It was a fuck to a standstill. I fell on top of her and chewed her lips to a frazzle.

Then suddenly I thought of the douche. "Get up! Get up!" I said, nudging her roughly.

"I don't need to," she said weakly, giving me a knowing smile.

"You mean . . . ?" I looked at her in astonishment.

"Yes, there's no need to worry. . . . Are you all right? Don't you want to wash?"

In the bathroom she confessed that she had been to the doctor—another doctor. There would be nothing to fear any more.

"So that's it?" I whistled.

She powdered my cock for me, stretched it like a glovefitter, and then bent over and kissed it. "Oh God," she said, flinging her arms around me, "if only. . . ."

"If only what?"

"You know what I mean. . . ."

I unglued myself and turning my head away, I said:

"Yes, I guess I do. Anyway, you don't hate me any more, do you?"

"I don't hate any one," she answered. "I'm sorry it's turned out the way it has. Now I'll have to share you . . . with her."

"You must be hungry," she added quickly. "Let me fix you something before you go." She powdered her face carefully first, rouged her lips, and did her hair up negligently but attractively. Her wrap was open from the waist up. She looked a thousand times better than I had ever seen her look. She was like a bright voracious animal.

I walked around in the kitchen with my prick hanging out and helped her fix a cold snack. To my surprise she unearthed a bottle of home made wine—elderberry wine that a neighbor had given her. We closed the doors and kept the gas burning to keep warm. Jesus, it was quite wonderful. It was like getting to know one another all over again. Now and then I got up and put my arms around her, kissed her passionately while my hand slid into her crack. She wasn't at all shy or balky. On the contrary. When I pulled away, she held my hand, and then with a quick dive, she fastened her mouth over my prick and sucked it in.

"You don't have to go immediately, do you?" she asked, as I sat down and resumed eating.

"Not if you don't want me to," I said, in the most amiable state of acquiescence.

"Was it my fault," she said, "that this never happened before? Was I such a squeamish creature?" She looked at me with such frankness and sincerity I hardly recognized the woman I had lived with all these years.

"I guess we were both to blame," I said, downing another glass of elderberry wine.

She went to the ice-box to ferret out some delicacy.

"You know what I feel like doing?" she said, coming

back to the table with arms laden. "I'd like to bring the gramophone down and dance. I have some very soft needles. . . . Would you like that?"

"Sure," I said, "it sounds fine."

"And let's get a bit drunk . . . would you mind? I feel so wonderful. I want to celebrate."

"What about the wine?" I said. "Is that all you have?"

"I can get some more from the girl upstairs," she said. "Or maybe some cognac—would you like that?"

"I'll drink anything . . . if it will make you happy."

She started to go at once. I jumped up and caught her by the waist. I raised her wrap and kissed her ass.

"Let me go," she murmured. "I'll be back in a minute."

As she came back I heard her whispering to the girl from upstairs. She tapped lightly on the glass panel. "Put something on," she cooed, "I've got Elsie with me."

I went into the bathroom and wrapped a towel around my loins. Elsie went into a fit of laughter when she saw me. We hadn't met since the day she found me lying in bed with Mona. She seemed in excellent good humor and not at all embarrassed by the turn of events. They had brought down another bottle of wine and some cognac. And the gramophone and the records.

Elsie was in just the mood to share our little celebration. I had expected Maude to offer her a drink and then get rid of her more or less politely. But no, nothing of the kind. She wasn't at all disturbed by Elsie's presence. She did excuse herself for being half-naked, but with a good-natured laugh, as though it were just one of those things. We put a record on and I danced with Maude. The towel slipped off but neither of us made any attempt to pick it up. When we ungrappled I stood there with my prick standing out like a flagpole and calmly reached for my glass. Elsie gave one startled look and then turned her head away. Maude handed me the towel, or rather slung it over my prick. "You don't mind, do you, Elsie?" she said. Elsie was terribly quiet—you could hear her temples hammering. Presently she went over to the machine and turned the record over. Then she reached for her glass without looking at us and gulped it down.

"Why don't you dance with her?" said Maude. "I won't stop you. Go ahead, Elsie, dance with him."

I went up to Elsie with the towel hanging from my prick. As she turned her back to Maude she pulled the towel off and grabbed it with a feverish hand. I felt her whole body quiver, as though a chill had come over her.

"I'm going to get some candles," said Maude. "It's too bright in here." She disappeared into the next room. Immediately Elsie stopped dancing, put her lips to mine and thrust her tongue down my throat. I put my hand on her cunt and squeezed it. She was still holding my cock. The record stopped. Neither of us pulled away to shut the machine off. I heard Maude coming back. Still I remained locked in Elsie's arms.

This is where the trouble starts, I thought to myself. But Maude seemed to pay no attention. She lit the candles and then turned the electric light off. I was pulling away from Elsie when I felt her standing beside us. "It's all right," she said. "I don't mind. Let me join in." And with that she put her arms around the two of us and we all three began kissing one another.

"Whew! it's hot!" said Elsie, breaking away at last.

"Take your dress off, if you like," said Maude. "I'm taking this off," and suiting action to word she slipped out of the wrap and stood naked before us.

The next moment we were all stark naked.

I sat down with Maude on my lap. Her cunt was wet

again. Elsie stood beside us with her arm around Maude's neck. She was a little taller than Maude and well built. I rubbed my hand over her belly and twined my fingers in the bush that was almost on a level with my mouth. Maude looked on with a pleasant smile of satisfaction. I leaned forward and kissed Elsie's cunt.

"It's wonderful not to be jealous any more," said Maude very simply.

Elsie's face was scarlet. She didn't quite know what her role was, how far she dared go. She studied Maude intently, as though not altogether convinced of her sincerity. Now I was kissing Maude passionately, my fingers in Elsie's cunt the while. I felt Elsie pressing closer, moving herself. The juice was pouring over my fingers. At the same time Maude raised herself and, shifting her bottom, adroitly managed to sink down again with my prick neatly fitted inside her. She was facing forward now, her face pressed against Elsie's breasts. She raised her head and took the nipple in her mouth. Elsie gave a shudder and her cunt began to quiver with silken spasms. Now Maude's hand, which had been resting on Elsie's waist, slid down and caressed the smooth cheeks. In another moment it had slipped farther down and encountered mine. I drew my hand away instinctively. Elsie shifted a little and then Maude leaned forward and placed her mouth on Elsie's cunt. At the same time Elsie bent forward, over Maude, and put her lips to mine. The three of us were now quivering as if we had the ague.

As I felt Maude coming I held myself in, determined to save it for Elsie. My prick still taut, I gently raised Maude from my lap and reached for Elsie. She straddled me face forward and with uncontrollable passion she flung her arms around me, glued her lips to mine, and fucked away for dear life. Maude had discreetly gone to the bathroom. When she returned Elsie was sitting in my lap, her arm around my neck, her face on fire. Then Elsie got up and went to the bathroom. I went to the sink and washed myself there.

"I've never been so happy," said Maude, going to the machine and putting on another record. "Give me your glass," she said, and as she filled it she murmured: "What will you say when you get home?" I said nothing. Then she added under her breath: "You could say one of us was taken ill."

"It doesn't matter," I said. "I'll think of something."

"You won't be angry with me?"

"Angry? What for?"

"For keeping you so long."

"Nonsense," I said.

She put her arms around me and kissed me tenderly. And with arms around each other's waist we reached for the glasses and gulped down a silent toast. At this moment Elsie returned. We stood there, naked as hat racks, our arms entwined, and drank to one another.

We began to dance again, with the candles guttering. I knew that in a few moments they would be extinguished and no one would make a move to get fresh ones. We changed off at rapid intervals, to avoid giving one another the embarrassment of standing apart and watching. Sometimes Maude and Elsie danced together, rubbing their cunts together obscenely, then pulling apart laughingly, and one or the other making a grab for me. There was such a feeling of freedom and intimacy that any gesture, any act, became permissible. We began to laugh and joke more and more. When finally the candles guttered out, first one, then the other, and only a pale shaft of moonlight streamed through the windows, all pretense at restraint or decency vanished.

It was Maude who had the idea of clearing the table. Elsie assisted uncomprehendingly, like someone who had been mesmerized. Quickly the things were whisked to the tubs. There was a quick dash to the next room for a soft blanket which was stretched over the table. Even a pillow. Elsie was beginning to get the drift. She looked on goggle-eyed.

Before getting down to actualities, however, Maude had another inspiration—to make eggnogs. We had to switch the light on for that. The two of them worked swiftly, almost frantically. They poured a liberal dose of cognac into the concoction. As I felt it slipping down my gullet I felt it going straight into my pecker, into my balls. As I was drinking, my head thrown back, Elsie cupped her hand around my balls. "One of them's bigger than the other," she said laughingly. Then, after a slight hesitation: "Couldn't we all do something together?" She looked at Maude. Maude grinned, as if to say—why not? "Let's put the top light out," said Elsie, "we don't need that any more, do we?" She sat down on the chair beside the table. "I want to watch you," she said, patting the blanket with her hand. She got hold of Maude and lifted her up and on to the table. "This is a new one to me," she said. "Wait a minute?" She took my hand and drew me to her. Then, looking at Maude. . . . "May I? "And without waiting for an answer she bent forward and reaching for my cock placed it in her mouth. After a few moments she withdrew her mouth. "*Now* . . . let me watch!" She gave me a little push, as if to hurry me on. Maude stretched out like a cat, her ass hanging over the edge of the table, the pillow under her head. She twined her legs around my waist. Then, suddenly, she untwined them and slung them over my shoulders. Elsie was standing beside me, her head down, watching with breathless absorption. "Pull it out a little," she said in a hoarse whisper, "I want to see it go in again." Then swiftly she ran to the window and raised the shades. "Do it!" she said. "Go on, fuck her!" As I plunged it in I felt Elsie slipping down beside me. The next moment I felt her tongue on my balls, lapping them vigorously.

Suddenly, utterly astounded, I heard Maude say: "Don't come yet. Wait. . . . Give Elsie a chance."

I pulled out, pushing my ass in Elsie's face in doing so, and tumbling her backwards on the floor. She gave a squeal of delight and quickly sprang to her feet. Maude climbed down from the table and Elsie nimbly placed herself in position. "Couldn't you do something too?" she said to Maude, sitting bolt upright. "I have an idea . . ." and she sprang off the table and threw the blanket on the floor and the pillow after it. It didn't take her long to figure out an interesting configuration.

Maude was stretched out on her back, Elsie squatting over her on bent knees, her head facing Maude's feet but the mouth glued to Maude's crack. I was on my knees, giving it to Elsie from behind. Maude was playing with my balls, a light, delicate manipulation with the fingertips. I could feel Maude squirming around as Elsie licked her furiously and avidly. There was a weird pale light playing over the room and the taste of cunt in my mouth. I had one of those final erections which threaten never to break. Now and then I took it out and, pushing Elsie forward, I sank down farther and offered it to Maude's nimble tongue. Then I would sink it in again and Elsie would squirm like mad and bury her nozzle in Maude's crotch, shaking her head like a terrier. Finally I pulled out and pushing Elsie aside I fell on Maude and buried it in her with a vengeance. "Do it, do it!" she begged, as if she were waiting for the axe. Again I felt Elsie's tongue on my balls. Then Maude came, like a star bursting, with a volley of half-finished words and phrases rippling off her tongue. I pulled away, still stiff as a poker, fearful now that I would never come again, and groped for Elsie. She was terribly gooey, and her mouth was just like a cunt now. "Do you want it?" I said, shoving it around inside her like a drunken fiend. "Go on, fuck, fuck!" she cried, slinging her legs up over my shoulders and dragging her bottom closer. "Give it to me, give it to me, you bugger!" She was almost yelling now. "Yes, I'll fuck you . . . I'll fuck you!" and she squirmed and writhed and twisted and bit and clawed me.

"Oh, oh! Don't. Please don't. It hurts!" she yelled.

"Shut up, you bitch you!" I said. "It hurts, does it? You wanted it, didn't you?" I held her tightly, raised myself a little higher to get it in to the hilt, and pushed until I thought her womb would give way. Then I came—right into that snail-like mouth which was wide open. She went into a convulsion, delirious with joy and pain. Then her legs slid off my shoulders and fell to the floor with a thud. She lay there like a dead one, completely fucked out.

"Jesus," I said, standing astraddle over her, and the sperm still coming out, dropping on her breast, her face, her hair, "Jesus Christ, I'm exhausted. I'm fucked out, do you know that?" I addressed myself to the room.

Maude was lighting a candle. "It's getting late," she said.

"I'm not going home," I said. "I'm going to sleep here."

"You are?" said Maude, an irrepressible thrill creeping into her voice.

"Yes, I can't go back in this condition, can I? Jesus, I'm groggy and boozy and woozy." I flopped on to a chair. "Give me a drop of that cognac, will you, I need a bracer."

She poured out a good stiff one and held it to my lips, as if she were giving me medicine. Elsie had risen to her feet, a bit wobbly and lurchy. "Give me one too," she begged. "What a night! We ought to do this again some time."

"Yeah, tomorrow," I said.

"It was a wonderful performance," she said, stroking

my dome. "I never thought you were like that. . . . You almost killed me, do you know it?"

"You'd better take a douche," said Maude.

"I guess so," Elsie sighed. "I don't seem to give a damn. If I'm caught I'm caught."

"Go on in there, Elsie," I said. "Don't be a damned fool."

"I'm too tired," said Elsie.

"Wait a minute," said I. "I want to have a look at you before you go in there." I made her climb on the table and open her legs wide. With the glass in one hand I pried her cunt open with the thumb and forefinger of my other hand. The sperm was still oozing out.

"It's a beautiful cunt, Elsie."

Maude took a good look at it too. "Kiss it," I said, gently pushing her nose into Elsie's bush.

I sat there, watching Maude nibble away at Elsie's cunt. "It feels good," Elsie was saying. "Awfully good." She moved like a belly dancer tied to the floor. Maude's ass was sticking out temptingly. In spite of the fatigue my prick began to swell again. It stiffened like a blood-pudding. I got behind Maude and slipped it in. She spun her ass around and around, with just the tip of it in. Elsie was now contorting herself with pleasure; she had her finger in her mouth, and was biting the knuckle. We went on like this for several minutes, until Elsie had an orgasm. Then we disengaged ourselves and looked at one another as though we had never seen each other before. We were dazed.

"I'm going to bed," I said, determined to make an end of it. I started for the next room, thinking to lie on the couch.

"You can stay with me," said Maude, holding me by the arm. "Why not?" she said, seeing the surprised look in my eyes.

"Yes," said Elsie, "why not? Maybe I'll go to bed with

you too. Would you let me?" she asked Maude point blank. "I won't bother you," she added. "I just hate to leave you now."

"But what will your folks say?" said Maude.

"They won't know that Henry stayed, will they?"

"No, of course not!" said Maude, a little frightened at the thought.

"And Melanie?" I said.

"Oh, she leaves early in the morning. She has a job now."

Suddenly I wondered what the devil I would say to Mona. I was almost panic-stricken.

"I think I ought to phone home," I said.

"Oh, not now," said Elsie coaxingly. "It's so late. . . . Wait."

We hid the bottles away, piled the dishes up in the sink, and took the phonograph upstairs with us. It was just as well that Melanie shouldn't suspect too much. We tip-toed through the hall and up the stairs, our arms loaded.

I lay between the two of them, a hand on either cunt. They lay quietly for a long while, sound asleep I thought. I was too tired to sleep. I lay with eyes wide open, staring up into the darkness. Finally I turned over on my side. Towards Maude. Instantly she turned towards me, putting her arms around me and glueing her lips to mine. Then she removed them and placed them to my ear. "I love you," she whispered faintly. I made no answer. "Did you hear?" she whispered. "I love you!" I pressed her close and put my hand between her legs. Just then I felt Elsie turning round, cuddling up to me spoon fashion. I felt her hand crawling between my legs, squeezing my balls. She had her lips against my neck and was kissing me softly, warmly, with wet, cool lips.

After a time I turned back to a prone position. Elsie did the same. I closed my eyes, tried to summon sleep. It was impossible. The bed felt deliciously soft, the bodies beside me were soft and clinging, and the odor of hair and sex was in my nostrils. From the garden came the heavy fragrance of rain-soaked earth. It was strange, soothingly strange, to be back in this big bed, the marital bed, with a third person beside us, and the three of us enveloped in frank, sensual lust. It was too good to be true. I expected the door to be flung open any moment and an accusing voice scream: "Get out of there, you brazen creatures!" But there was only the silence of the night, the blackness, the heavy, sensual odors of earth and sex.

When I shifted again it was towards Elsie. She was waiting for me, eager to press her cunt against me, slip her thick, taut tongue down my throat.

"Is she asleep?" she whispered. "Do it once more," she begged.

I lay motionless, my cock limp, my arm drooping over her waist.

"Not now," I whispered. "In the morning maybe."

"No, now!" she begged. My prick was curled up in her hand like a dead snail. "Please, please," she whispered, "I want it. Just one more fuck, Henry."

"Let him sleep," said Maude, snuggling up. Her voice sounded as if she were drugged.

"All right," said Elsie, patting Maude's arm. Then, after a few moments of silence, her lips pressed against my ear, she whispered slowly, allowing a pause between each word: "When she falls asleep, yes?" I nodded. Suddenly I felt that I was dropping off. "Thank God," I said to myself.

There was a blank, a long blank, it seemed to me, during which I was completely out. I awakened gradually, dimly conscious that my prick was in Elsie's mouth. I ran my hand over her head and stroked her back. She put her hand up and placed her fingers over my mouth, as if to warn me not to protest. A useless warning because, curiously enough, I had awakened with a full knowledge of what was coming. My prick was already responding to Elsie's labial caresses. It was a new prick; it seemed thinner, longer, pointed—a dog-like prick. And it had life in it, as though it had refreshed itself independently, as though it had taken a nap all by itself.

Gently, slowly, stealthily—why had we become furtive now? I wondered—I pulled Elsie up and over me. Her cunt was different than Maude's—longer, narrower, like the finger of a glove slipping over my prick. I made comparisons as I cautiously jogged her up and down. I ran my fingers along the edge and grabbed her bush and tugged it gently. Not a whisper passed our lips. Her teeth were fastened into the hump of my shoulder. She was arched so that only the tip of it was in her and around that she was slowly, skillfully, torturingly twirling her cunt. Now and then she sank down on it and dug away like an animal.

"God, I love it!" she finally whispered. "I'd like to fuck you every night."

We rolled over on our sides and lay there glued together, making no movement, no sound. With extraordinary muscular contractions her cunt played with my prick as if it had a life and will of its own.

"Where do you live?" she whispered. "Where can I see you . . . *alone?* Write me tomorrow . . . tell me where to meet you. I want a fuck every day . . . do you hear? Don't come yet, *please.* I want it to last forever."

Silence. Just the beating of her pulse between the legs. I never felt such a tight fit, such a long, smooth, silky, clean, fresh tight fit. She couldn't have been fucked more than a dozen times. And the roots of her hair, so strong and fragrant. And her breasts, firm and smooth, almost like apples. The fingers too, strong, supple, greedy, always wandering, clutching, caressing, tickling. How she loved to grab my balls, to cup them, weigh them, then ring the scrotum with two fingers, as if she were going to milk me. And her tongue always active, her teeth biting, pinching, nipping. . . .

She's very quiet now, not a muscle stirring. Whispers again.

"Am I doing all right? You'll teach me, won't you? I'm rooty. I could fuck forever. . . . You're not tired any more, are you? Just leave it like that . . . don't move. If I come don't take it out . . . you won't will you? God, this is heaven. . . ."

Quiet again. I have the feeling I could lie this way indefinitely. I want to hear more.

"I've got a friend," she whispers. "We could meet there . . . she wouldn't say anything. Jesus, Henry, I never thought it could be like this. Can you fuck like this every night?"

I smiled in the dark.

"What's the matter?" she whispered.

"Not every night," I whispered, almost breaking into a giggle.

"Henry, fuck! Quick, fuck me . . . I'm coming."

We came off simultaneously, a prolonged orgasm which made me wonder where the damned juice came from.

"You did it!" she whispered. Then: "It's all right . . . it was marvelous."

Maude turned over heavily in her sleep.

"Good-night," I whispered. "I'm going to sleep. . . . I'm dead."

"Write me tomorrow," she whispered, kissing my cheek. "Or phone me . . . *promise*."

I grunted. She cuddled up to me, her arm around my waist. We fell into a trance.

* * *

. . . Towards dawn Mona returned, wide awake, lovelier than ever, her skin glowing like calcium. She hardly listened to my explanations about the night before; she was exalted, infatuated with herself. So many things had happened since then—she didn't know where to begin. First of all, they had promised her the role of understudy for the leading part in their next production. That is, the director had—no one else knew anything about it as yet. He was in love with her, the director. Had been slipping love notes in her pay envelopes for the last weeks. And the leading actor, he too was in love with her—madly in love. It was he who had been coaching her all along. He had been teaching her how to breathe, how to relax, how to stand, how to walk, how to use her voice. It was marvelous. She was a new person, with unknown powers. She had faith in herself, a boundless faith. Soon she would have the world at her feet. She'd take New York by storm, tour the country, go abroad maybe . . . Who could predict what lay ahead? Just the same, she was a little frightened of it all, too. She wanted me to help her; I was to listen to her read the script of her new part. There were so many things she didn't know—and she didn't want to reveal her ignorance before her infatuated lovers. Maybe she'd look up that old fossil at the Ritz-Carlton, make him buy her a new outfit. She needed hats, shoes, dresses, blouses, gloves, stockings . . . so many, many things. It was important now to look the part. She was going to wear her hair differently too. I had to go with her into the hall and observe the new carriage, the new gait she had acquired. Hadn't I noticed the change in her voice? Well, I would very soon. She would be completely remade—and I would love her even more. She would be a hundred different women to me now. Suddenly she thought of an old beau whom she had forgotten about, a clerk at the Imperial Hotel. He would buy her everything she needed—without a word. Yes, she must telephone him in the morning. I could meet her at dinner, in her new togs. I wasn't going to be jealous, was I? He was a young man, the clerk, but a perfect fool, a ninny, a sap. The only reason he saved his money was that she might spend it. He had no use for it otherwise—he was too dumb to know what to do with it. If he could only hold her hand furtively he was grateful. Maybe she would give him a kiss sometime—when she needed some unusual favor.

On and on she ran . . . the kind of gloves she liked, the way to place the voice, how the Indians walked, the value of Yoga exercises, the way to train the memory, the perfume that suited her mood, the superstitiousness of theatrical people, their generosity, their intrigues, their amours, their pride, their conceit. How it felt to rehearse in an empty house, the jokes and pranks that occurred in the wings, the attitude of the stage hands, the peculiar aroma of the dressing rooms. And the jealousy! Everyone jealous of everyone else. Fever, commotion, distraction, grandeur. A world within a world. One became intoxicated, drugged, hallucinated.

And the discussions! A mere trifle could bring about a raging controversy, ending sometimes in a brawl, a hair-pulling match. Some of them seemed to have the very devil in them, especially the women. There was only one decent one, and she was quite young and inexperienced. The others were veritable maenads, furies, harpies. They swore like troopers. By comparison the girls at the dance hall were angelic.

A long pause.

Then, à propos of nothing, she asked when the divorce trial was taking place.

"This week," I said, surprised at the sudden turn of her mind.

"We'll get married right away," she said.

"Of course," I responded.

She didn't like the way I said "of course." "You don't have to marry me, if you don't want," she said.

"But I do want to," I said. "And then we'll get out of this place . . . find a place of our own."

"Do you mean that?" she exclaimed. "I'm so glad. I've been waiting to hear you say that. I want to start a new life with you. Let's get away from all these people! And I want you to quit that awful job. I'll find a place where you can write. You won't need to earn any money. I'll soon be making lots of money. You can have anything you want. I'll get you all the books you want to read. . . . Maybe you'll write a play—and I'll act in it! That would be wonderful, wouldn't it?"

I wondered what Rebecca would have said of this speech, had she been listening. Would she have heard only the actress, or would she have detected the germ of a new being expressing itself? Perhaps that mysterious quality of Mona's lay not in obscuration but in germination. True enough, the contours of her personality were not sharply defined, but that was no reason to accuse her of falsity. She was mimetic, chameleonesque, and not outwardly, but inwardly. Outwardly everything about her was pronounced and definite; she stamped her impress upon you immediately. Inwardly she was like a column of smoke; the slightest pressure of her will altered the configuration of her personality instantly. She was sensitive to pressures, not the pressure of others' wills but of their desires. The histrionic rôle with her was not something to be put on and off—it was her way of meeting reality. What she thought she believed; what she believed was real; what was real she acted upon. Nothing was unreal to her, except that which she was not thinking about. But the moment her attention was brought to bear, no matter how monstrous, fantastic or incredible, the thing became real. In her the frontiers were never closed. People who credited her with having a strong will were utterly mistaken. She had a will, yes, but it was not the will which swept her headlong into new and startling situations—it was her ever-present readiness, her alertness, to act out her ideas. She could change with devastating swiftness from rôle to rôle; she changed before your eyes, with that incredible and elusive prestidigitation of the vaudeville star who impersonates the most diverse types. What she had been doing all her life unconsciously the theatre was now teaching her to do deliberately. They were only making an actress of her in the sense that they were revealing to her the boundaries of art; they were indicating the limitations which surround creation. They could make a failure of her only by giving her free rein.

* * *

The day of the trial I presented myself at court in a bright and supercilious mood. Everything had been agreed upon beforehand. I had only to raise my hand, swear a silly oath, admit my guilt and take the punishment. The judge looked like a scarecrow fitted with a pair of lunar binoculars; his black wings flapped lugubriously in the hushed silence of the room. He seemed to be slightly annoyed by my serene complacency; it did not bolster the illusion of his importance, which was absolutely nil. I could make no distinction between him and the brass rail, between him and the cuspidor. The brass rail, the Bible, the cuspidor, the American flag, the blotter on his desk, the thugs in uniform who preserved order and decorum, the knowledge that was tucked away in his brain cells, the musty books in his study, the philosophy that underlay the whole structure of the law, the eye-glasses he wore, his B. V. D.'s, his person and his personality, the whole ensemble was a senseless collaboration in the name of a blind machine about which I didn't give a fuck in the dark. All I wanted was to know that I was definitely free to put my head in the noose again.

It was all going like tic-tac-toe, one thing cancelling another, and at the end of course the law squashing you down as if you were a fat, juicy bedbug, when suddenly I realized that he was asking me if I were willing to pay such and such an amount of alimony regularly for the rest of my days.

"*What's that?*" I demanded. The prospect of at last encountering some opposition caused him to brighten appreciably. He reeled off some gibberish about solemnly agreeing to pay the sum of something or other.

"I agree to no such thing," I said emphatically. "I intend to pay"—and here I mentioned a sum that was double the amount he had named.

It was his turn to say "*What's that?*"

I repeated myself. He looked at me as though I had lost my senses, then, swiftly, as though he were trapping me, he snapped out: "Very good! We'll make it as you wish. It's your funeral."

"It's my pleasure and privilege," I retorted.

"Sir!"

I repeated myself. He gave me a withering look, beckoned to the lawyer to approach, leaned over and whispered something in his ear. I had the distinct impression that he was asking the lawyer if I were in my sound senses. Apparently assured that I was, he looked up and, fixing a stony gaze upon me, he said: "Young man, do you know what the penalty is for failure to meet your obligations?"

"No sir," I said, "nor do I care to hear it. Are we through now? I've got to get back to my job."

It was a beautiful day outdoors. I started walking aimlessly. Soon I was at the Brooklyn Bridge. I started walking over the Bridge, but after a few minutes I lost heart, turned around and dove into the subway. I had no intention of going back to the office; I had been given a day off and I intended to make the most of it.

At Times Square I got off and walked instinctively towards the French-Italian restaurant over near Third Avenue. It was cool and dark in the back of the grocery store where they served the food. At lunch time there never were many customers. Soon there was only myself and a big, sprawling Irish girl who had already made herself quite drunk. We fell into a strange conversation about the Catholic Church during the course of which she repeated like a refrain: "The Pope's all right, but I refuse to kiss his ass."

Finally she pushed her chair back, struggled to her feet, and tried to walk towards the lavatory. The lavatory was used by men and women alike and was in the hall. I saw that she would never make it alone. I got up and held her by the arm. She was thoroughly potted and lurching like a storm-tossed ship.

As we got to the door of the lavatory she begged me to help her onto the seat. I stood her by the seat so that all she had to do was to sit down. She hitched up her skirt and tried to pull her panties down, but the effort was too much. "Pull 'em down for me, will you," she begged with a sleepy grin. I did as she asked, patted her cunt affectionately, and sat her down on the seat. Then I turned to go.

"Don't go!" she whined, clutching my hand, and with that she began emptying her tank. I held on while she finished the job, Nos. 1 and 2, with stink bombs and everything. Throughout the operation she repeated over and over: "No, I *won't* kiss the Pope's ass!" She looked so absolutely helpless that I thought perhaps I'd have to wipe her ass for her. However, from long years of training she managed to do this much for herself, though it took an incredibly long time. I was about ready to throw up when finally she asked me to lift her up. As I was pulling her bloomers up I couldn't help rubbing my hand over her rose-bush. It was tempting, but the stench was too powerful to dally with that idea.

As I assisted her out of the toilet the patronne espied us and nodded her head sadly. I wondered if she realized what chivalry it took for me to perform this act. Anyway, we went back to the table, ordered some black coffee, and sat talking a little while longer. As she sobered up she became almost disgustingly grateful. She said if I would take her home I could have her—she wanted to make it up to me. "I'll take a bath and change my things," she said. "I feel filthy. It *was* filthy too, God help me."

I told her I would see her home in a taxi, but that I wouldn't be able to stay with her.

"Now you're getting delicate," she said. "What's the matter, ain't I good enough for you? It ain't my fault, is it, if I had to go to the toilet? You go to the toilet, don't you? Wait till I take a bath—you'll see what I look like. Listen, give me your hand!" I gave her my hand and she put it under her skirt, right on her bushy cunt. "Take a good feel of it," she urged. "You like it? Well, it's all yours. I'll scrub it and perfume it for you. You can take all you like of it. I'm not a bad lay. And I'm not a tart either, see! I got cock-eyed, that's all. A guy walked out on me, and I was crazy enough to take it to heart. He'll come crawling back before long, don't you worry. But Jesus, I did have my heart set on him. I told him I wouldn't kiss the Pope's ass—and that got him sore. I'm a good Catholic, same as he, but I can't see the Pope as Christ Almighty, can you?"

She went on with her monologue, jumping from one thing to another like a goat. I gathered that she was a switchboard operator in a big hotel. She wasn't such a bad sort, either, down under her Irish skin. I could see that she might be very attractive, once the fumes of the alcohol cleared away. She had very blue eyes and jet black hair, and a smile that was sly and puckish. Maybe I would run up and help her with her bath. I could always run out on her if anything went amiss. The thing that bothered me was that I was to meet Mona for dinner. I was to wait for her in the Rose Room of the McAlpin Hotel.

We got in a taxi and drove uptown. In the cab she rested her head on my shoulder. "You're awfully good to me," she said in a sleepy voice. "I don't know who you are, but you're O. K. with me. Jesus, I wish I could take a nap first. Would you wait for me?"

"Sure," I said. "Maybe I'll take a nap, too."

The apartment was cosy and attractive, better than I had expected it to be. She had no sooner opened the door than she kicked off her shoes. I helped her undress.

As she stood before the mirror, nude except for her panties, I had to admit that she possessed a beautiful figure. Her breasts were white and full, round and taut, with bright, strawberry-colored nipples.

"Why don't you take those off, too?" I said, pointing to the panties.

"No, not now," she said, suddenly becoming coy, her cheeks coloring slightly.

"I took them off before," I said. "What's the difference now?" I put my hand on her waist as if to pull them down. "Don't, please!" she begged. "Wait till I have my bath." She paused a moment, then added: "I'm just getting over my period."

That settled it for me. I saw the ring-worms flowering again. I got panicky.

"All right," I said, "take your bath! I'll stretch out in here while you're at it."

"Won't you scrub my back for me?" she said, her lips curling in that puckish smile of hers.

"Why sure I will . . . certainly," I said. I led her to the bathroom, half-pushing her along in my haste to get rid of her.

As she slipped out of the panties I noticed a dark bloodstain. Not on your life, I thought to myself. No sir, not in my sound senses I don't. *Kiss the Pope's ass—never!*

But as she lay there soaping herself I felt myself weakening. I took the soap from her hand and scrubbed her bush for her. She squirmed with pleasure as my soapy fingers entwined themselves in her hair.

"I think it's finished," she said, arching her pelvis and spreading her cunt open with her two hands. "You look . . . do you see anything?"

I put the soapy middle finger of my right hand up her cunt and massaged it gently. She lay back with her hands clasped behind her head and slowly gyrated her pelvis. "Jesus, that feels good," she said. "Go on, do it some more. Maybe I won't need a nap."

As she got worked up she began to move more violently. Suddenly she unclasped her hands and with wet fingers she unbuttoned my fly, took my prick out and made a dive for it with her mouth. She went at it like a professional, teasing it, worrying it, fluting her lips, then choking on it. I came off in her mouth; she swallowed it as if it were nectar and ambrosia.

Then she sank back into the tub, sighed heavily and closed her eyes.

Now is the time to beat it, I said to myself, and pretending that I was going to look for a cigarette I grabbed my hat and bolted. As I ran down the stairs I put my finger to my nostrils and smelled it. It wasn't a bad odor. It smelled of soap more than anything else.

* * *

When I arrived at Riverside Drive it was almost dawn. Mona had not returned. I lay listening for her step. I began to fear that she had met with an accident—worse, that perhaps she had killed herself, or tried to, at least. It was possible, too, that she had gone home to her parents. But then why had she left the cab? Perhaps to run to the subway. But then the subway was not in that direction. I could of course telephone her home, but I knew she would interpret that badly. I wondered if she had telephoned during the night. Neither Rebecca nor Arthur ever bothered to leave a message for me; they always waited until they saw me.

Towards eight o'clock I knocked at their door. They were still asleep. I had to knock loudly before they answered. And then I learned nothing—they had come home very late themselves.

In despair I went to Kronski's room. He too was muffled in sleep. He didn't seem to know what I was driving at.

Finally he said: "What's the matter—has she been out all night again? No, there wasn't any call for you. Get out of here . . . leave me alone!"

I hadn't slept a wink. I felt exhausted. But then the reassuring thought came to me that she might telephone me at the office. I almost expected a message to be lying on my desk waiting for me.

Most of the day went by in taking cat naps. I slept at my desk, my head buried in my folded arms. Several times I called Rebecca to see if she had received any message, but it was always the same answer. When it came time to close shop I lingered on. No matter what had happened I could not believe that she would let the day pass without telephoning me. It was just incredible.

A strange, nervous vitality possessed me. Suddenly I was wide awake, more wide awake than I could have been had I rested three days in bed. I would wait another half hour and if she didn't phone I would go directly to her home.

As I was pacing back and forth with pantherish strides the stairway door opened and a little shaver with dark skin entered. He closed the door behind him quickly as if he were shutting out a pursuer. There was something jolly and mysterious about him which his Cuban voice exaggerated.

"You *will* give me a job, won't you, Mr. Miller?" he burst out. "I must have the messenger job to complete my studies. Everybody tells me that you are a kind man—and I can see it myself—you have a good face. I am proficient in many things, as you will discover when you know me better. Juan Rico is my name. I am eighteen years old. I am a poet too."

"Well, well," I said, chuckling and stroking him under the chin—he was the size of a midget and looked like one—"so you're a poet? Then I'm surely going to give you a job."

"I'm an acrobat, too," he said. "My father had a circus once. You will find me very speedy on my legs. I love to go hither and about with zest and alacrity. I am also extremely courteous and when delivering a message I would say, 'Thank you sir,' and doff my cap respectfully. I know all the streets by heart, including the Bronx. And if you would put me in the Spanish neighborhood you would find me very effective. Do I please you, sir?" He gave me a bewitching grin which implied that he knew very well how to sell himself.

"Go over there and sit down," I said. "I'll give you a blank to fill out. Tomorrow morning you can start in bright and early—with a smile."

"Oh I can smile, sir—beautifully," and he did.

"You're sure you're eighteen?"

"Oh yes, sir, that I can prove. I have all my papers with me."

I gave him an application blank and went to the adjoining room—the rink—to leave him in peace. Suddenly the telephone rang. I bounded back to the desk and picked up the receiver. It was Mona speaking, in a subdued, restrained, unnatural voice, as though she had been drained hollow.

"He died a little while ago," she said. "I've been at his side ever since I left you. . . ."

I mumbled some inadequate words of consolation and then I asked her when she was coming back. She wasn't sure just when . . . she wanted me to do her a little favor . . . to go to the department store and buy her a mourning dress and some black gloves. Size sixteen. *What sort of material?* She didn't know—anything I chose. . . . A few more words and she hung up.

Little Juan Rico was looking up into my eyes like a faithful dog. He had understood everything and was trying in his delicate Cuban way to let me know that he wished to share my sorrow.

"It's all right, Juan," I said, "everybody has to die some time."

"Was that your wife who telephoned?" he asked. His eyes were moist and glistening.

"Yes," I said, "that was my wife."

"I'm sure she must be beautiful."

"What makes you say that?"

"The way you talked to her . . . I could almost see her. I wish I could marry a beautiful woman someday. I think about it very often."

"You're a funny lad," I said. "Thinking about marriage already. Why, you're just a boy."

"Here's my application, sir. Will you kindly look it over now so that I may be sure I can come tomorrow?"

I gave it a quick glance and assured him it was satisfactory.

"Then I am at your service, sir. And now, sir, if you will pardon me, may I suggest that you let me stay with you a little while? I don't think it is good for you to be alone at this moment. When the heart is sad one needs a friend."

I burst out laughing. "A good idea," I said. "We'll go to dinner together, how's that? And a movie afterwards—does that suit you?"

He got up and began to frisk about like a trained dog. Suddenly he became curious about the empty room in the rear. I followed him in and watched him good-naturedly as he examined the paraphernalia. The roller skates intrigued him. He had picked up a pair and was examining them as if he had never seen such things before.

"Put them on," I said, "and do a turn. This is the skating rink."

"Can you skate also?" he asked.

"Sure I can. Do you want to see me skate?"

"Yes," he said, "and let me skate with you. I haven't done it for years and years. It's a rather comical diversion, is it not?"

We slipped the skates on. I shot forward with hands behind my back. Little Juan Rico followed at my heels. In the center of the room there were slender pillars; I looped in and around the pillars as if I were giving an exhibition.

"I say, but it's very exhilarating, isn't it?" said Juan breathlessly. "You glide like a zephyr."

"Like a what?"

"Like a *zephyr* . . . a mild, pleasant breeze."

"Oh, *zephyr!*"

"I wrote a poem once about a zephyr—that was long ago."

I took his hand and swung him around. Then I placed him in front of me and with my hands on his waist I pushed him along, guiding him lightly and dexterously about the floor. Finally I gave him a good push and sent him skedaddling to the other end of the room.

"Now I'll show you a few fancy turns that I learned in the Tyrol," I said, folding my arms in front of me and raising one leg in the air. The thought that never in her life would Mona suspect what I was doing this minute gave me a demonic joy. As I passed and repassed little Juan, who was now sitting on the window-sill absorbed in the spectacle, I made faces at him—first sad and mournful, then gay, then insouciant, then hilarious, then meditative, then stern, then menacing, then idiotic. I tickled myself in the arm-pits, like a monkey; I waltzed like a trained bear; I squatted low like a cripple; I sang in a cracked key, then shouted like a maniac. Round and round, ceaselessly, merrily, free as a bird. Juan joined in. We stalked each other like animals, we turned into waltzing mice, we did the deaf and dumb act.

And all the time I was thinking of Mona wandering about in the house of mourning, waiting for her mourning dress, her black gloves, and what not.

Round and round, with never a care. A little kerosene, a match, and we would go up in flames, like a burning merry-go-round. I looked at Juan's poll—it was like dry tinder. I had an insane desire to set him on fire, set him aflame and send him hurtling down the elevator shaft. Then two or three wild turns, à la Breughel, and out the window!

I calmed down a little. Not Breughel, but Hieronymous Bosch. A season in hell, amidst the traps and pulleys of the medieval mind. First time around they yank off an arm. Second time around a leg. Finally just a torso rolling around. And the music playing with vibrant twangs. The iron harp of Prague. A sunken street near the synagogue. A dolorous peal of the bells. A woman's guttural lament.

Not Bosch any longer, but Chagall. An angel in mufti descending slantwise just above the roof. Snow on the ground and in the gutters little pieces of meat for the rats. Cracow in the violet light of evisceration. Weddings, births, funerals. A man in an overcoat and only one string to his violin. The bride has lost her mind; she dances with broken legs.

Round and round, ringing door-bells, ringing sleigh-bells. The cosmococcic round of grief and slats. At the roots of my hair a touch of frost, in the tips of my toes a fire. The world is a merry-go-round in flames, the horses burn down to the hocks. A cold, stiff father lying on a feather-bed. A mother green as gangrene. And the bridegroom rolling along.

First we'll bury him in the cold ground. Then we'll bury his name, his legend, his kites and race horses. And for the widow a bon-fire, a suttee Viennoise. I will marry the widow's daughter—in her mourning gown and black gloves. I will do atonement and anoint my head with ashes.

Round and round. . . . Now the figure eight. Now the dollar sign. Now the spread eagle. A little kerosene and a match, and I would go up like a Christmas tree.

"Mr. Miller! Mr. Miller!" calls Juan. "Mr. Miller, stop it! Please stop it!"

The boy looks frightened. What can it be that makes him stare at me so?

"Mr. Miller," he says, clutching me by the coat tail, "please don't laugh so! *Please,* I'm afraid for you."

I relaxed. A broad grin came over my face, then softened to an amiable smile.

"That's better, sir. You had me worried. Hadn't we better go now?"

"I think so, Juan. I think we've had enough exercise for today. Tomorrow you will get a bicycle. *Are you hungry?*"

"Yes sir, I am indeed. I always have a fabulous appetite. Once I ate a whole chicken all by myself. That was when my aunt died."

"We'll have chicken tonight, Juan me lad. Two chickens—one for you and one for me."

"You're very kind, sir. . . . Are you sure you're all right now?"

"Fine as a fiddle, Juan. Now where do you suppose we could buy a mourning dress at this hour?"

"I'm sure I don't know," said Juan.

In the street I hailed a taxi. I had an idea that on the East Side there would be shops still open. The driver was certain he could find one.

"It's very lively down here, isn't it?" said Juan, as we alighted in front of a dress shop. "Is it always this way?"

"Always," I said. "A perpetual fiesta. Only the poor enjoy life."

"I should like to work down here some time," said Juan. "What language do they speak here?"

"All languages," I said. "You can also speak English."

The proprietor was standing at the door. He gave Juan a friendly pat on the head.

"I would like a mourning dress, size 16," I said. "Not too expensive. It must be delivered tonight, C. O. D."

A dark young Jewess with a Russian accent stepped forward. "Is it for a young or an old woman?" she said.

"A young woman, about your size. For my wife."

She began showing me various models. I told her to choose the one she thought most suitable. "Not an ugly one," I begged, "and not too chic either. You know what I mean."

"And the gloves," said Juan. "Don't forget the gloves."

"What size?" asked the young lady.

"Let me see your hands," I said. I studied them a moment. "A little larger than yours."

I gave the address and left a generous tip for the errand boy. The proprietor now came up, began talking to Juan. He seemed to take a great fancy to him.

"Where do you come from, sonny?" he asked. "From Puerto Rico?"

"From Cuba," said Juan.

"Do you speak Spanish?"

"Yes sir, and French and Portuguese."

"You're very young to know so many languages."

"My father taught me them. My father was the editor of a newspaper in Havana."

"Well, well," said the proprietor. "You remind me of a little boy I knew in Odessa."

"Odessa!" said Juan. "I was in Odessa once. I was a cabin boy on a trading ship."

"What!" exclaimed the proprietor. "You were in Odessa? It's unbelievable. How old are you?"

"I'm eighteen, sir."

The proprietor turned to me. He wanted to know if he couldn't invite us to have a drink with him in the ice cream parlor next door.

We accepted the invitation with pleasure. Our host, whose name was Eisenstein, began to talk about Russia. He had been a medical student originally. The boy who resembled Juan was his son who had died. "He was a strange boy," said Mr. Eisenstein. "He didn't resemble any of the family. And he had his own way of thinking. He wanted to tramp around the world. No matter what you told him he had a different idea. He was a little philosopher. Once he ran away to Egypt—because he wanted to study the pyramids. When we told him we were going to America he said he would go to China. He said he didn't want to become rich, like the Americans. A strange boy! Such independence! Nothing frightened him—not even the Cossacks. I was almost afraid of him sometimes. Where did he come from? He didn't even look like a Jew. . . ."

He went into a monologue about the strange blood that had been poured into the veins of the Jews in their wanderings. He spoke of strange tribes in Arabia, Africa, China. He thought even the Eskimos might have Jewish blood in them. As he talked he became intoxicated by this idea of the mixture of races and bloods. The world would be a stagnant pool had it not been for the Jews. "We are like seeds carried by the wind," he said. "We blossom everywhere. Hardy plants. Until we are pulled up by the roots. Even then we don't perish. We can live upside down. We can grow between stones."

All this time he had taken me for a Jew. Finally I explained that I was not a Jew, but that my wife was.

"And she became a Christian?"

"No, I'm becoming a Jew."

Juan was looking at me with big, questioning eyes. Mr. Eisenstein didn't know whether I was joking or not.

"When I come down here," I said, "I feel happy. I don't know what it is, but I feel more at home here. Maybe I have Jewish blood and don't know it."

"I'm afraid not," said Mr. Eisenstein. "You're attracted, because you're not a Jew. You like what is different, that's all. Maybe you hated the Jews once. That happens sometimes. Suddenly a man sees that he was mistaken and then he becomes violently in love with what he once hated. He goes to the other extreme. I know a Gentile who became converted to Judaism. We don't try to convert, you know that. If you're a good Christian it's better that you stay a Christian."

"But I don't care about the religion," I said.

"The religion is everything," he said. "If you can't be a good Christian you can't be a good Jew. We are not a people or a race—we're a religion."

"That's what you say, but I don't believe it. It's more than that. It's as though you were a kind of bacteria. Nothing can explain your survival, certainly not your faith. That's why I'm so curious, why I get excited when I'm with your people. I would like to possess the secret."

"Well, study your wife," said he.

"I do but I don't make her out. She's a mystery."

"But you love her?"

"Yes," I said, "I love her passionately."

"And why aren't you with her now? Why do you have the dress sent to her? Who is it that died?"

"Her father," I answered. "But I never met him," I added rapidly. "I've never been inside her home."

"That's bad," he said. "There's something wrong there. You should go to her. Never mind if she didn't ask you. Go to her! Don't let her be ashamed of her parents. You don't have to go to the funeral, but you should let her see that you care for her family. You are only an accident in her life. When you die the family will go on. They will absorb your blood. We have drunk the blood of every race. We go on like a river. You must not think you are marrying her alone—you are marrying the Jewish race, the Jewish people. We give you life and strength. We nourish you. In the end all peoples will come together. We will have peace. We will make a new world. And there will be room for everybody. . . . No, don't leave her alone now. You will regret it, if you do. She is proud, that's what it is. You must be soft and gentle. You must woo her like a pigeon. Maybe she loves you now, but later she will love you more. She will hold you like a vise. There is no love like that of the Jewish woman for the man she gives her heart to. *Especially if he is of Gentile blood.* It is a great victory for her. It is better for you to surrender than to be the master. . . . You will excuse me for speaking this way, but I know what I am talking about. And I see you are not an ordinary Gentile. You are one of those lost Gentiles—you are searching for something . . . you don't know what exactly. We know your kind. We are not always eager to have your love. We have been betrayed so often. Sometimes it is better to have a good enemy—then we know where we stand. With your kind we are never sure where we stand. You are like water—and we are rocks. You eat us away little by little—not with malice, but with kindness. You lap against us like the waves of the sea.

The big waves we can meet—but the gentle lapping, that takes our strength away."

I was so excited by this unexpected excursus that I had to interrupt his speech.

"Yes, I know," he said. "I know how you feel. You see, we know all about you—but you have everything to learn about us. You can be married a thousand times, to a thousand Jewish women, and still you will not know what we know. We are right inside of you all the time. Bacteria, yes, maybe. If you are strong we support you; if you are weak, we destroy you. We live not in the world, as it seems to the Gentile, but in the spirit. The world passes away, but the spirit is eternal. My little boy understood that. He wanted to remain pure. The world was not good enough for him. He died of shame—shame for the world. . . ."

* * *

Some minutes later, when we sauntered out into the violet light of early evening, I saw the ghetto with new eyes. There are Summer nights in New York when the sky is pure azure, when the buildings are immediate and palpable, not only in their substance but in their essence. That dirty streaked light which reveals only the ugliness of factories and sordid tenements disappears very often with sunset, the dust settles down, the contours of the buildings become more sharply defined, like the lineaments of an ogre in a calcium spotlight. Pigeons appear in the sky, wheeling above the rooftops. A cupola bobs up, sometimes out of a Turkish Bath. There is always the stately simplicity of St. Marks-on-the-Bouwerie, the great foreign square abutting Avenue A., the low Dutch buildings above which the ruddy gas tanks loom, the intimate side streets with their incongruous American names, the triangles which bear the stamp of old landmarks, the waterfront with the Brooklyn shore so close that one can almost recognize the people walking on the other side. All the glamour of New York is squeezed into this pullulating area which is marked off by formaldehyde and sweat and tears. Nothing is so familiar, so intimate, so nostalgic to the New Yorker as this district which he spurns and rejects. The whole of New York should have been one vast ghetto: the poison should have been drained off, the misery apportioned; the joy should have been communicated through every vein and artery. The rest of New York is an abstraction; it is cold, geometrical, rigid as *rigor mortis* and, I might as well add, *insane*—if one can only stand apart and look at it undauntedly. Only in the beehive can one find the human touch, find that city of sights, sounds, smells which one hunts for in vain beyond the margins of the ghetto. To live outside the pale is to wither and die. Beyond the pale there are only dressed-up cadavers. They are wound up each day, like alarm clocks. They perform like seals; they die like box office receipts. But in the seething honey-comb there is a growth as of plants, an animal warmth almost suffocating, a vitality which accrues from rubbing and glueing together, a hope which is physical as well as spiritual, a contamination which is dangerous but salutary. Small souls perhaps, burning like tapers, but burning steadily—and capable of throwing portentous shadows on the walls which hem them in.

Walk down any street in the soft violet light. Make the mind blank. A thousand sensations assault you at once from every direction. Here man is still furred and feathered; here cyst and quartz still speak. There are audible, voluble buildings with sheet metal vizors and windows that sweat; places of worship too, where the children drape themselves about the porticos like contortionists; rolling, ambulant streets where nothing stands still, nothing is fixed, nothing is comprehensible except through the eyes and mind of a dreamer. Hallucinating streets too, where suddenly all is silence, all is barren, as if after the passing of a plague. Streets that cough, streets that throb like a fevered temple, streets to die on and not a soul take notice. Strange, frangipanic streets, in which the attar of roses mingles with the acrid bite of leek and scallion. Slippered streets, which echo with the pat and slap of lazy feet. Streets out of Euclid, which can be explained only by logic and theorem. . . .

Pervading all, suspended between the layers of the skin like a distillate of ruddy smoke, is the secondary sexual sweat—pubic, Orphic, mammalian—a heavy incense smuggled in by night on velvet pads of musk. No one is immune, not even the Mongoloid idiot. It washes over you like the brush and passage of camisoled breasts. In a light rain it makes an invisible aetherial mud. It is of every hour, even when rabbits are boiled to a stew. It glistens in the tubes, the follicles, the papillaries. As the earth slowly wheels, the stoops and banisters turn and the children with them; in the murky haze of sultry nights all that is terrene, volupt and fatidical hums like a zither. A heavy wheel plated with fodder and featherbeds, with little sweet-oil lamps and drops of pure animal sweat. All goes round and round, creaking, wobbling, lumbering, whimpering sometimes, but round and round and round. Then, if you become very still, standing on a stoop, for instance, and carefully think no thoughts, a myopic, bestial clarity besets your vision. There is a wheel, there are spokes, and there is a hub. And in the center of the hub there is—exactly nothing. It is where the grease goes, and the axle. And you are there, in the center of nothingness, sentient, fully expanded, whirring with the whir of planetary wheels. Everything becomes alive and meaningful, even yesterday's snot which clings to the doorknob. Everything sags and droops, is mossed with wear and care; everything has been looked at thousands of times, rubbed and caressed by the occipital eye. . . .

A man of an olden race standing in a stone trance. He smells the food which his ancestors cooked in the millenary past: the chicken, the liver paste, the stuffed fish, the herrings, the eiderdown ducks. He has lived with them and they have lived in him. Feathers float through the air, the feathers of winged creatures caged in crates—as it was in Ur, in Babylon, in Egypt and Palestine. The same shiny silks, blacks turning green with age: the silks of other times, of other cities, other ghettos, other pogroms. Now and then a coffee grinder or a samovar, a little wooden casket for spices, for the myrrh and aloes of the East. Little strips of carpet—from the souks and bazaars, from the emporiums of the Levant; bits of astrakhan, laces, shawls, nubies, and petticoats of flaming, flouncing flamingo. Some bring their birds, their little pets—warm, tender things pulsing with tremulous beat, learning no new language, no new melodies, but pining away, droopy, listless, languishing in their super-heated cages suspended above the fire-escapes. The iron balconies are festooned with meat and bedding, with plants and pets—a crawling still life in which even the rust is rapturously eaten away. With the cool of the evening the young are exposed like egg-plants; they lie back under the stars, lulled to dream by the obscene jabberwocky of the American street. Below, in wooden casks, are the pickles floating in brine. Without the pickle, the pretzel, the Turkish sweets, the ghetto would be without savour. Bread of every variety, with seeds and without. White, black, brown, even gray bread—of all weights, all consistencies. . . .

The ghetto! A marble table top with a basket of bread. A bottle of seltzer water, preferably blue. A soup with egg drops. And two men talking. Talking, talking, talking, with burning cigarettes hanging from their blenched lips. Nearby a cellar with music: strange instruments, strange costumes, strange airs. The birds begin to warble, the air becomes overheated, the bread piles up, the seltzer bottles smoke and sweat. Words are dragged like ermine through the spittled sawdust; growling, guttural dogs paw the air. Spangled women choked with tiaras doze heavily in their richly upholstered caskets of flesh. The magnetic fury of lust concentrates in dark, mahogany eyes.

In another cellar an old man sits in his overcoat on a pile of wood, counting his coal. He sits in the dark, as he did in Cracow, stroking his beard. His life is all coal and wood, little voyages from darkness to daylight. In his ears is still the ring of hoofs on cobbled streets, the sound of shrieks and screams, the clatter of sabres, the splash of bullets against a blank wall. In the cinema, in the synagogue, in the coffee house, wherever one sits, two kinds of music playing—one bitter, one sweet. One sits in the middle of a river called Nostalgia. A river filled with little souvenirs gathered from the wreckage of the world. Souvenirs of the homeless, of birds of refuge building again and again with sticks and twigs. Everywhere broken nests, egg-shells, fledgelings with twisted necks and dead eyes staring into space. Nostalgic river dreams under tin copings, under rusty sheds, under capsized boats. A world of mutilated hopes, of strangled aspirations, of bullet-proof starvation. A world where even the warm breath of life has to be smuggled in, where gems big as pigeons' hearts are traded for a yard of space, an ounce of freedom. All is compounded into a familiar liver paste which is swallowed on a tasteless wafer. In one gulp there is swallowed down five thousand years of bitterness, five thousand years of ashes, five thousand years of broken twigs, smashed egg-shells, strangled fledgelings. . . .

In the deep sub-cellar of the human heart the dolorous twang of the iron harp rings out.

Build your cities proud and high. Lay your sewers. Span your rivers. Work feverishly. Sleep dreamlessly. Sing madly, like the bulbul. Underneath, below the deepest foundations, there lives another race of men. They are dark, sombre, passionate. They muscle into the bowels of the earth. They wait with a patience which is terrifying. They are the scavengers, the devourers, the avengers. They emerge when everything topples into dust.

* * *

For seven days and nights I was alone. I began to think that she had left me. Twice she telephoned, but she sounded far away, lost, swallowed up by grief. I remembered Mr. Eisenstein's words. I wondered, wondered if she had been reclaimed.

Then one day, towards closing time, she stepped out of the elevator and stood before me. She was all in black except for a mauve turban which gave her an exotic cast. A transformation had taken place. The eyes had grown still softer, the skin more translucent. Her figure had become seductively suave, her carriage more majestic. She had the poise of a somnambulist.

For a moment I could scarcely believe my eyes. There was something hypnotic about her. She radiated power, magnetism, enchantment. She was like one of those Italian women of the Renaissance who gaze at you steadily with enigmatic smile from a canvas which recedes into infinity. In those few strides which she took before throwing herself into my arms I felt a gulf, such as I had never known could exist between two people, closing up. It was as though the earth had opened up between us, as if, by a supreme and magical effort of will, she had leaped the void and rejoined me. The ground on which she stood a moment ago fell away, slipped into a past altogether unknown to me, just as the shelf of a continent slips into the sea. Nothing so clear and tangible as this formulated itself in my mind then; it was only afterwards, because I rehearsed this moment time and again later, that I understood the nature of our reunion.

Her whole body felt strangely different, as I pressed her close. It was the body of a creature who had been reborn. It was an entirely new body that she surrendered, new because it contained some element which hitherto had been missing. It was, strange as it may seem to say so, as if she had returned with her soul—and not her private, individual soul, but the soul of her race. She seemed to be offering it to me, like a talisman.

Words came to our lips with difficulty. We simply gurgled and stared at one another. Then I saw her glance roving over the place, taking everything in with a remorseless eye, and finally resting on my desk and on me. "What are you doing here?" she seemed to say. And then, as it softened, as she gathered me up in the folds of the tribe—"*What have they done to you?*" Yes, I felt the power and the pride of her people. I have not chosen you, it said, to sit among the lowly. I am taking you out of this world. I am going to enthrone you.

And this was Mona, the Mona who had come to me from the center of the dance floor and offered herself, as she had offered herself to hundreds and perhaps thousands of others before me. Such a strange, wondrous flower is the human being! You hold it in your hand and while you sleep it grows, it becomes transformed, it exhales a narcotic fragrance.

In a few seconds I had become worshipful. It was almost unbearable to look at her steadily. To think that she would follow me home, accept the life I had to offer her, seemed unbelievable. I had asked for a woman and I had been given a queen.

What happened at dinner is a complete blank. We must

have eaten in a restaurant, we must have talked, we must have made plans. I remember nothing of all this. I remember her face, her new soulful look, the brilliance and magnetism of the eyes, the translucent tone of the flesh.

I remember that we walked for a time through deserted streets. And perhaps, listening only to the sound of her voice, perhaps then she told me everything, all that I had ever longed to know about her. I remember not a word of it. Nothing had any importance or meaning except the future. I held her hand, clasped it firmly, the fingers entwined, walking with her into the overabundant future. Nothing could possibly be what it had been before. The ground had opened up, the past had been swept away, drowned, drowned as deep as a lost continent. And miraculously—how miraculously I only realized as the moments prolonged themselves!—she had been saved, had been restored to me. It was my duty, my mission, my destiny in this life to cherish and protect her. As I thought of all that lay ahead I began to grow, from within, as if from a small seed. I grew inches in the space of a block. It was in my heart that I felt the seed bursting.

And then, as we stood at a corner, a bus came along. We jumped in and went upstairs on the deck. To the very front seat. As soon as the fare had been paid I took her in my arms and smothered her with kisses. We were alone and the bus was careening over the bumpy pavement.

Suddenly I saw her give a wild look around, raise her dress feverishly, and the next moment she was straddling me. We fucked like mad in the space of a few drunken blocks. She sat on my lap, even after it was over, and continued to caress me passionately.

When we entered Arthur Raymond's home the place was ablaze. It was as if they had been expecting her return. Kronski was there and Arthur's two sisters, Rebecca, and some of her friends. They greeted Mona with the utmost warmth and affection. They almost wept over her.

It was the moment to celebrate. Bottles were brought out, the table was spread, the phonograph wound up. "Yes, yes, let us rejoice!" every one seemed to say. We literally flung ourselves at one another. We danced, we sang, we talked, we ate, we drank. More and more joyous it became. Every one loved every one. Union and reunion. On and on into the night, even Kronski singing at the top of his lungs. It was like a bridal feast. The bride had come back from the grave. The bride was young again. The bride had blossomed.

Yes, it was a marriage. That night I knew that we were joined on the ashes of the past.

"My wife, my wife!" I murmured, as we fell asleep.

5. Surrealism

It is not certain that Anaïs Nin had a wholly beneficial influence on Henry Miller. That she was good for his character is not hard to believe.

> Without his writing, I don't know what Henry would be. It completes him. People who know him as gentle, wonder at the writing. Yet sometimes I have the feeling that this gentleness is not entirely genuine. It is his way of charming. Of disarming. It allows his entry anywhere, he is trusted. It is like a disguise of the observant, the critical, the accusing man within. His severity is disguised. His hatreds and his rebellions. They are not apparent, or acted out. It is always a shock to others. I am aware at times, while he speaks in a mellow way to others, of that small, round, hard photographic lens in his blue eyes.
>
> *The Diary of Anaïs Nin*

In clarity and severity must Anaïs Nin have looked upon herself and her friends. Her beauty is in the sharpness of her features and the tender precision of her intelligence. She perceives. She pins. She practices a species of acupuncture.

> I dislike Henry's blind attacks on everything, like Lawrence's. When he is unhappy he is ready to destroy the world.
>
> Women are so much more honest than men. A woman says: "I am jealous." A man covers it up with a

> system of philosophy, a book of literary criticism, a study of psychology.
>
> *The Diary of Anaïs Nin*

The victims are her friends. They seem to prosper from the accuracy of her needle and the comprehension with which she coats it. She is a spirit of civilization so long as the word will possess any good meaning.

The Henry Miller who leaves Paris ten years after coming to it in 1930 is already that established literary figure we think of as an agent of humanity. Indeed, he will think of himself that way, and more and more on alternate days. There seems no question that the combination of literary success and friendship with Anaïs Nin has done wonders for his generosity. Taken right in his shoes—as he stands—he has become a nicer man.

Nonetheless, his literary work is subtly diminished. Huge literary vanities have developed in him and finally come close to spoiling Black Spring *and* Tropic of Capricorn. *He, too, can write like a successful ass, pompous, full of word-tricks, employing the absurd too cheaply. One sample may stand for five hundred such paragraphs:*

> Aye, the great sun of syphilis is setting. *Low visibility:* forecast for the Bronx, for America, for the whole modern world. Low visibility accompanied by great gales of laughter. No new stars on the horizon. *Catastrophes. . . .* only catastrophes!
>
> *Black Spring*

It is too easy. The old carnal Miller has become too happy with himself. Purple shot never fails nor icicles of grass and certainly not the odor of thanatos in Terre Haute. Sprouts of pubic hair spit gold pollen and cadmium yellow is the rose madder gravy of white fiesta midnights.

To blame Anaïs Nin might be an act of misplaced lit-

erary judgment. Miller was living in the Paris of the thirties, incubator of Patagonians, whole womb of surrealism. In that air of Europe, the memory of the old horror of the trenches dissipated less slowly than intimations of the new horror approached. It was as if the mind of Europe comprehended that the oncoming disproportions of the concentration camps would induce a violence into logic that only surrealism could absorb. One breathed the air of the absurd and labored in the vineyards of the absurd rather than surrender to dread. In the world of the dream every stone covered a horror.

Besides, half of Miller's nature was surrealistic. To feel lust for a woman you despise is the oxymoronic mulch of surrealism. Every sexy statue and cunty deaf-mute of his past had built up his rage to announce a world of no confidence and no meaning—at least no meaning in which one consequence could follow upon another. Tropic of Cancer had indeed been saying as much. We can hardly blame Anaïs Nin for that.

It was just that her presence, her home, her ambience was European culture to him. If some part of Miller must have secretly grovelled before it, he was never without the blood in his nostrils to absorb it, eat it, engorge it, and finally do better than the style he admired. So he took in her literary delicacies along with her psychological punctilio. He began to write fancy. Tropic of Capricorn is the book which could have been better than Cancer and on the same terms—even today, at its least, it is a tidal wave of prose. But it is spoiled by avalanches of over-writing. The man with the latest and best balls to come along in American letters turned arty in Paris. He had to. That self-acquired Brooklyn culture, that sense of himself as an impostor (am I the greatest writer alive, or do not even know how to construct a novel?), his prodigious competitiveness, had to take on all forms, all manners, even all vices of avant-garde writing.

Where Anaïs Nin was a natural child of avant-garde, and looked to create a poetic medium of ellipse which might convey her sense of many a special human relation, Miller was out to overpower each one of his techniques. Living with the volcano of energy the success of Tropic of Cancer gave him, he could hardly have been a sober writer in those years. Surrealism would have appealed in any case. Knowing her, however, had to exacerbate his most extravagant tendencies. Through his eyes, there must have been a fascinating and maddening calm at the civilized center of everything Anaïs Nin did. It must have been a goad that she would not believe altogether in men like himself who wanted to go out and wrestle with the gods. Centuries of acquired proportion lived in her restraint. She had had a Catholic childhood after all calculated to raise her by slow stages from the XIVth century to the present.

> I was so exalted by the idea of eating Jesus's flesh and drinking His blood that I couldn't swallow the Host well, and I dreaded harming it. On my knees, lost to my surroundings, eyes closed, I visualized Christ descending into my heart so realistically (I was a realist then!) that I could see Him walking down the stairs and entering the room of my heart like a sacred visitor. The state of this room was a subject of great preoccupation for me. I fancied that if I had not been good, this room would appear ugly in the eyes of Christ; I fancied He would see as soon as He entered whether it was clear, empty, luminous, or cluttered, dark, chaotic. At that age, nine, ten, eleven, I believe I approximated sainthood. And then, at sixteen, resentful of controls, disillusioned with a God who had not granted my prayers (the return of my father), who performed no miracles, who left me fatherless and in a strange country, I rejected all Catholicism with exaggeration.
>
> *The Diary of Anaïs Nin*

We may clap our psychoanalytical hands. Miller has been motherless; she is fatherless. They are virtually intended to have a lifelong friendship.

> His life. The lower depths, the underworlds. Violence, ruthlessness, gold-digging, debauch. What a torrent of bestial life. His language, descriptions of a world I never knew. The streets of Brooklyn. Broadway. The Village. Poverty. Associations with illiterates, with all kinds of people.
>
> Mine was, from childhood, growth in an atmosphere of music and books and artists, always constructing, creating, writing, drawing, inventing plays, acting in them, writing a diary, living in created dreams as inside a cocoon, dreams born of reading, always reading, growing, disciplining myself to learn, to study, skirting abysses and dangers with incredible innocence, the body always sensitive but in flight from ugliness. The eroticism of Paris awakened me but I remained a romantic. I studied dancing, painting, sculpture, costuming, decoration. I created beautiful homes.
>
> *The Diary of Anaïs Nin*

Nonetheless she guided him very well. And right into the full trap of good criticism. The irony is that the more accurately we point out the vice in another writer, the more likely is the vice to reinforce itself. There is every indication she tried to keep him working in the best direction for himself. She penetrated instantly through his lack of philosophy and his full conceit that he could philosophize.

A bona fide philosophical novelist like Proust or Joyce or Mann, Tolstoy or Dostoyevsky, Melville, Jane Austen, or Henry James, has a mind which permeates his work like an herb. By that measure, Miller was a philosopher who cooked only with garlic, chopping boards full of garlic. Dependably would his philosophy fight the ingredients of his novels, overwhelm them, savage them, betray his own comprehension of what he had to offer, and then betray that he did not know exactly what he was offering. Anaïs Nin saw that Miller was without philosophy—he had only sentiments, at their best likely to be some of the most eloquent sentiments voiced in English. Still there was nothing near to an underlying idea which might contain his characters.

She would beg him to ignore the problem altogether. In a letter written as early as June 1933 she tells him:

> You do not have a philosophy. You have feelings about living . . . You are at war with yourself, with the intellectual you.
>
> I say, let the intellectual alone, the savant, the philosopher. Enjoy life. Intoxicate yourself with life. Describe it. Do not comment on it, or draw false conclusions. You have had your cerebral winter—your mental fervors. You were not happy. *Black Spring* will make you happier. I beg you, give up cerebration. You are in rebellion without knowing why.
>
> *The Diary of Anaïs Nin*

Naturally, she will confirm him in his pride that he is *a philosopher. Nothing will stop him now, not for the rest of his career. Since he becomes progressively more genial, compassionate, generous, and conceivably saintly as the decades go by, the philosophy he will insist on becomes more and more general. A page from* The World of Sex *written around 1940 may reveal her critical influence.*

> Given half a chance, a woman offers her whole being. It's instinctive with her. Not man! A man is usually plagued with all kinds of disturbing notions, with regard to love, sex, politics, art, religion, and so on. A man is always more muddled than a woman. He needs woman if for no other purpose than to be straightened out. Sometimes it takes nothing more than a good, clean, healthy fuck to do the trick. Yes, sometimes an honest fuck is all it needs to dissipate the notion that directing world affairs isn't exclusively *his* responsibil-

> ity. Men have a way of taking things seriously rather than tragically. They are always looking beyond their noses for something more important than what's to hand. Love, when it occurs, is something to be carried on in the wings, as it were. For them the real drama is always taking place on the world stage.
>
> *The World of Sex*

Needless to say, since the idea is not quite his own, neither is the style. He is beginning to sound a little more like other writers, and they are not the best writers. She has been so perfect a critic as to incarcerate him into his vices, and so good a civilized friend that the barbarian at the center of him has become ready to mellow. She could not know that he would never fulfill this prescription.

> I said to Henry: "In the books, you are really creating yourself. In *Tropic of Cancer* you were only a sex and a stomach. In the second book, *Black Spring,* you begin to have eyes, a heart, ears, hands. By and by, with each book, you will create a complete man, and then you will be able to write about women, but not until then. . . ."
>
> *The Diary of Anaïs Nin*

Some organs he never did pick up. Any man who could describe a pussy so well from the outside was not likely to succeed in imagining it from the inside.

> ". . . you will need her and you will call it love. You will always fall back on that excuse when you are sucking the life out of a woman."
>
> "That is where you are wrong," I interrupted with some heat. "It's me who gets sucked dry, not the woman."
>
> "That is your way of deceiving yourself. Because the woman can never give you what you want you make yourself out to be a martyr. A woman wants love and your're incapable of giving love. If you were a lower type of man you would be a monster; but you will convert

your frustration into something useful. Yes, by all means go on writing. Art can transform the hideous into the beautiful. Better a monstrous book than a monstrous life. Art is painful, tedious, softening. If you don't die in the attempt, your work may transform you into a sociable, charitable human being. . . ." (We looked at one another keenly.) "For you are not as intelligent as you think you are. That is your weakness, your overweening intellectual pride. If you rely exclusively on that you defeat yourself. You have all the feminine virtues, but you are ashamed to acknowledge them to yourself. You think because you are strong sexually that you are a virile man, but you are more of a woman than a man. Your sexual virility is only the sign of a greater power which you haven't begun to use. Don't try to prove yourself a man by exploiting your powers of seduction. Women are not fooled by that sort of strength and charm. Women, even when they are subjugated mentally, are always master of the situation. A woman may be enslaved, sexually, and yet dominate the man. You will have a harder time than other men because to dominate another doesn't interest you. You will always be trying to dominate yourself; the woman you love will only be an instrument for you to practice on. . . ."

Sexus

From **Tropic of Capricorn**

Ah yes, if I had known then that these birds existed—Cendrars, Vaché, Grosz, Ernst, Apollinaire—if I had known that then, if I had known that in their own way they were thinking exactly the same things as I was, I think I'd have blown up. Yes, I think I'd have gone off like a bomb. But I was ignorant. Ignorant of the fact that almost fifty years previously a crazy Jew in South America had given birth to such startlingly marvelous phrases as "doubt's duck with the vermouth lips" or "I have seen a fig eat an onager"—that about the same time a Frenchman, who was only a boy, was saying: "Find flowers that are chairs" . . . "my hunger is the black air's bits" . . . "his heart, amber and spunk." Maybe at the same time, or thereabouts, while Jarry was saying "in eating the sound of moths," and Apollinaire repeating after him "near a gentleman swallowing himself," and Breton murmuring softly "night's pedals move uninterruptedly," perhaps "in the air beautiful and black" which the lone Jew had found under the Southern Cross another man, also lonely and exiled and of Spanish origin, was preparing to put down on paper these memorable words: "I seek, all in all, to console myself for my exile, for my exile from eternity, for that *unearthing* (*destierro*) which I am fond of referring to as my unheavening. . . . At present, I think that the best way to write this novel is to tell how it should be written. It is the novel of the novel, the creation of creation. Or God of God, *Deus de Deo*." Had I known he was going to add this, this which follows, I would surely have gone off like a bomb. . . . "By being crazy is understood losing one's reason. Reason, but not the truth, for there are madmen who speak truths while others keep silent. . . ." Speaking of these things, speaking of the war and the war dead, I cannot refrain from mentioning that some twenty years later I ran across this in French by a Frenchman. O miracles of miracles! "*Il faut le dire, il y a des cadavres que je ne respecte qu'à moitié.*" Yes, yes, and again yes! O, let us do some rash thing—for the sheer pleasure of it! Let us do something live and magnificent, even if destructive! Said the mad cobbler: "All things are generated out of the grand mystery, and proceed out of one degree into another. Whatever goes forward in its degree, the same receives no abominate."

* * *

Not long ago I was walking the streets of New York. Dear old Broadway. It was night and the sky was an Oriental blue, as blue as the gold in the ceiling of the *Pagode*, rue de Babylone, when the machine starts clicking. I was passing exactly below the place where we first met. I stood there a moment looking up at the red lights in the windows. The music sounded as it always sounded—light, peppery, enchanting. I was alone and there were millions of people around me. It came over me, as I stood there, that I wasn't thinking of her any more; I was thinking of this book which I am writing, and the book had become more important to me than her, than all that had happened to us. Will this book be the truth, the whole truth, and nothing but the truth, so help me God? Plunging into the crowd again I wrestled with this question of "truth." For years I have been trying to tell this story and always the question of truth has weighed upon me like a nightmare. Time and again I have related to others the circumstances of our life, and I have always told the truth. But the truth can also be a lie. The truth is not enough. Truth is only the core of a totality which is inexhaustible.

I remember that the first time we were ever separated this idea of totality seized me by the hair. She pretended, when she left me, or maybe she believed it herself, that it was necessary for our welfare. I knew in my heart that she was trying to be free of me, but I was too cowardly to admit it to myself. But when I realized that she could do without me, even for a limited time, the truth which I had tried to shut out began to grow with alarming rapidity. It was more painful than anything I had ever experienced before, but it was also healing. When I was completely emptied, when the loneliness had reached such a point that it could not be sharpened any further, I suddenly felt that, to go on living, this intolerable truth had to be incorporated into something greater than the frame of personal misfortune. I felt that I had made an imperceptible switch into another realm, a realm of tougher, more elastic fiber, which the most horrible truth was powerless to destroy. I sat down to write her a letter telling her that I was so miserable over the thought of losing her that I had decided to begin a book about her, a book which would immortalize her. It would be a book, I said, such as no one had ever seen before. I rambled on ecstatically, and in the midst of it I suddenly broke off to ask myself why I was so happy.

Passing beneath the dance hall, thinking again of this book, I realized suddenly that our life had come to an end: I realized that the book I was planning was nothing more than a tomb in which to bury her—and the me which had belonged to her. That was some time ago, and ever since I have been trying to write it. Why is it so difficult? Why? Because the idea of an "end" is intolerable to me.

Truth lies in this knowledge of the end which is ruthless and remorseless. We can know the truth and accept it, or we can refuse the knowledge of it and neither die nor be born again. In this manner it is possible to live forever, a negative life as solid and complete, or as dispersed and fragmentary, as the atom. And if we pursue this road far enough, even this atomic eternity can yield to nothingness and the universe itself fall apart.

For years now I have been trying to tell this story; each time I have started out I have chosen a different route. I am like an explorer who, wishing to circumnavigate the globe, deems it unnecessary to carry even a compass. Moreover, from dreaming over it so long, the story itself has come to resemble a vast, fortified city, and I who dream it over and over, am outside the city, a wanderer, arriving before one gate after another too exhausted to enter. And as with the wanderer, this city in which my story is situated eludes me perpetually. Always in sight it nevertheless remains unattainable, a sort of ghostly citadel floating in the clouds. From the soaring, crenelated battlements flocks of huge white geese swoop down in steady, wedge-shaped formation. With the tips of their blue-white wings they brush the dreams that dazzle my vision. My feet move confusedly; no sooner do I gain a foothold than I am lost again. I wander aimlessly, trying to gain a solid, unshakable foothold whence I can command a view of my life, but behind me there lies only a welter of crisscrossed tracks, a groping, confused, encircling, the spasmodic gambit of the chicken whose head has just been lopped off.

Whenever I try to explain to myself the peculiar pattern

which my life has taken, when I reach back to the first cause, as it were, I think inevitably of the girl I first loved. It seems to me that everything dates from that aborted affair. A strange, masochistic affair it was, ridiculous and tragic at the same time. Perhaps I had the pleasure of kissing her two or three times, the sort of kiss one reserves for a goddess. Perhaps I saw her alone several times. Certainly she could never have dreamed that for over a year I walked past her home every night hoping to catch a glimpse of her at the window. Every night after dinner I would get up from the table and take the long route which led to her home. She was never at the window when I passed and I never had the courage to stand in front of the house and wait. Back and forth I passed, back and forth, but never hide nor hair of her. Why didn't I write her? Why didn't I call her up? Once I remember summoning enough pluck to invite her to the theater. I arrived at her home with a bunch of violets, the first and only time I ever bought flowers for a woman. As we were leaving the theater the violets dropped from her corsage, and in my confusion I stepped on them. I begged her to leave them there, but she insisted on gathering them up. I was thinking how awkward I was—it was only long afterwards that I recalled the smile she had given me as she stooped down to pick up the violets.

It was a complete fiasco. In the end I ran away. Actually I was running away from another woman, but the day before leaving town I decided to see her once again. It was midafternoon and she came out to talk to me in the street, in the little areaway which was fenced off. She was already engaged to another man; she pretended to be happy about it but I could see, blind as I was, that she wasn't as happy as she pretended to be. If I had only said the word I am sure she would have dropped the other fellow; perhaps she would even have gone away with me. I preferred to punish myself. I said good-by nonchalantly and I went down the street like a dead man. The next morning I was bound for the Coast, determined to start a new life.

The new life was also a fiasco. I ended up on a ranch in Chula Vista, the most miserable man that ever walked the earth. There was this girl I loved and there was the other woman, for whom I felt only a profound pity. I had been living with her for two years, this other woman, but it seemed like a lifetime. I was twenty-one and she admitted to be thirty-six. Every time I looked at her I said to myself—when I am thirty she will be forty-five, when I am forty she will be fifty-five, when I am fifty she will be sixty-five. She had fine wrinkles under the eyes, laughing wrinkles, but wrinkles just the same. When I kissed her they were magnified a dozen times. She laughed easily, but her eyes were sad, terribly sad. They were Armenian eyes. Her hair, which had been red once, was now a peroxide blonde. Otherwise she was adorable—a Venusian body, a Venusian soul, loyal, lovable, grateful, everything a woman should be, *except that she was fifteen years older*. The fifteen years' difference drove me crazy. When I went out with her I thought only—how will it be ten years hence? Or else, what age does she seem to have now? Do I look old enough for her? Once we got back to the house it was all right. Climbing the stairs I would run my finger up her crotch, which used to make her whinny like a horse. If her son, who was almost my age, were in bed we would close the doors and lock ourselves in the kitchen. She'd lie on the narrow kitchen table and I'd slough it into her. It was marvelous. And what made it more marvelous was that with each performance I would say to myself—*This is the last time . . . tomorrow I will beat it!* And then, since she was the janitress, I would go down to the cellar and roll the ash barrels out for her. In the morning, when the son had left for work, I would climb up to the room and air the bedding.

Both she and the son had T.B. . . . Sometimes there were no table bouts. Sometimes the hopelessness of it all got me by the throat and I would put on my things and go for a walk. Now and then I forgot to return. And when I did that I was more miserable than ever, because I knew that she would be waiting for me with those large sorrowful eyes. I'd go back to her like a man who had a sacred duty to perform, I'd lie down on the bed and let her caress me; I'd study the wrinkles under her eyes and the roots of her hair which were turning red. Lying there like that, I would often think about the other one, the one I loved, would wonder if she were lying down for it too, or . . . Those long walks I took three hundred and sixty-five days of the year!—I would go over them in my mind lying beside the other woman. How many times since have I relived these walks! The dreariest, bleakest, ugliest streets man ever created. In anguish I relive these walks, these streets, these first smashed hopes. The window is there, but no Melisande; the garden too is there, but no sheen of gold. Pass and repass, the window always vacant. The evening star hangs low; Tristan appears, then Fidelio, and then Oberon. The hydra-headed dog barks with all his mouths and though there are no swamps I hear the frogs croaking everywhere. Same houses, same car lines, same everything. She is hiding behind the curtain, she is waiting for me to pass, she is doing this or doing that . . . *but she is not there, never, never, never.* Is it a grand opera or is it a hurdy-gurdy playing? It is Amato bursting his golden lung; it is the *Rubaiyat,* it is Mount Everest, it is a moonless night, it is a sob at dawn, it is a boy making believe, it is Puss in the Boot, it is Mauna Loa, it is fox or astrakhan, it is of no stuff and no time, it is endless and it begins over and over, under the heart, in the back of the throat, in the soles of the feet, and why not just once, just once, for the love of Christ, just a shadow or a rustle of the curtain, or a breath on the windowpane, something once, if only a lie, something to stop the pain, to stop this walking up and down, up and down. . . . Walking homeward. Same houses, same lampposts, same everything. I walk past my own home, past the cemetery, past the gas tanks, past the car barns, past the reservoir, out into the open country. I sit beside the road with my head in my hands and sob. Poor bugger that I am, I can't contract my heart enough to burst the veins. I would like to suffocate with grief but instead I give birth to a rock.

Meanwhile the other one is waiting. I can see her again as she sat on the low stoop waiting for me, her eyes large and dolorous, her face pale and trembling with eagerness. *Pity* I always thought it was brought me back, but now as I walk toward her and see the look in her eyes I don't know any more what it is, only that we will go inside and lie together and she will get up half weeping, half laughing, and she will grow very silent and watch me, study me as I move about, and never ask me what is torturing me, never, never, because that is the one thing she fears, the one thing she dreads to know. *I don't love you!* Can't she hear me screaming it? *I don't love you!* Over and over I yell it, with lips tight, with hatred in my heart, with despair, with hopeless rage. But the words never leave my lips. I look at her and I am tongue-tied. I can't do it. . . . Time, time, endless time on our hands and nothing to fill it but lies.

* * *

She wants to go. To go. . . . Again her haunch, that slippery glide as when she came down from the dance hall and moved into me. Again her words . . . "suddenly for no reason at all, he bent down and lifted up my dress." She's slipping the fur around her neck; the little black bonnet sets her face off like a cameo. The round, full face, with Slavic cheekbones.

How could I dream this, never having seen it? How could I know that she would rise like this, close and full, the face full white and blooming like a magnolia? I tremble as the fullness of her thigh brushes me. She seems even a little taller than I, though she is not. It's the way she holds her chin. She doesn't notice where she's walking. She walks *over* things, on, on, with eyes wide open and staring into space. No past, no future. Even the present seems dubious. The self seems to have left her, and the body rushes forward, the neck full and taut, white as the face, full like the face. The talk goes on, in that low, throaty voice. No beginning, no end. I'm aware not of time nor the passing of time, but of timelessness. She's got the little womb in the throat hooked up to the big womb in the pelvis. The cab is at the curb and she is still chewing the cosmological chaff of the outer ego. I pick up the speaking tube and connect with the double uterus. Hello, hello, are you there? Let's go! Let's get on with it—cabs, boats, trains, naphtha launches; beaches, bedbugs, highways, byways, ruins; relics, old world, new world, pier, jetty; the high forceps, the swinging trapeze, the ditch, the delta, the alligators, the crocodiles, talk, talk, and more talk; then roads again and more dust in the eyes, more rainbows, more cloudbursts, more breakfast foods, more creams, more lotions. And when all the roads have been traversed and there is left only the dust of our frantic feet there will still remain the memory of your large full face so white, and the wide mouth with fresh lips parted, the teeth chalk white and each one perfect, and in this remembrance nothing can possibly change because this, like your teeth, is perfect. . . .

It is Sunday, the first Sunday of my new life, and I am wearing the dog collar you fastened around my neck. A new life stretches before me. It begins with the day of rest. I lie back on a broad green leaf and I watch the sun bursting in your womb. What a clabber and clatter it makes! All this expressly for me, what? If only you had a million suns in you! If only I could lie here forever enjoying the celestial fireworks!

I lie suspended over the surface of the moon. The world is in a womblike trance: the inner and the outer ego are in equilibrium. You promised me so much that if I never come out of this it will make no difference. It seems to me that it is exactly 25,960 years since I have been asleep in the black womb of sex. It seems to me that I slept perhaps 365 years too many. But at any rate I am now in the right house, among the sixes, and what lies behind me is well and what lies ahead is well. You come to me disguised as Venus, but you are Lilith, and I know it. My whole life is in the balance; I will enjoy the luxury of this for one day. Tomorrow I shall tip the scales. Tomorrow the equilibrium will be finished; if I ever find it again it will be in the blood and not in the stars. It is well that you promise me so much. I need to be promised nearly everything, for I have lived in the shadow of the sun too long. I want light and chastity—and a solar fire in the guts. I want to be deceived and disillusioned so that I may complete the upper triangle and not be continually flying off the planet into space. I believe everything you tell me, but I know also that it will all turn out differently. I take you as a star and a trap, as a stone to tip the scales, as a judge that is blindfolded, as a hole to fall into, as a path to walk, as a cross and an arrow. Up to the present I traveled the opposite way of the sun; henceforth I travel two ways, as sun and as moon. Henceforth I take on two sexes, two hemispheres, two skies, two sets of everything. Henceforth I shall be double-jointed and double-sexed. Everything that happens will happen twice. I shall be as a visitor to this earth, partaking of its blessings and carrying off its gifts. I shall neither serve nor be served. I shall seek the end in myself.

I look out again at the sun—my first full gaze. It is

blood-red and men are walking about on the rooftops. Everything above the horizon is clear to me. It is like Easter Sunday. Death is behind me and birth too. I am going to live now among the life maladies. I am going to live the spiritual life of the pygmy, the secret life of the little man in the wilderness of the bush. Inner and outer have changed places. Equilibrium is no longer the goal—the scales must be destroyed. Let me hear you promise again all those sunny things you carry inside you. Let me try to believe for one day, while I rest in the open, that the sun brings good tidings. Let me rot in splendor while the sun bursts in your womb. I believe all your lies implicitly. I take you as the personification of evil, as the destroyer of the soul, as the maharanee of the night. Tack your womb up on my wall, so that I may remember you. We must get going. Tomorrow, tomorrow. . . .

From **Black Spring**

. . . No need to write about China. Write about *that!* About what's inside of you . . . the great vertiginous vertebration . . . the zoospores and the leucocytes . . . the wamroths and the holenlindens . . . every one's a poem. The jellyfish is a pocm too—thc finest kind of poem. You poke him here, you poke him there, he slithers and slathers, he's dithy and clabberous, he has a colon and intestines, he's vermiform and ubisquishous. And Mowgli in the garden whistling for the rent, he's a poem too, a poem with big ears, a wambly bretzular poem with logamundiddy of the goo-goo. He has round, auricular daedali, round robin-breasted ruches that open up like an open barouche. He wambles in the wambhorst whilst the whelkin winkles . . . he wabbles through the wendish wikes whirking his worstish wights. . . . Mowgli . . . owgli . . . whist and wurst. . . ."

"He's losing his mind," says Jill.

"Wrong again," says Jabber. "I've just found my mind, only it's a different sort of mind than you imagined. You think a poem must have covers around it. The moment you write a thing the poem ceases. The poem is the present which you can't define. You live it. Anything is a poem if it has time in it. You don't have to take a ferryboat or go to China to write a poem. The finest poem I ever lived was a kitchen sink. Did I ever tell you about it? There were two faucets, one called Froid and the other Chaud. Froid lived a life *in extenso*, by means of a rubber hose attached to his schnausel. Chaud was bright and modest. Chaud dripped all the time, as if he had the clap. On Tuesdays and Fridays he went to the Mosque where there was a clinic for venereal faucets. Tuesdays and Fridays Froid had to do all the work. He was a bugger for work. It was his whole world. Chaud on the other hand had to be petted and coaxed. You had to say "not so fast," or he'd scald the skin off you. Once in a while they worked in unison, Froid and Chaud, but that was seldom. Saturday nights, when I washed my feet at the sink, I'd get to thinking how perfect was the world over which these twain ruled. Never anything more than this iron sink with its two faucets. No beginnings and no ends. Chaud the alpha and Froid the omega. Perpetuity. The Gemini, ruling over life and death. Alpha-Chaud running out through all degrees of Fahrenheit and Reaumur, through magnetic filings and comets' tails, through the boiling cauldron of Mauna Loa into the dry light of the Tertiary moon; Omega-Froid running out through the Gulf Stream into the paludal bed of the Sargasso Sea, running through the marsupials and the foraminifera, through the mammal whales and the Polar fissures, running down through island universes, through dead cathodes, through dead bone and dry rot, through the follicles and tentacles of worlds unformed, worlds untouched, worlds unseen, worlds unborn and forever lost. Alpha-Chaud dripping, dripping; Omega-Froid working, working. Hand, feet, hair, face, dishes, vegetables, fish washed clean and away; despair, ennui, hatred, love, jealousy, crime. . . dripping, dripping. I, Jabberwhorl, and my wife Jill, and after us legions upon legions. . . all standing at the iron sink. Seeds falling down through the drain; young canteloupes, squash, caviar, macaroni, bile, spittle, phlegm, lettuce leaves, sardines' bones, Worcestershire sauce, stale beer, urine, bloodclots, Kruschen salts, oatmeal, chew tobacco, pollen, dust, grease, wool, cotton threads, match sticks, live worms, shredded wheat, scalded milk, castor oil. Seeds of waste falling away forever and forever coming back in pure draughts of a miraculous chemical substance which refuses to be named, classified, labeled, analyzed, or drawn and quartered. Coming back as Froid and Chaud perpetually, like a truth that can't be drowned. You can take it hot or cold, or you can take it tepid. You can wash your feet or gargle your throat; you can rinse the soap out of your eyes or drive the grit out of the lettuce leaves; you can bathe the new-born babe or swab the rigid limbs of the dead; you can soak bread for fricadellas or dilute your wine. First and last things. Elixir. I, Jabberwhorl, tasting the elixir of life and death. I, Jabberwhorl, of waste and H2O composed, of hot and cold and all the intermediate realms, of scum and rind, of finest, tiniest substance never lost, of great sutures and compact bone, of ice fissures and test tubes, of semen and ova fused, dissolved, dispersed, of rubber schnausel and brass spigot, of dead cathodes and squirming infusoria, of lettuce leaves and bottled sunlight . . . I, Jabberwhorl, sitting at the iron sink am perplexed and exalted, never less and never more than a poem, an iron stanza, a boiling follicle, a lost leucocyte. The iron sink where I spat out my heart, where I bathed my tender feet, where I held my first child, where I washed my sore gums, where I sang like a diamond-backed terrapin and I am singing now and will sing forever though the drains clog and the faucets rust, though time runs out and I be all there is of present, past and future. *Sing,* Froid, sing transitive! *Sing,* Chaud, sing intransitive! Sing Alpha and Omega! Sing Hallelujah! Sing out, O sink! Sing while the world sinks. . . ."

And singing loud and clear like a dead and stricken swan on the bed we laid him out.

* * *

A night of bitter cold. Walking along with head down a whore sidles up to me and putting her arm in mine leads me to a hotel with a blue enamel sign over the door. Upstairs in the room I take a good look at her. She is young and athletic, and best of all, she is ignorant. She doesn't know the name of a single king. She doesn't even speak her own language. Whatever I relate to her she licks up like hot fat. She lards herself with it. The whole process is one of getting warm, of putting on a coat of grease for the winter, as she explains to me in her simple way. When she has extracted all the grease from my marrow bones she pulls back the coverlet and with the most astounding sprightliness she commences her trapezoid flights. The room is like a humming bird's nest. Nude as a berry she rolls herself into a ball, her head tucked between her breasts, her arms pinned to her crotch. She looks like a green berry out of which a pea is about to burst.

Suddenly, in that silly American way, I hear her say: "Look, I can do *this*, but I can't do *that!*" Whereupon she does it. Does what? Why, she commences to flap the lips of her vagina, just like a hummingbird. She has a furry little head with frank doglike eyes. Like a picture of the devil when the Palatinate was in flower. The incongruity of it sledges me. I sit down under a trip-hammer: every time I glance at her face I see an iron slit and behind it a man in an iron mask winking at me. A terrifying drollery because he winks with a blind eye, a blind, teary eye that threatens to turn into a cataract.

If it weren't that her arms and legs were all entangled, if she weren't a slippery, coiling snake strangled by a mask, I could swear that it was my wife Alberta, or if not my wife Alberta then another wife, though I think it's Alberta. I thought I'd always know Alberta's crack, but twisted into a knot with a mask between her legs one crack is as good as another and over every sewer there's a grating, in every pod there's a pea, behind every slit there's a man with an iron mask.

Sitting in the chair by the iron bedstead, with my suspenders down and a trip-hammer pounding the dome of my skull, I begin to dream of the women I have known. Women who deliberately cracked their pelvis in order to have a doctor stick a rubber finger inside them and swab the crannies of their epiglottis. Women with such thin diaphragms that the scratch of a needle sounded like Niagara Falls in their fallen bladders. Women who could sit by the hour turning their womb inside out in order to prick it with a darning needle. Queer doglike women with furry heads and always an alarm clock or a jigsaw puzzle hidden in the wrong place; just at the wrong moment the alarm goes off; just when the sky is blazing with Roman candles and out of the wet sparks crabs and star fish, just then always and without fail a broken saw, a wire snapping, a nail through the finger, a corset rotting with perspiration. Queer dogfaced women in stiff collars, the lips drooping, the eyes twitching. Devil dancers from the Palatinate with fat behinds and the door always on a crack and a spittoon where the umbrella stand should be. Celluloid athletes who burst like ping-pong balls when they shoot through the gaslight. Strange women—and I'm always sitting in a chair beside an iron bedstead. Such skilful fingers they have that the hammer always falls in the dead center of my skull and cracks the glue of the joints. The brain pan is like a hamburger steak in a steaming window.

Passing through the lobby of the hotel I see a crowd gathered around the bar. I walk in and suddenly I hear a child howling with pain. The child is standing on a table in the midst of the crowd. It's a girl and she has a slit in the side of her head, just at the temple. The blood is bubbling from her temple. It just bubbles—it doesn't run down the side of her face. Every time the slit in her temple opens I see something stirring inside. It looks like a chick in there. I watch closely. This time I catch a good glimpse of it. It's a cuckoo! People are laughing. Meanwhile the child is howling with pain.

In the anteroom I hear the patients coughing and scraping their feet; I hear the pages of a magazine closing and the rumble of a milk wagon on the cobblestones outside. My wife is sitting on a white stool, the child's head is against my breast. The wound in her temple is throbbing, throbbing as if it were a pulse laid against my heart. The surgeon is dressed in white; he walks up and down, up and down, puffing at his cigarette. Now and then he stops at the window to see how the weather looks. Finally he washes his hands and puts on the rubber gloves. With the sterilized gloves on his hands he lights a flame under the instruments; then he looks at his watch absent-mindedly and fingers the bills lying on the desk. The child is groaning now; her whole body is twitching with pain. I've got her arms and legs pinned. I'm waiting for the instruments to boil.

At last the surgeon is ready. Seating himself on a little white stool he selects a long, delicate instrument with a red-hot point and without a word of warning he plunges it into the open wound. The child lets out such a bloodcurdling scream that my wife collapses on the floor. "Don't pay any attention to *her!*" says the cool, collected surgeon, shoving her body aside with his foot. "Hold tight now!" And dipping his cruelest instrument into a boiling antiseptic he plunges the blade into the temple and holds it there until the wound bursts into flames. Then, with the same diabolical swiftness, he suddenly withdraws the instrument to which there is attached, by an eyelet, a long white cord which changes gradually into red flannel and then into chewing gum and then into popcorn and finally into sawdust. As the last flake of sawdust spills out the wound closes up clean and solid, leaving not even the suggestion of a scar. The child looks up at me with a peaceful smile and, slipping off my lap, walks steadily to the corner of the room where she sits down to play.

"That was excellent!" says the surgeon. "Really quite excellent!"

"Oh, it was, eh?" I scream. And jumping up like a maniac I knock him off the stool and with my knees firmly planted in his chest I grab the nearest instrument and commence to gouge him with it. I work on him like a demon. I gouge out his eyes, I burst his eardrums, I slit his tongue, I break his windpipe, I flatten his nose. Ripping the clothes off him I burn his chest until it smokes, and while the flesh is still raw and quivering from the hot iron I roll back the outer layers and I pour nitric acid inside—until I hear the heart and lungs sizzling. Until the fumes almost keel me over.

The child meanwhile is clapping her hands with glee.

6. Grease

After ten years in Paris, Miller is almost fifty, and his career is about to go through another large bend. A few months before the Second World War will begin he decides to take a long vacation. He has not had a real one in twenty years, not since going to work as employment manager of the messenger department at Western Union. He has been writing and scuffling and performing heavy duty in the Land of Fuck, engaged in the constant if artistic borrowing of money, shelter, wine and food from friends. Looking back, it has been a tough twenty years, and he has finished one great book plus two fabulously rich books and he has working manuscripts in plenty, plus a few other publications.* He has been recognized by all the avant-garde outposts of the literary establishment and is already on his way to becoming his own confused half-legend. (To the Freshman Class which entered Harvard in September of 1939, he was notorious already as a great dirty writer different from everybody else alive. "Too much for me" was the comment of any good prep school boy on his way to a good eating club in Plympton Street.)

It was time for Miller to take a rest. Time to take that one

---

* They are *Aller Retour, New York; Max and the White Phagocytes; Scenario; Money and How It Got That Way*, and later the Hamlet correspondence with Michael Fraenkel. He has also an enormous manuscript on D. H. Lawrence which he can never finish.

long good breath which is permitted a few men and women as they cross the ridge-line of their life. He took off a year and went to Greece. Nothing prepares us for the change so well as the first few hundred words of The Colossus of Maroussi.

> I would never have gone to Greece had it not been for a girl named Betty Ryan who lived in the same house with me in Paris. One evening, over a glass of white wine, she began to talk of her experiences in roaming about the world. I always listened to her with great attention, not only because her experiences were strange but because when she talked about her wanderings she seemed to paint them: everything she described remained in my head like finished canvases by a master. It was a peculiar conversation that evening: we began by talking about China and the Chinese language which she had begun to study. Soon we were in North Africa, in the desert, among peoples I had never heard of before. And then suddenly she was all alone, walking beside a river, and the light was intense and I was following her as best I could in the blinding sun but she got lost and I found myself wandering about in a strange land listening to a language I had never heard before. She is not exactly a story teller, this girl, but she is an artist of some sort because nobody has ever given me the ambiance of a place so thoroughly as she did Greece. Long afterwards I discovered that it was near Olympia that she had gone astray and I with her, but at the time it was just Greece to me, a world of light such as I had never dreamed of and never hoped to see.
>
> *The Colossus of Maroussi*

He went to visit Lawrence Durrell in Corfu. He did not know it, but the months in Greece would soon become the best period of his life, and we are suddenly offered a full glimpse of the view on the other side of the mountain. Crossing the watershed, Miller ascends out of all the dark funky magic caverns in his Land of Fuck and comes into the Land of Light and we have a new author we are going to read on many an occasion for the rest of his life, the effulgent, the plangent, the lambent Henry Miller so full of light he can be a pain to all the dark places, so rich in his admiration of good humanity that one almost weeps to hear his hard-tooled cunts moan again.

There is no doubt. Greece performed a miracle. The curd of whatever love had been kept for decades in the rocky crevice of his heart turned to milk. He is the only writer in Christendom to prove that old piss may, on occasion, taste better than new milk. The Colossus of Maroussi is a lovely book, a charming book, and by reputation one of the best, perhaps the best, travel book ever written. Perhaps it is not. It swims in delight, it tintinnabulates in rhapsody, but sometimes it neglects to describe the very terrain which is furnishing this spiritual equivalent of the old personal hard-on. After awhile, it becomes a trifle suspicious as a book. It is too nice. The unhappy thought arises that there may have been some unconscious calculation in the working: the purest spirit of the Anglo-American literary world may even have been engaging in a subtle species of corruption.

The thought gives heart to a critic. It is onerous to write about a great artist whose personality is only deployed on the rare spectrum from ogre to saint. It is an intensity of personalities too incorruptible. A corrupt man can never comprehend a man without corruption. So it is life-enhancing to a critic to be able to suspect that once in his life Henry Miller had a self-serving idea.

His situation was as follows: The war had begun while he was in Greece. The American consul picked up his passport and forced him to return to America directly from Athens. If he had left New York ten years ago with ten dollars in his pocket (the sum of good will left among his Brooklyn and Manhattan friends after years of borrowing), a lonely man rejected by his wife and unknown in his talents, he was coming back now as a literary figure with his own variety of enormous cultural arrogance which he had to install next to his immense cultural timidity: how could there have been an hour in his life until now when he did not have to wonder if he was a great intellectual or essentially incompetent as a thinker? The same ambiguity could be applied to his qualifications as a novelist. Brilliant young men like Durrell might applaud him, eminences like Eliot could recognize the life-like verisimilitudes in his very lack of narrative construction, but Miller was on the inside working out.

For years a young writer (which is to say an unpublished writer whatever his age) must live with his lacks and his vices. If the talent is large enough, there comes a point where he turns some principle of literature inside-out. The weakness our author is trying to improve begins to be seen by critics as his strength. Hemingway as a young author must always have lived in the unspoken fear that he was not really a writer because he could not handle a complex sentence (particularly if it was long). Life in the twenties, however, was giving its intimations that society would soon move from an architectural class structure (with foundations, lower stories, upper stories and roof) to a more serial arrangement like ranch houses, superhighways, and unstressed narrative. (I climbed up over the hill and saw this girl and we made it under the trees for a while and then I turned her over to some friends of mine and we said so long.) That is unstressed narrative. Hemingway's short repetitive sentences and long unstressed serial sentences produced a note which would vibrate through that architectonic society so ready to deteriorate in its forms. So, too, did Faulkner's long sentences (which may once have made him despair of his ability to see anything straight and clear and fast) succeed in exciting critics precisely because they brought back to life a world of firm and sensuous vales being eaten out already by the entropy. That is not, of course, the full explanation for the success of Hemingway and Faulkner—nobody is going to argue there was no more to them than that. The point is rather that they may have passed through the disorienting experience of being applauded for what privately they saw as weaknesses. It hurts one's balance, hurts it in all those inflamed joints and sockets of the psyche where a suddenly successful artist tries to keep his vanity, arrogance, and sense of his own limitations in proportion. Passing more slowly through this transposition, Faulkner may have been gradually encouraged to become more gnomic, but at least he was not plucked out of his roots. Hemingway and Miller were given more of a turn. Indeed their literary self-esteem rose at the rate of a man ascending in a high-speed elevator; their insecurity could be gauged by the intensity of their private conviction that there was nothing really, if you looked at it, to keep the cable from snapping.

This sense of wild advancement and whole lack of vehicle security may never have left Hemingway—there is reason to believe as we shall see that Miller came to a grim truce with all his divergent realities. He learned to live with upturned roots three times uprooted. Miller leaves us happy finally when we think of him. But he is another man today than the figure who reluctantly came back to America. That notorious underground celebrity, age fifty, heard a small chorus on his return which told him that he was the greatest American writer alive and ought to be recognized as such. And if one were a literary handicapper, it could have seemed for a little while as if not too much was in his way. Thomas Wolfe, the nearest we had to a major popular American writer, was dead hardly a year, Dos Passos, author of the closest approach to the possibility of the great American novel, was about to enter his years of decline—it was known already in leftist literary circles that he was moving to the right, and powerful critical attitudes were getting ready to depose him. Hemingway with For Whom the Bell Tolls was king—all the more reason to assume he could be forced to abdicate in a year (people with real taste were beginning to wonder if For Whom the Bell Tolls was really that good) and Faulkner, unaccountably, was not being taken at full value. Not yet. Besides Faulkner was parochial when not provincial. So was Steinbeck; so was Farrell. If one were looking for long shots, Miller was the best dark horse around, and friends and new friends and literary acquaintances must have tried to tell him so. "If only you were publishable, there'd be no stopping you," he must have heard a thousand times.

The thought had to enter some part of his head that right there in 1940, back in America, the title belonged to him. Apart from talent and his private ambivalence about how huge or overblown his talent might be, it was possible he had suffered more than any of the other writers. He had certainly taken more chances. There was no reason to believe he had not had a range of experience more comprehensive than any of his competitors. The handicapper could have said to him, "Write a straight novel we can publish. Make it full of characters and put in every corner of society. Make it as good as U.S.A. and you'll go three times as far as Dos Passos."

Miller, however, would do it in his own fashion. Comparable to no one else in any other way, he would not be too quickly predictable here either. It is possible he was as secretly competitive as Hemingway, but he was not about to compete. Not for Miller to get into a contest if he was the only English-speaking author in the world with something divine to say. In the circumstances, he may have made his compromise, and he wrote a book which could be published in America. The irony is that it was never a book to put him into any literary races. You would not get the literary championship of America in 1940 by writing a book about Greece, not unless there were hordes of Americans in Greece rather than one euphoric Henry Miller. The Colossus of Maroussi became his private paean to respectability, and it is, as described, a lovely book and the first of Miller's works which could be given to the eighty-year-old mother of the minister of the First Episcopalian Church in you-may-name-the-suburb-of-Philadelphia and she will love it and love it so much she could even take a trip to Greece in her eighty-first year: at his most benign Miller still has the power to change people's lives. Nonetheless, it is a different Henry Miller who writes this book. As if to show to his detractors that he can do it, he is altogether separated from the Land of Fuck. He is also unbelievably circumspect about his friends. On page 25 for instance: "Here a terrible wrangle ensued between Durrell and his wife. I felt quite helpless and could only pity them both from the depths of my heart. It was really a private quarrel. . . ." Can this be Miller, our own Henry who once would rush to tell how Carl, his closest friend, could get on his knees to inspect a lady's open vagina, separate the lips and then report back that it had made the unforgettable sound of "squish-squish"? Yes, Miller is writing like a respectable this year.

We cannot discount the real possibility: Miller wrote the book (1) out of his love for Greece and (2) to tuck a little grease up the hole of the American establishment.

If Miller is not being done an injustice, and there is any purchase to the possibility that just once he put on his good literary suit and paid a call on the literary academy, then we can shake our head at his lack of profound judgment when it comes to playing literary steeplechase. No book like The Colossus of Maroussi was going to get him forgiven in all the right places (which is to say all the worst of the literary places) for Tropic of Cancer.

If he thought to take America by storm with an absolutely charming book, he simply never understood the virulence of the literary establishment as it was then constituted. He did not comprehend that the literary establishment had not raised verse, respectability and mediocrity as their approved canon—recall us to William Lyon Phelps, J. Donald Adams, and the panache of Clifton Fadiman—in order to hand the keys over to a writer of dirty books. Return us in imagination to the kind of people who did reviewing then, spavined AP wire-service types afraid the copy-desk editor would carve his initials in their sphincter if they did not protect the American family from writers like Miller. Henry knew that, knew it profoundly in the best part of him—it was what had driven him underground in the first place. But how could he not be feverish on his return? The Colossus of Maroussi is the book of a man in an ecstatic fever; if he had once accomplished the impossible by proving victorious over his ten years in France why did he not have the right to assume some kind of equal decade in America? He lost sight of that law which kept the best of American writers inside the walls of non-obscene language, even Hemingway with "muck" for "fuck" all through For Whom the Bell Tolls ("Señor Jordan, the mucking tanks are coming to the obscenity-bridge where we must muck the tanks or by them be mucked.") Hemingway stayed clear of just such perils in muck but not by much, and it may have mucked up his machismo. He knew the enemy was implacable. If the American literary establishment had already given ground to realism and naturalism, to the proletarian novel and left-wing sentiments, if it offered space to the avant-garde and even some room for the restrained explication of promiscuous behavior, it did not put up in any way with fuck, cock and cunt. Piss and shit could not leave a calling card more often than a new dog on a white rug. A dirty book was simply forbidden—that was the final line of defense. All of society might be swept up into the pent oncoming sexual chaos if the dirty book became acceptable. It was even wise to build fences against that possibility, and take care not to let anyone who wrote a dirty book be rewarded later for a clean book. That, after all, would be equal to Newport giving reception to an ex-madame merely because she had married a rich man.

So Miller ran into the huge American indifference machine. The Colossus of Maroussi was beautiful and he was an underground legend, but somehow no established publisher was interested in a book about Greece. Finally put out by The Colt Press in San Francisco, it would eventually receive its small intense critical applause, its small steady sale—he was naturally penniless again—and its total lack of impact on the American scene. Miller was beached in America, lost in the huge disruptions of the approaching American entrance into war, and utterly failed in his secret project (if it existed) of taking back by storm the country which had rejected him a decade ago. He had had his right to issue a book with calculation—maybe no major American author had ever paid greater dues for his individuality—he had a simple right to do the publishable book which would work for him in America, but there is nonetheless a subtle fall from literary grace in The Colossus of Maroussi; whatever adulation he received for it would probably contribute to a few more dubious literary habits.

Ready to begin The Rosy Crucifixion he may have been more in need of a great editor than at any other hour in his life. Given his pride, his crazy speed, his fear of his own readiness to be over-influenced, and his curious unpublishability, now confirmed by the trip to Colt Press—with the exception of Big Sur and The Oranges of Hieronymus Bosch there is not a single one of the books he will be able to publish in America over the next two decades which will not, by the measure of his major work, be other than minor. They are also singularly unobscene. It is a loss. Obscenity is not a pose with him, but the natural blood of his mind and the steel in his tools of analysis. He can write just so bad as a twit, a fart or an old hat when he does not swear. His wisdom breathes in the sap of filthy speech because, as he remarks himself, his deepest and truest education was on the streets. Now, he is back on American streets, and soon will be on American roads, and before too many years will arrive like many another pioneer before him to the shores of the Pacific where he will eventually come to rest. Odds are he is passing through the last major shift of his life. If like every other American author, he loved America more than he would ever begin to allow, the love affair must have had some final disappointment in the limited reception given The Colossus of Maroussi. He will spend the rest of his life fulminating at the monstrosities of a country which had not the wit-at-large to accept him as one of its foremost men. In retrospect, considering how often he was right, the monstrosities were there. Perhaps his voice is harsh, hysterical and strident so much of the time because he was the first to take a walk through the halls of non-responsiveness, those all-pervasive corporate surfaces which would end by linking plastic hands across every road, building and instrument in America.

From

The Colossus of Maroussi

Here one evening on his way back to Amaroussion I met Katsimbalis. It was definitely a meeting. As far as encounters with men go I have only known two others to compare with it in my whole life—when I met Blaise Cendrars and when I met Lawrence Durrell. I didn't have very much to say that first evening; I listened spellbound, enchanted by every phrase he let drop. I saw that he was made for the monologue, like Cendrars; like Moricand the astrologer. I like the monologue even more than the duet, when it is good. It's like watching a man write a book expressly for you: he writes it, reads it aloud, acts it, revises it, savours it, enjoys it, enjoys your enjoyment of it, and then tears it up and throws it to the winds. It's a sublime performance, because while he's going through with it you are God for him—unless you happen to be an insensitive and impatient dolt. But in that case the kind of monologue I refer to never happens.

He was a curious mixture of things to me on that first occasion; he had the general physique of a bull, the tenacity of a vulture, the agility of a leopard, the tenderness of a lamb, and the coyness of a dove. He had a curious overgrown head which fascinated me and which, for some reason, I took to be singularly Athenian. His hands were rather small for his body, and overly delicate. He was a vital, powerful man, capable of brutal gestures and rough words, yet somehow conveying a sense of warmth which was soft and feminine. There was also a great element of the tragic in him which his adroit mimicry only enhanced. He was extremely sympathetic and at the same time ruthless as a boor. He seemed to be talking about himself all the time, but never egotistically. He talked about himself because he himself was the most interesting person he knew. I liked that quality very much—I have a little of it myself.

We met a few days later to have dinner together— he, his wife Aspasia and the Durrells. After dinner we were to meet some friends of his. From the time he met us he was bubbling over. He was always that way, even on bad days when he complained of headache or dizziness or any of the hundred and one ailments which pestered him. He was taking us to a *taverna* in Piraeus, he said, because he wanted us to enjoy Greek cooking in the Greek way. It was one of his favorite hang-outs in the old days. "I made a mistake to get married," he said—his wife listening and smiling indulgently—"I wasn't cut out for marriage—it's ruining me. I can't sleep, I can't smoke, I can't drink any more. . . . I'm finished." He was always talking about himself as of some one who was done for: it was a little motif which he wove into the monologue by way of warming up to a subject. Things which happened only yesterday fell into this same nostalgic done-for past. Sometimes, when he talked this way, he gave me the impression of being an enormous tortoise which had slipped out of its shell, a creature which was spending itself in a desperate struggle to get back into the shell which it had outgrown. In this struggle he always made himself look grotesque and ridiculous—he did it deliberately. He would laugh at himself, in the tragic way of the buffoon. We would all laugh, his wife too. No matter how sad or morbid or pathetic the story might be he would have us laughing continuously. He saw the humorous aspect of everything, which is the real test of the tragic sense.

The food . . . food was something he was passionate about. He had been enjoying good food since childhood and I guess he will go on enjoying it until he dies. His father had been a great gourmet and Katsimbalis, though perhaps lacking some of his father's sensual refinements and accomplishments, was following the family tradition. Between great carnivorous gulps of food he would pound his chest like a gorilla before washing it down with a hogshead of *rezina.* He had drunk a lot of *rezina* in his time: he said it was good for one, good for the kidneys, good for the liver, good for the lungs, good for the bowels and for the mind, good for everything. Everything he took into his system was good, whether it was poison or ambrosia. He didn't believe in moderation nor good sense nor anything that was inhibitory. He believed in going the whole hog and then taking your punishment. There were a lot of things he couldn't do any more—the war had bunged him up a bit. But despite the bad arm, the dislocated knee, the damaged eye, the disorganized liver, the rheumatic twinges, the arthritic disturbances, the migraine, the dizziness and God knows what, what was left of the catastrophe was alive and flourishing like a smoking dung-heap. He could galvanize the dead with his talk. It was a sort of devouring process: when he described a place he ate into it, like a goat attacking a carpet. If he described a person he ate him alive from head to toe. If it were an event he would devour every detail, like an army of white ants descending upon a forest. He was everywhere at once, in his talk. He attacked from above and below, from the front, rear and flanks. If he couldn't dispose of a thing at once, for lack of a phrase or an image, he would spike it temporarily and move on, coming back to it later and devouring it piecemeal. Or like a juggler, he would toss it in the air and, just when you thought he had forgotten it, that it would fall and break, he would deftly put an arm behind his back and catch it in his palm without even turning his eye. It wasn't just talk he handed out, but *language*—food and beast language. He always talked against a landscape, like the protagonist of a lost world. The Attic landscape was best of all for his purpose: it contains the necessary ingredients for the dramatic monologue. One has only to see the open air theatres buried in the hillsides to understand the importance of this setting. Even if his talk carried him to Paris, for example, to a place like the Faubourg Montmartre, he spiced and flavored it with his Attic ingredients, with thyme, sage, tufa, asphodel, honey, red clay, blue roofs, acanthus trimmings, violet light, hot rocks, dry winds, dust, *rezina*, arthritis and the electrical crackle that plays over the low hills like a swift serpent with a broken spine. He was a strange contradiction, even in his talk. With his snake-like tongue which struck like lightning, with fingers moving nervously, as though wandering over an imaginary spinet, with pounding, brutal gestures which somehow never smashed anything but simply raised a din, with all the boom of surf and the roar and sizzle and razzle-dazzle, if you suddenly observed him closely you got the impression that he was sitting there immobile, that only the round falcon's eye was alert, that he was a bird which had been hypnotized, or had hypnotized itself, and that his claws were fastened to the wrist of an invisible giant, a giant like the earth. All this flurry and din, all these kaleidoscopic prestidigitations of his, was only a sort of wizardry which he employed to conceal the fact that he was a prisoner—that was the impression he gave me when I studied him, when I could break the spell for a moment and observe him attentively. But to break the spell required a power and a magic almost equal to his own; it made one feel foolish and impotent, as one always does when one succeeds in destroying the power of illusion. Magic is never destroyed—the most we can do is to cut ourselves off, amputate the mysterious antennae which serve to connect us with forces beyond our power of understanding. Many a time, as Katsimbalis talked, I caught that look on the face of a listener which told me that the invisible wires had been connected, that something was being communicated which was over and above language, over and above personality, something magical which we recognize in dream and which makes the face of the sleeper relax and expand with a bloom such as we rarely see in waking life. Often when meditating on this quality of his I thought of his frequent allusions to the incomparable honey which is stored by the bees on the slopes of his beloved Hymettos. Over and over he would try to explain the reasons why this honey from Mount Hymettos was unique. Nobody can explain it satisfactorily. Nobody can explain anything which is unique. One can describe, worship and adore. And that is all I can do with Katsimbalis' talk.

It was later, after I had returned to Corfu and had had a good taste of solitude, that I appreciated the Katsimbalistic monologue even more. Lying nude in the sun on a ledge of rock by the sea I would often close my eyes and try to reweave the pattern of his talks. It was then that I made the discovery that his talk created reverberations, that the echo took a long time to reach one's ears. I began to compare it with French talk in which I had been enveloped for so long. The latter seemed more like the play of light on an alabaster vase, something reflective, nimble, dancing, liquid, evanescent, whereas the other, the Katsimbalistic language, was opaque, cloudy, pregnant with resonances which could only be understood long afterwards when the reverberations announced the collision with thoughts, people, objects located in distant parts of the earth. The Frenchman puts walls about his talk, as he does about his garden: he puts limits about everything in order to feel at home. At bottom he lacks confidence in his fellow-man; he is skeptical because he doesn't believe in the innate goodness of human beings. He has become a realist because it is safe and practical. The Greek, on the other hand, is an adventurer: he is reckless and adaptable, he makes friends easily. The walls which you see in Greece, when they are not of Turkish or Venetian origin, go back to Cyclopean age. Of my own experience I would say that there is no more direct, approachable, easy man to deal with than the Greek. He becomes a friend immediately: he goes out to you. With the Frenchman friendship is a long and laborious process: it may take a lifetime to make a friend of him. He is best in acquaintanceship where there is little to risk and where there are no aftermaths. The very word *ami* contains almost nothing of the flavor of friend, as we feel it in English. *C'est mon ami* can not be translated by "this is my friend." There is no counterpart to this English phrase in the French language. It is a gap which has never been filled, like the word "home." These things affect conversation. One can converse all right, but it is difficult to have a heart to heart talk. All France, it has often been said, is a garden, and if you love France, as I do, it can be a very beautiful garden. For myself I found it healing and soothing to the spirit; I recovered from the shocks and bruises which I had received in my own country. But there comes a day, when you are well again and strong, when this atmosphere ceases to be nourishing. You long to break out and test your powers. Then the French spirit seems inadequate. You long to make friends, to create enemies, to look beyond walls and cultivated patches of earth. You want to cease thinking in terms of life insurance, sick benefits, old age pensions and so on.

* * *

I'd rather talk about something more interesting—about Katsimbalis, for instance, about the visit to his home in

Amaroussion one day towards twilight. Another marvelous day, another red letter day in my life! We had been asked to come early in order to watch the sunset. Stephanides had made a translation of some Greek poems—we were going to hear them in English. When we arrived Katsimbalis hadn't quite finished his nap. He was rather ashamed of being caught napping because he was always bragging about how little sleep he required. He came downstairs looking a bit foggy and pasty. He was talking as if to himself, making little futile gestures with his hands as if to get the damned spinet working. He was mumbling something about a word which he had remembered in his dream a few moments ago. He was always rummaging about in his brain for adequate English words and phrases to express some remarkable Greek image which he had just stumbled on in a book. Anyway, as I say, we had roused him from a sound sleep and he was moving about in a drugged way, muttering and gesturing like a man trying to shake off the cobwebs which still enveloped him. His talk began on the fringe of this dream which he had not wholly shaken clear of. To begin you begin anywhere, and since he had just been dreaming he talked dream. The dream was unimportant, forgotten in a moment, but the remembrance of the dream led him back to the word which had been bothering him, which he had been tracking down for days, so he said, and which was now becoming clearer as he himself became clearer, as the cobwebs fell away. The word, whatever it was, led to language and language led to honey and honey was good for one, as were other things, *rezina* for example, especially *rezina*, good for the lungs, good for the liver, good for anything that ailed you, especially too much of it, which one should not do, not take too much of it, but which he did anyway regardless of the doctor's orders, particularly if it were a good *rezina* such as the one we had the other night at the *taverna* in Piraeus. The young lamb was good too, had we noticed? He made the gesture of licking his fingers, wiped his mouth with the back of his hand, sniffed the air as though to breathe again the aromatic smoke from the oven. He paused a moment and looked about him, as if searching for something with which to wet his tongue before going into the monologue full tilt. Nobody said anything. Nobody dared to interrupt now just as he was getting into his stride. The poems were lying on the table; Seferiades was expected any moment and the captain with him. I could feel that he was growing a bit frantic inwardly, that he was making a rapid calculation to see if there were time enough to get it off his chest before his friends arrived. He was fluttering a bit, like a bird whose wing is caught. He kept on mumbling and muttering, just to keep the engine going until he had decided on his direction. And then somehow, without being aware of the transition, we were standing on the aerial verandah overlooking the low hills, on one of which there was a lone windmill, and Katsimbalis was in full flight, a spread eagle performance about the clear atmosphere and the blue-violet hues that descend with the twilight, about the ascending and descending varieties of monotony, about individualistic herbs and trees, about exotic fruits and inland voyages, about thyme and honey and the sap of the arbutus which makes one drunk, about islanders and highlanders, about the men of the Peloponnesus, about the crazy Russian woman who got moonstruck one night and threw off her clothes, how she danced about in the moonlight without a stitch on while her lover ran to get a strait-jacket. As he talked I was taking in for the first time with my own eyes the true splendor of the Attic landscape, observing with a growing exhilaration that here and there over the bare brown sward, amidst anomalous and eccentric growths, men and women, single solitary figures, were strolling about in the clear fading light, and for some reason they appeared to me as being very Greek, walking as no other people walk, making clear-cut patterns in their ethereal meandering, patterns such as I had seen earlier in the day on the vases in the museum. There are so many ways of walking about and the best, in my opinion, is the Greek way, because it is aimless, anarchic, thoroughly and discordantly human. And this walking about on the brown sward amidst the eccentric, inelegant trees, the thick foliage flying like hair stiff-brushed in the well of the distant mountains, blended strangely with the Katsimbalistic monologue which I heard, digested and silently communicated to the Asiatic loungers below who were fading softly now in the dimming light. . . . On the high verandah in Amaroussion, just as the light from the other worlds began to shed its brilliance, I caught the old and the new Greece in their soft translucence and thus they remain in my memory. I realized at that moment that there is no old or new, only Greece, a world conceived and created in perpetuity. The man who was talking had ceased to be of human size or proportions but had become a Colossus whose silhouette swooned backwards and forwards with the deep droning rhythm of his drug-laden phrases. He went on and on and on, unhurried, unruffled, inexhaustible, inextinguishable, a voice that had taken form and shape and substance, a figure that had outgrown its human frame, a silhouette whose reverberations rumbled in the depths of the distant mountain sides.

* * *

If there is one dream which I like above all others it is that of sailing on land. Coming into Poros gives the illusion of the deep dream. Suddenly the land converges on all sides and the boat is squeezed into a narrow strait from which there seems to be no egress. The men and women of Poros are hanging out of the windows just above your head. You pull in right under their friendly nostrils, as though for a shave and hair cut en route. The loungers on the quay are walking with the same speed as the boat; they can walk faster than the boat if they choose to quicken their pace. The island revolves in cubistic planes, one of walls and windows, one of rocks and goats, one of stiff-blown trees and shrubs, and so on. Yonder, where the mainland curves like a whip, lie the wild lemon groves and there in the Spring young and old go mad from the fragrance of sap and blossom. You enter the harbor of Poros swaying and swirling, a gentle idiot tossed about amidst masts and nets in a world which only the painter knows and which he has made live again because like you, when he first saw this world, he was drunk and happy and care-free. To sail slowly through the streets of Poros is to recapture the joy of passing through the neck of the womb. It is a joy too deep almost to be remembered. It is a kind of numb idiot's delight which produces legends such as that of the birth of an island out of a foundering ship. The ship, the passage, the revolving walls, the gentle undulating tremor under the belly of the boat, the dazzling light, the green snake-like curve of the shore, the beards hanging down over your scalp from the inhabitants suspended above you, all these and the palpitant breath of friendship, sympathy, guidance, envelop and entrance you until you are blown out like a star fulfilled and your heart with its molten smithereens scattered far and wide.

* * *

It was a Sunday morning when Katsimbalis and I left Nauplia for Mycenae. It was hardly eight o'clock when we arrived at the little station bearing this legendary name. Passing through Argos the magic of this world suddenly penetrated my bowels. Things long forgotten came back with frightening clarity. I was not sure whether I was recalling things I had read as a child or whether I was tapping the universal memory of the race. The fact that these places still existed, still bore their ancient names, seemed incredible. It was like a resurrection and the day we had chosen for the journey was more like Easter than Thanksgiving Day. From the station to the ruins was a walk of several kilometers. As at Epidaurus there was a sublime stillness all about. We walked leisurely towards the encircling hills which rise up from the gleaming Argive plain. A few birds were wheeling overhead in the unbroken vault of blue. Suddenly we came upon a little boy crying as if his heart would break. He was standing in the field beside the road. His weeping had absolutely no relation to the hushed and tranquil world in which he stood; it was as if he had been set down in the green field by a spirit from the outside world. What could a little boy be crying about at such an hour in such a wondrous world? Katsimbalis went over and spoke to him. He was crying because his sister had stolen his money. How much money? Three drachmas. Money, money. . . . Even here there was such a thing as money. The word money never sounded so preposterous to me before. How could one think such a word in this world of terror and beauty and magic? If he had lost a donkey or a parrot I could have understood. But three drachmas—I just couldn't visualize the meaning of three drachmas. I couldn't believe he was weeping. It was an hallucination. Let him stand there and weep—the spirit would come and fetch him again; he didn't belong, he was an anomaly.

After you pass the little hostelry run by Agamemnon and his wife, which faces a field of Irish green, you become immediately aware that the earth is sown with the bodies and relics of legendary figures. Even before Katsimbalis opened his mouth I knew they were lying all about us—the earth tells you so. The approach to the place of horror is fantastically inviting. There are smooth green mounds, hummocks, hillocks, tumuli everywhere, and beneath them, not very deep either, lie the warriors, the heroes, the fabulous innovators who without machinery erected the most formidable fortifications. The sleep of the dead is so deep that the earth and all who walk it dream; even the huge carrion birds who wheel above seem drugged and hypnotized. As one rises slowly with the rising terrain the blood thickens, the heart slows down, the mind comes to rest obsessively on the shuddering image of an endless chain of assassinations. There are two distinct worlds impinging on one another—the heroic world of daylight and the claustral world of dagger and poison. Mycenae, like Epidaurus, swims in light. But Epidaurus is all open, exposed, irrevocably devoted to the spirit. Mycenae folds in upon itself, like a fresh-cut navel, dragging its glory down into the bowels of the earth where the bats and the lizards feed upon it gloatingly. Epidaurus is a bowl from which to drink the pure spirit: the blue of the sky is in it and the stars and the winged creatures who fly between, scattering song and melody. Mycenae, after one turns the last bend, suddenly folds up into a menacing crouch, grim, defiant, impenetrable. Mycenae is closed in, huddled up, writhing with muscular contortions like a wrestler. Even the light, which falls on it with merciless clarity, gets sucked in, shunted off, grayed, beribboned. There were never two worlds so closely juxtaposed and yet so antagonistic. It is Greenwich here with respect to everything that concerns the soul of man. Move a hair's breadth either way and you are in a totally different world. This is the great shining bulge of horror, the high slope whence man, having attained his zenith, slipped back and fell into the bottomless pit.

It was still early morning when we slipped through the lion's gate. No sign of a guardian about. Not a soul in sight.

The sun is steadily rising and everything is clearly exposed to view. And yet we proceed timidly, cautiously, fearing we know not what. Here and there are open pits looking ominously smooth and slimy. We walk between the huge slabs of stone that form the circular enclosure. My book knowledge is nil. I can look on this mass of rubble with the eyes of a savage. I am amazed at the diminutive proportions of the palace chambers, of the dwelling places up above. What colossal walls to protect a mere handful of people! Was each and every inhabitant a giant? What dread darkness fell upon them in their evil days to make them burrow into the earth, to hide their treasures from the light, to murder incestuously in the deep bowels of the earth? We of the New World, with millions of acres lying waste and millions unfed, unwashed, unsheltered, we who dig into the earth, who work, eat, sleep, love, walk, ride, fight, buy, sell and murder there below ground, are we going the same way? I am a native of New York, the grandest and the emptiest city in the world; I am standing now at Mycenae, trying to understand what happened here over a period of centuries. I feel like a cockroach crawling about amidst dismantled splendors. It is hard to believe that somewhere back in the leaves and branches of the great genealogical tree of life my progenitors knew this spot, asked the same questions, fell back senseless into the void, were swallowed up and left no trace of thought save these ruins, the scattered relics in museums, a sword, an axle, a helmet, a death mask of beaten gold, a bee-hive tomb, an heraldic lion carved in stone, an exquisite drinking vase. I stand at the summit of the walled citadel and in the early morning I feel the approach of the cold breath from the shaggy gray mountain towering above us. Below, from the great Argive plain the mist is rising. It might be Pueblo, Colorado, so dislocated is it from time and boundary. Down there in that steaming plain where the automotrice crawls like a caterpillar, is it not possible there once stood wigwams? Can I be sure there never were any Indians here? Everything connected with Argos, shimmering now in the distance as in the romantic illustrations for text-books, smacks of the American Indian. I must be crazy to think thus, but I am honest enough to admit the thought. Argos gleams resplendent, a point of light shooting arrows of gold into the blue. Argos belongs to myth and fable: her heroes never took on flesh. But Mycenae, like Tiryns, is peopled with the ghosts of antediluvial men, Cyclopean monsters washed up from the sunken ridges of Atlantis. Mycenae was first heavy-footed, slow, sluggish, ponderous, though embodied in dinosaurian frames, war reared in anthropophagous luxury, reptilian, ataraxic, stunning and stunned. Mycenae swung full circle, from limbo to limbo. The monsters devoured one another, like crocodiles. The rhinoceros man gored the hippopotamic man. The walls fell on them, crushed them, flattened them into the primeval ooze. A brief night. Lurid lightning flashes, thunder cannonading between the fierce shoulders of the hills. The eagles fly out, the plain is scavengered, the grass shoots forth. (This is a Brooklyn lad talking. Not a word of truth in it, until the gods bring forth the evidence.) The eagles, the hawks, the snot-knobbed vultures, gray with greed like the parched and barren mountain-sides. The air is alive with winged scavengers. Silence—century upon century of silence, during which the earth puts on a coat of soft green. A mysterious race out of nowhere swoops down upon the country of Argolis. Mysterious only because men have forgotten the sight of the gods. The gods are returning, in full panoply, man-like, making use of the horse, the buckler, the javelin, carving precious jewels, smelting ores, blowing fresh vivid images of war and love on bright dagger blades. The gods stride forth over the sun-lit swards, full-statured, fearless, the gaze frighteningly candid and open. A world of light is born. Man looks at man with new eyes. He is awed, smitten by his own gleaming image reflected everywhere. It goes on thus, century upon century swallowed like cough-drops, a poem, an heraldic poem, as my friend Durrell would say. While the magic is on the lesser men, the initiates, the Druids of the Peloponnesus, prepare the tombs of the gods, hide them away in the soft flanks of the hillocks and hummocks. The gods will depart one day, as mysteriously as they came, leaving behind the human-like shell which deceives the unbelieving, the poor in spirit, the timid souls who have turned the earth into a furnace and a factory.

We have just come up from the slippery staircase, Katsimbalis and I. We have not descended it, only peered down with lighted matches. The heavy roof is buckling with the weight of time. To breathe too heavily is enough to pull the world down over our ears. Katsimbalis was for crawling down on all fours, on his belly if needs be. He has been in many a tight spot before; he has played the mole on the Balkan front, has wormed his way through mud and blood, has danced like a madman from fear and frenzy, killed all in sight including his own men, has been blown skyward clinging to a tree, has had his brain concussed, his rear blunderbussed, his arms hanging in shreds, his face blackened with powder, his bones and sinews wrenched and unsocketed. He is telling me it all over again as we stand midway to earth and sky, the lintel sagging more and more, the matches giving out. "We don't want to miss this," he pleads. But I refuse to go back down into that slimy well of horrors. Not if there were a pot of gold to be filched would I make the descent. I want to see the sky, the big birds, the short grass, the waves of blinding light, the swamp mist rising over the plain.

We come out on the far hillside into a panorama of blinding clarity. A shepherd with his flock moves about on a distant mountain side. He is larger than life, his sheep are covered with golden locks. He moves leisurely in the amplitude of forgotten time. He is moving amidst the still bodies of the dead, their fingers clasped in the short grass. He stops to talk with them, to stroke their beards. He was moving thus in Homeric times when the legend was being embroidered with copperish strands. He added a lie here and there, he pointed to the wrong direction, he altered his itinerary. For the shepherd the poet is too facile, too easily satiated. The poet would say "there *was* . . . they *were*. . . ." But the shepherd says *he lives, he is, he does*. . . . The poet is always a thousand years too late—and blind to boot. The shepherd is eternal, an earth-bound spirit, a renunciator. On these hillsides forever and ever there will be the shepherd with his flock: he will survive everything, including the tradition of all that ever was.

Now we are passing over the little bridge above the sundered vault of Clytemnestra's resting place. The earth is flamy with spirit as if it were an invisible compass we are treading and only the needle quivering luminously as it catches a flash of solar radiance. We are veering towards Agamemnon's tomb over the vault of which only the thinnest patch of earth now rests like a quilt of down. The nudity of this divine caché is magnificent. Stop before the heart glows through. Stoop to pick a flower. Shards everywhere and sheep droppings. The clock has stopped. The earth sways for a fraction of a second, waiting to resume its eternal beat.

I have not yet crossed the threshold. I am outside, between the Cyclopean blocks which flank the entrance to the shaft. I am still the man I might have become, assuming every benefit of civilization to be showered upon me with regal indulgence. I am gathering all of this potential civilized muck into a hard, tiny knot of understanding. I am blown to the maximum, like a great bowl of molten glass hanging from the stem of a glass-blower. Make me into any fantastic shape, use all your art, exhaust your lung-power—still I shall only be a thing fabricated, at the best a beautiful cultured soul. I know this, I despise it. I stand outside full-blown, the most beautiful, the most cultured, the most marvellously fabricated soul on earth. I am going to put my foot over the threshold—*now*. I do so. I hear nothing. I am not even there to hear myself shattering into a billion splintered smithereens. Only Agamemnon is there. The body fell apart when they lifted the mask from his face. But he is there, he fills the still bee-hive: he spills out into the open, floods the fields, lifts the sky a little higher. The shepherd walks and talks with him by day and by night. Shepherds are crazy folk. So am I. I am done with civilization and its spawn of cultured souls. I gave myself up when I entered the tomb. From now on I am a nomad, a spiritual body. Take your fabricated world and put it away in the museums, I don't want it, can't use it. I don't believe any civilized being knows, or ever did know, what took place in this sacred precinct. A civilized man can't possibly know or understand—he is on the other side of that slope whose summit was scaled long before he or his progenitors came into being. They call it Agamemnon's tomb. Well, possibly some one called Agamemnon was here laid to rest. What of it? Am I to stop there, gaping like an idiot? I do not. I refuse to rest on that too-too-solid fact. I take flight here, not as poet, not as recreator, fabulist, mythologist, but as pure spirit. I say the whole world, fanning out in every direction from this spot, was once alive in a way that no man has ever dreamed of. I say there were gods who roamed everywhere, men like us in form and substance, but free, electrically free. When they departed this earth they took with them the one secret which we shall never wrest from them until we too have made ourselves free again. We are to know one day what it is to have life eternal—*when we have ceased to murder*. Here at this spot, now dedicated to the memory of Agamemnon, some foul and hidden crime blasted the hopes of man. Two worlds lie juxtaposed, the one before, the one after the crime. The crime contains the riddle, as deep as salvation itself. Spades and shovels will uncover nothing of any import. The diggers are blind, feeling their way towards something they will never see. Everything that is unmasked crumbles at the touch. Worlds crumble too, in the same way. We can dig in eternally, like moles, but fear will be ever upon us, clawing us, raping us from the rear.

It seems scarcely credible to me now that what I relate was the enchanting work of a brief morning. By noon we were already winding down the road to the little inn. On the way we came across the guardian who, though he had arrived too late, insisted on filling me with facts and dates which are utterly without sense. He spoke first in Greek and then, when he discovered I was an American, in English. When he had finished his learned recital he began talking about Coney Island. He had been a molasses-thrower on the board-walk. He might just as well have said that he had been a wasp glued to the ceiling of an abandoned chateau for all the interest I showed. Why had he come back? The truth is he hadn't come back. Nobody comes back who has once made the transatlantic voyage westward. He is still throwing molasses on the board-walk. He came back to incarnate as a parrot, to talk this senseless parrot-language to other parrots who pay to listen. This is the language in which it is said that the early Greeks believed in gods, the word god no longer having any meaning but used just the same, thrown out like counterfeit money. Men who believe in nothing write learned tomes about gods who never existed. This is part of the cultural rigmarole. If you are very proficient at it you finally get a seat in the academy where you slowly degenerate into a full-fledged chimpanzee.

Here is Agamemnon and his spouse. Would we like something à la carte or a full banquet, a royal gorge, so to speak? Where is the wine list? A good cold wine while we wait would be in order. Katsimbalis is smacking his lips; his palate is dry. We flop down on the lawn and Agamemnon brings us a de luxe edition of a book by an English archaeologist. This is the hors d'oeuvre, apparently, for the bloody English tourist. The book stinks of learning: it is about upper and lower strata, breast-plates, chicken bones and grave relics. I chuck it aside when Agamemnon has turned his back. He is a tender fellow, this Agamemnon, and is almost a diplomat from force of habit. His wife has the air of being a good cook. Katsimbalis is dozing off under a big tree. Some German sauerkrauts, disguised as human beings, are sitting at a table under another tree. They look frightfully learned and repulsive; they are swollen like toads.

I am gazing blankly at the field of Irish green. It is a Lawrence Durrell field, heraldic in every sense of the word. Looking blankly into that field I suddenly realize what Durrell was trying to tell me in those long rambling poems he called letters. I used to think, when these heraldic messages arrived at the Villa Seurat on a cold summer's day in Paris, that he had taken a sniff of coke before oiling his pen. Once a big fulsome sheaf which looked like prose fell out of the envelope—it was called "Zero" and it was dedicated to me by this same Lawrence Durrell who said he lived in Corfu. I had heard of chicken tracks and of liver mantic and I once came near grasping the idea of absolute Zero, even though the thermometer has yet to be made which could register it, but not until I sat gazing into the field of Irish green in front of Agamemnon's Inn did I ever get the idea of Zero in the heraldic sense. There never was a field so fieldishly green as this. When you spot anything true and clear you are at Zero. Zero is Greek for pure vision. It means what Lawrence Durrell says when he writes Ionian. It means, and now for example, I can tell you more precisely because what I am trying to describe is happening right before my very eyes. . . . Two men and a woman are standing in the field. One man has a tape measure in his hand. He is going to measure off the plot of land which he has received for a wedding present. His bride is there to make certain that not a millimetre of land is miscalculated. They are down on all fours. They are arguing about a tiny piece in the southwest corner. Perhaps a twig has diverted the tape measure the fraction of a millimetre. One can't be too careful. Never look a gift horse in the mouth! They are measuring something which heretofore was only a word to me—*land*. The dead heroes, the gold cups, the bucklers, the jewels, the chased daggers—these items have nothing to do with the business in hand. What is vital here is land, just land. I roll it over and over on my tongue—land, land, land. Why yes, *land*, that's it—I had almost forgotten it meant such a simple, eternal thing. One gets twisted, derouted, spavined and indoctrinated shouting "Land of the Free" et cetera. Land is something on which to grow crops, build a home, raise cows and sheep. Land is land, what a grand, simple word! Yes, Lawrence Durrell, zero is what you make it: you take a piece of wet earth and as you squeeze it between your fingers you get two men and a woman standing in the field of Irish green measuring land. The wine has come. I raise my glass. *Salute, Larry me lad, and keep the flag at zero!* In a few more pages we shall revisit Mycenae together and Nancy will lead the way down the bat-slimed stairs to the bottomless well.

* * *

When I think of Katsimbalis bending over to pick a flower from the bare soil of Attica the whole Greek world, past, present and future, rises before me. I see again the soft, low mounds in which the illustrious dead were hidden away; I see the violet light in which the stiff scrub, the worn rocks, the huge boulders of the dry river beds gleam like mica; I see the miniature islands floating above the surface of the sea, ringed with dazzling white bands; I see the eagles swooping out from the dizzy crags of inaccessible mountain tops, their sombre shadows slowly staining the bright carpet of earth below; I see the figures of solitary men trailing their flocks over the naked spine of the hills and the fleece of their beasts all golden fuzz as in the days of legend; I see the women gathered at the wells amidst the olive groves, their dress, their manners, their talk no different now than in Biblical times; I see the grand patriarchal figure of the priest, the perfect blend of male and female, his countenance serene, frank, full of peace and dignity; I see the geometrical pattern of nature expounded by the earth itself in a silence which is deafening. The Greek earth opens before me like the Book of Revelation. I never knew that the earth contains so much; I had walked blindfolded, with faltering, hesitant steps; I was proud and arrogant, content to live the false, restricted life of the city man. The light of Greece opened my eyes, penetrated my pores, expanded my whole being. I came home to the world, having found the true center and the real meaning of revolution. No warring conflicts between the nations of the earth can disturb this equilibrium. Greece herself may become embroiled, as we ourselves are now becoming embroiled, but I refuse categorically to become anything less than the citizen of the world which I silently declared myself to be when I stood in Agamemnon's tomb. From that day forth my life was dedicated to the recovery of the divinity of man. Peace to all men, I say, and life more abundant!

7. Henry the First

On reflection, a liberty may have been taken with Miller's honor in judging The Colossus of Maroussi. In the absence of evidence harder than his remark in Remember to Remember, "Even when I write an innocent and beautiful book of my impressions of a foreign land . . . they find me unacceptable,"* Miller's motives may have been less practical than the desire to pay a social call on the literary establishment. Rather something in his long-denied German upbringing might have worshipped at the chalice of the old idea that kunst is beauty and light, and he was trying therefore with the Greek book to be no champion of the literary world so much as a good artist, clean, and upright. Who can know the lusts of such a mix in Miller? It is better to remind ourselves that in search for the factors of his elusive motivation, it is useful to think of him by a new polarity: immigrant and aristocrat. A part of Miller has to dwell forever in the psychic stance of a minority man. While such inferiority is not to be compared to the inner lack of status of a Negro or Jew at the turn of the century, nor even an Italian or Irishman, since Germans were more ubiquitously lower-middle-class and respectable, nonetheless, by Miller's own measure of self-esteem, he was not cultured. A part of him has to look at America from the bottom up. By bone cells, nerve and marrow, he is then

---

* *The Colossus of Maroussi* (New York: New Directions Publishing Corp., 1941), p. 140.

equal to many another major American writer: it is not quite his country. In the pit of his psyche a part of him can always feel less located than any small businessman in Des Moines. So he is always having a love affair with America. One can go so far as to suppose he never has a fornication where he is not fucking America too (an old American habit which has contributed much to our upward social mobility—and would account for that gloom the members of a minority group often have when fornicating each other). It is no accident, when he meets Mona in the rhapsodic conclusion to Tropic of Capricorn, *that he will compare her to America. We have to go back to the passage printed in this book already.*

> Opulence she has, and magnificence; it's America right or wrong, and the ocean on either side. For the first time in my life the whole continent hits me full force, hits me between the eyes. This is America, buffaloes or no buffaloes, America the emery wheel of hope and disillusionment. Whatever made America made her, bone, blood, muscle, eyeball, gait, rhythm, poise, confidence, brass and hollow gut. She's almost on top of me, the full face gleaming like calcium. The big soft fur is slipping from her shoulder. She doesn't notice it. She doesn't seem to care if her clothes should drop off. She doesn't give a fuck about anything. It's America moving like a streak of lightning toward the glass warehouse of red-blooded hysteria. Amurrica, fur or no fur, shoes or no shoes. Amurrica C.O.D.
>
> *Tropic of Capricorn*

That recollection was, of course, written in Paris. Back in America he is discovering what every other expatriate will encounter on return. America is a damnably difficult country to fuck. It sits on morale like a hundred-pound bag of potatoes. It's stupid. *America—goes the depressed recognition—is cold cunt.*

If he can feel like an immigrant equal to his grandparents all over again, there is, fortunately, the other pole of the spec-

trum. He is a citizen of the world as well, one of nature's aristocrats. Given that admiration—whether he would banish it or not—for things Prussian that are buried, nay, plastered into his genes, he is a royal family to himself, king of a universe of one, King Henry. Rejected by America on his return, he has every habit for holding his head high, he is Henry the First, Henry the very first you may be certain of his line. When was there ever a great artist who did not have some private sense of the mentality of a king?

After The Colossus of Maroussi, Miller must have set out on a double venture. Over the next few years he would cross America several times and write about it. To the first of his travel books about Greece, he would add a work on America, The Air-Conditioned Nightmare (with a second volume Remember to Remember) and in company with this effort would begin The Rosy Crucifixion. The powerful near wholly pornographic passages in the first half of Sexus must have been done in this period. If Mona was America, he was shoving it up the sluice of America, one wild new immigrant, yes, take that, America! Good old barbarian grunting. But in The Air-Conditioned Nightmare, he would speak as an aristocrat, with the tastes of an aristocrat, nothing to please him so much as southern mansions, nor anything to depress him like the middle class. His tone is grand, even monarchical. As usual, it works powerfully at its best, and is liblab at its worst. It is worthwhile to take one look at Miller at his absolute worst—his sententiousness can give heart to minor artists. Even the king flats out his dull days on the throne. So thunders Henry I, the Philosopher-King, when phumphering.

> Man in revolt against his own cloying nature—that is real war. And that is a bloodless war which goes on forever, under the peaceful name of evolution. In *this* war man ranges himself once and for all on the side of the angels. Though he may, as individual, be de-

> feated, he can be certain of the outcome—because the whole universe is with him.
>
> There are experiments which are made with cunning and precision, because the outcome is divined beforehand. The scientist, for example, always sets himself soluble problems. But man's experiment is not of this order. The answer to the grand experiment is in the heart; the search must be conducted inwardly. We are afraid to trust the heart. We inhabit a mental world, a labyrinth in whose dark recesses a monster waits to devour us. Thus far we have been moving in mythological dream sequence, finding no solutions because we are posing the wrong questions. We find only what we look for, and we are looking in the wrong place. We have to come out of the darkness, abandon these explorations which are only flights of fear. We have to cease groping on all fours. We have to come out in the open, erect, and fully exposed.
>
> *The Air-Conditioned Nightmare*

Indeed, his writing reveals the shock that travel has let into him. His style is depressed and half as rich as it used to be. Long stretches of The Air-Conditioned Nightmare *are twice offensive: his authoritative arrogance never deserts him, only his style. Yet when next to his worst he is full of virtue, and dull with bile, he perceives in all nonetheless of the clarity of a guru. He is decades ahead of his time. It is just that he now writes as badly as any other guru. Clichés seem to offer him the ring of mantras. To find a good sentence in the passage presented half a page ago is not possible.* On the other hand, search for a single phrase which does not have truth. He is in all the misery of writing solid editorials for an America which will not read.*

> Everything is caricatural here. I take a plane to see my father on his death-bed and up there in the clouds,

---

* Except for the immortal remark: "The scientist, for example, always sets himself soluble problems."

in a raging storm, I overhear two men behind me discussing how to put over a big deal, the big deal involving paper boxes, no less. The stewardess, who has been trained to behave like a mother, a nurse, a mistress, a cook, a drudge, never to look untidy, never to lose her Marcel wave, never to show a sign of fatigue or disappointment or chagrin or loneliness, the stewardess puts her lily-white hand on the brow of one of the paper-box salesmen and in the voice of a ministering angel, says: "Do you feel tired this evening? Have you a headache? Would you like a little aspirin?" We are up in the clouds and she is going through this performance like a trained seal. When the plane lurches suddenly she falls and reveals a tempting pair of thighs. The two salesmen are now talking about buttons, where to get them cheaply, how to sell them dearly. Another man, a weary banker, is reading the war news. There is a great strike going on somewhere—several of them, in fact. We are going to build a fleet of merchant vessels to help England—*next December*. The storm rages. The girl falls down again—she's full of black and blue marks. But she comes up smiling, dispensing coffee and chewing gum, putting her lily-white hand on someone else's forehead, inquiring if he is a little low, a little tired perhaps. I ask her if she likes her job. For answer she says, "It's better than being a trained nurse." The salesmen are going over her points; they talk about her like a commodity. They buy and sell, buy and sell. For that they have to have the best rooms in the best hotels, the fastest, smoothest planes, the thickest, warmest overcoats, the biggest, fattest purses. We need their paper boxes, their buttons, their synthetic furs, their rubber goods, their hosiery, their plastic this and that. We need the banker, his genius for taking our money and making himself rich. The insurance man, his policies, his talk of security, of dividends—we need him too. *Do we?* I don't see that we need any of these vultures. I don't see that we need any of these cities, these hell-holes I've been in. I don't think we need a two-ocean fleet either. I was in Detroit a few nights ago. I saw the Mannerheim Line in the movies. I saw how the Russians pulverized it. I learned the lesson. *Did you?* Tell me what it is that man can build, to protect himself, which other men cannot destroy? What are we trying to defend? Only what is old, useless, dead, indefensible. Every defense is a provocation to assault. Why not surrender? Why not give—give all? It's so damned practical, so thoroughly effective and disarming. Here we are, we the people of the United States: the greatest people on earth, so we think. We have everything—everything it takes to make people happy. We have land, water, sky and all that goes with it. We could become the great shining example of the world; we could radiate peace, joy, power, benevolence. But there are ghosts all about, ghosts whom we can't seem to lay hands on. We are not happy, not contented, not radiant, not fearless.

The Air-Conditioned Nightmare

Nowhere is this new dichotomy more apparent than in what he has to say about crime. When has the psychology of a convicted criminal been put more revealingly into a single paragraph, yet when has Miller's vocabulary ever been so bland or general? One's intuition is forced to drill through each second-hand phrase in order to feel the heft of human meat behind every sorrowful remark.

To rehearse the story of his life is not my purpose. It was not so very unusual: it was in the tradition. In a moment of weakness, in the moment when it seemed that every man's hand was turned against him, he had crossed the line. Living in that other world each day that passed made it more and more difficult to rejoin the herd. Crimes born of necessity soon led to crimes of sheer bravado. While on parole, after serving his first sentence, he committed a purely gratuitous crime —the sort of thing an artist would do just to keep his hand in. Prison of course is the school of crime *par excellence.* Until one has gone through that school one is only an amateur. In prison bonds of friendship are established, often over a trifle, a kind word, a look, a bone. Later, out in the world, one will do anything to prove one's loyalty. Even if one wants with all his heart and soul to go straight, when the critical moment comes, when it is a toss-up between believing in the world or believing in one's friend, one will choose the latter. One has had a taste of the world; one knows enough not to expect justice or mercy from it. But one can never forget an act of kindness shown in a moment of great need. *Blow up a block house?* Why certainly, if that will help your friend out. *But that may mean life imprisonment, or death in the chair!* What of it? One good turn deserves another. You've been humiliated, you've been tortured, you've been reduced to the level of a wild beast. Who cared? Nobody. Nobody on the outside, no, not even God himself, knows what a man suffers on the inside. There's no language to convey it. It's beyond all human comprehension. It's so vast, so wide, so deep that even the angels with all their powers of understanding and all their powers of locomotion could never explore the whole of it. No, when a friend makes a call on you you've got to obey. You have to do for him what God himself wouldn't do. It's a law. Otherwise you'd fall apart, you'd bark in the night like a dog.

The Air-Conditioned Nightmare

Yet in the same piece, and not six pages further along, Miller finally erupts, says goodbye to his editorial duty, and dives off into glory, into his sea of words, surrealistic Henry, Prince-poet of Dada, knave-acrobat of the cosmos. Now he will string a zither across Tania's immortal navel once more and shit his metaphysical arpeggios. King Henry the First. Some day there will be a book about America's two Henrys and the study they offer, dazzling in contrast. The century may sit in the saddle between Henry I and Henry K.

And as though and as if these were not enough, there are the wild noumena, the pleistocene memories, the placental fuges and subterfuges. Memories that hang by a hair, and in dying give birth to dandruff; faces that burn in luminol, shedding hysterical light on cellular problems; names running back to lethal sources, reverberating like spun harps; words embedded in lymph and cyst, which no form of dynamite can blast away; tears that fall on warm fruit and make waterfalls in far-off Africa; birds that settle between the eyes only to singe their wings and fall like broken crutches; vapors that rise from the arteries and congeal into phosphorescent webs of mica; and devils who laugh like antelopes, bounding in and out of broken teeth or frazzled dreams; and monsters of the underwaters, who suck like the undertow or bleat like pregnant baboons; and hammerclaviers fitted with cloying geraniums, announcing stench and smoke and delirium; and kings like Ebenezer Sock, born blanched with terror, who prey on eupheme; and more of his ilk, and more, and then nothing but cube on cube, pillar upon pillar, tomb upon tomb, as far as the mind can reach and just a little beyond. And as though and as if there were at last a limit there is none, believe me, none, none. A little beyond looms the face of the beloved. Ever larger, ever fuller, ever clearer it grows: a moon-glow that saturates an empty sky. Slowly, slow as claustral fever, the nebulae arrive. Little medallions constellate the panic that clouds the orifices of fright. Intaglio depths gleam from the precipitous walls of new world hearts. Through the laughing mouth oceans leap into being and pain still-born is cried down again. The marvels of emptiness parade their defilement, the embryonic unsheath their splendor. Echolalia mounts her throne. The web stretches tighter, the ravisher is ravished. A slat gives way, an axe falls, little children drop like flowers on the burnished hearth beneath the open door. It is the morning of the day after the night before on the threshold of unsubjugated repetition. It fits like a silver-studded bracelet on a warm wrist.

The Air-Conditioned Nightmare

From
The Air-Conditioned Nightmare

January in Louisiana! Already the first signs of spring were manifesting themselves in the cabin door-yards: the paper-white narcissus and the German iris whose pale gray-green spikes are topped by a sort of disdainful white plume. In the transparent black waters of the bayous the indestructible cypress, symbol of silence and death, stands knee-deep. The sky is everywhere, dominating everything. How different the sky as one travels from region to region! What tremendous changes between Charleston, Asheville, Biloxi, Pensacola, Aiken, Vicksburg, St. Martinsville! Always the live oak, the cypress, the chinaball tree; always the swamp, the clearing, the jungle; cotton, rice, sugar cane; thickets of bamboo, banana trees, gum trees, magnolias, cucumber trees, swamp myrtle, sassafras. A wild profusion of flowers: camellias, azaleas, roses of all kinds, salvias, the giant spider lily, the aspidistra, jasmine, Michaelmas daisies; snakes, screech-owls, raccoons; moons of frightening dimensions, lurid, pregnant, heavy as mercury. And like a leit-motif to the immensity of sky are the tangled masses of Spanish moss, that peculiar spawn of the South which is allied to the pineapple family. An epiphyte, rather than a parasite, it lives an independent existence, sustaining itself on air and moisture; it flourishes just as triumphantly on a dead tree or a telegraph wire as on the live oak. "None but the Chinese," says Weeks Hall, "can ever hope to paint this moss. It has a baffling secret of line and mass which has never been remotely approached. It is as difficult to do as a veronica. The live oaks tolerate it—they do not seem to be at one with it. But to the Louisiana cypress it seems to want to act as a bodyguard. A strange phenomenon." It is also a profitable one, as the mattress and upholstery industry of Louisiana would indicate.

There are people from the North and the Mid-West who actually shudder when they first come upon the giant bewhiskered live oaks; they sense something dismal and forbidding in them. But when one sees them in majestic, stately rows, as on the great estates around Beaufort, S.C., or at Biloxi—at Biloxi they come to apotheosis!—one must bow down before them in humble adoration for they are, if not the monarchs of the tree world, certainly the sages or the magi.

It was in the shade of one of these great trees that the three of us stood admiring the back of the house. I say the three of us because our host—and that is one of the things I like about Weeks Hall—can stop and examine the place he lives in any hour of the day or night. He can talk for hours about any detail of the house or gardens; he speaks almost as if it were his own creation, though the house and the trees which surround it came into existence over a century ago. It is all that remains of estates which once comprised several thousand acres, including Weeks Island, a Spanish royal grant made to David Weeks by Baron Carondelet in 1792. The entrance to the property, now reduced to three acres, is on Main Street, which is a continuation of Highway 90. Driving past it in a car one would never in the world suspect what lies hidden behind the dense hedge of bamboo which encircles the grounds.

As we stood there talking, Theophile came up to inform our friend that some women were at the front gate demanding permission to visit the grounds. "Tell them I'm out," said our host. "The tourists!" he said wryly, turning to Rattner. "They pour through here like ants; they overrun the place. Thousands and thousands of them—it's like the plague." And then he began to relate one anecdote after another about the women who insist on inspecting the rooms, which is forbidden. "They would follow me into the bathroom," he said, "if I permitted them. It's almost impossible to have any privacy when you live in a place like this." Most of them were from the Middle West, I gathered. They were the type one sees in Paris, Rome, Florence, Egypt, Shanghai—harmless souls who have a mania for seeing the world and gathering information about anything and everything. A curious thing about these show places, and I have visited a number of them, is that the owners, despite the martyrdom inflicted upon them by the steady hordes of visitors, almost never feel at liberty to exclude the public. They all seem to possess a sense of guilt about living alone in such ancient splendor. Some of course can not afford to spurn the modest revenue which this traffic brings, but for the most part there exists a feeling of obligation towards the public, whether conscious or unconscious.

Later, in looking over the register, I came across many interesting names, that of Paul Claudel surprising me not a little. "Claudel, ah yes! He said a wonderful thing about the camellia—how in Japan, when the blossom falls, they speak of it as a beheading." He went on to talk about the camellia, of which he has some marvelous varieties, including the largest Lady Hume's Blush in America. Its rarity, I was informed, is almost legendary; a plant of this size, in fact, is comparable to a black pearl. He dwelt at length on the tones and colors, the Lady Hume's Blush, he insisted, being of the palest pink ivory, whereas the Madame Strekaloff was of a peach-blossom pink streaked with rose, a rose with reddish stripes. He spoke of the tight little blossoms which might have been born under the glass domes of wax flowers. "The new varieties are lush but never sensuous; they have a beauty which forbids. They are coldly unaffected by praise and admiration. Pink cabbages, that's what they are!" And so on and so forth. It seemed to me that the man had given his life to the study of camellias, to say nothing of his wealth. But the more I listened to him the more I realized that he had an almost encyclopaedic knowledge about a great diversity of things. A superabundant vitality also, which permits him, when he feels inclined to talk, to continue like a fount from morning till night. He had always been a great talker, I learned, even before the injury to his arm limited his painting. That first evening, after the dishes had been cleared away, I watched him in fascination as he paced up and down the room, lighting one cigarette after another—he smokes almost a hundred a day—and telling us of his travels, his dreams, his weaknesses and vices, his passions, his prejudices, his ambitions, his observations, his studies, his frustrations. At three in the morning, when we finally begged leave to retire, he was wide awake, making himself a fresh cup of black coffee which he shares with his dog, and preparing to take a stroll about the garden and meditate on things past and future. One of the weaknesses, shall I call it, which sometimes comes upon him in the wee hours of the morning is the desire to telephone some one in California or Oregon or Boston. The anecdotes about these early morning enthusiasms of his are related from one end of the country to the other. Telephoning is not the only one of his imperative impulses; the others are even more spectacular, more weird, such as impersonating a non-existent idiot twin brother. . . .

When the guests retire he communes with the dog. There is an unholy sort of bond between them, something quite out of the ordinary. I have forgotten the dog's name—Spot or Queenie, some common name like that. She is an

English setter, a bitch, and rather seedy now and smelly, though it would break her master's heart if he should hear me say a thing like that. Weeks Hall's contention about this Alice or Elsie is this—that she does not know that she is a dog. According to him, she does not like other dogs, doesn't even recognize them, so to speak. He contends that she has the most beautiful manners—the manners of a lady. Perhaps. I am no judge of dogs. But of one thing I am in agreement with him—she has absolutely human eyes. That her coat is like falling water, that her ears remind you of Mrs. Browning's portrait, that she makes things handsome with her casual languor—such subtleties are beyond me. But when you look into her eyes, no matter how much or how little you know about dogs, you must confess that this puzzling creature is no ordinary bitch. She looks at you with the soulful eyes of some departed human who has been condemned to crawl about on all fours in the body of this most companionable setter. Weeks Hall would have it that she is sad because of her inability to speak, but the feeling she gave me was that she was sad because nobody except her master had the intelligence to recognize her as a human being and not just a dog. I could never look her in the eyes for more than a few moments at a time. The expression, which I have caught now and then on the face of a writer or painter suddenly interrupted in the midst of an inspiration, was that of a wanderer between two worlds. It was the sort of look which makes one desire to withdraw discreetly, lest the separation between body and soul become irreparable.

The next morning, after breakfast, as I was about to open a door which had blown shut, I saw to my astonishment the signatures in pencil on the back of the door of hundreds of celebrities, written in every scrawl imaginable. Of course we had to add our own to the collection. I signed mine under that of a Hungarian named Bloor Schleppey, a fascinating name which unleashed a story about the door that is worth recounting. The present names, it seems, are all of recent origin. Originally there was an even more scintillating array of names, but about the time of Bloor Schleppey, perhaps because the name had such an uncommon effect upon our host, the latter, after a debauch lasting several days, was so disgusted with the condition of the house that he ordered the servants to clean it from top to bottom. "I want it to be immaculate when I wake up," were his orders. They tried to tell him that it was impossible to put a house of such proportions in order in such a short space of time. There were only two of them. "Well, then, hire a gang," said our host. And they did. And when he awoke from his slumber the house was indeed spic and span, as he had commanded it to be. Certain things, to be sure, had disappeared, what with the zeal and frenzy of the house-cleaners. The real coup came when he observed, in the course of his inspection, that the door with the names had been washed down and the names obliterated. That was a blow. At first he stormed and cussed, but when he had quieted down suddenly an inspiration came to him. He would unhinge the door, crate it, and send it on a round robin to be re-signed by his distinguished visitors. What a journey! The idea was so fascinating that presently he began to think it was too good a treat to offer a mere door—he would go himself from place to place, carrying the door along, and begging like a monk for a fresh signature. Some of the visitors had come from China, some from Africa, some from India. Better to supervise it personally than entrust it to the post or express agencies. Nobody, as far as he knew, had ever travelled around the world with a door. It would be quite a feat, a sensation, in fact. To find Bloor Schleppey, that would be something. God only knew where he had disappeared. The others he thought of as relatively fixed, like certain stars. But Bloor Schleppey—he hadn't the faintest idea where Bloor Schleppey had departed to. And then, as he was planning his itinerary—a delight which lasted for weeks—who should arrive, unheralded, in the dead of night, accompanied by three great Danes on a leash, but Bloor Schleppey himself! Well, to make the story short, the door was put back on its hinges, Bloor Schleppey inscribed his signature again, and the idea of a world tour with a door on his back gradually faded away, like all whimsical ideas. A strange thing about the people identified with this door, which I feel compelled to add in conclusion, is this—that many of them, as if in answer to a silent summons, have returned to sign their names again. It may also be, of course, that some of them were summoned back by an early morning telephone call—who can say?

In the course of a century or more curious events must naturally have occurred in a remote and idyllic domain of this sort. At night, lying in the center of a huge four-poster bed staring at the brass ornament in the center of the tester, the stillness of the house seemed the stillness not of an empty house but of one in which a great family was sleeping the profound and peaceful sleep of the dead. Awakened from a light sleep by the buzz of a mosquito I would get to thinking about the statues in the garden, about that fluid, silent communion which went on like music between these guardians of the Four Seasons. Sometimes I would get up and go out on the broad balcony overlooking the garden, stand there half-naked puffing a cigarette, hypnotized by the warmth, the silence, the fragrance which enveloped me. So many strange, startling phrases were dropped in the course of a day—they would come back to me at night and plague me. Little remarks, such as the one he dropped about the pool, for instance. "A dozen square feet of pool mean more to them than all the soil: it is a transparent mystery." The pool! It brought back memories of the dead fountain which graces the entrance to the now abandoned Mississippi Lunatic Asylum. I know that water is soothing to the insane, just as music is. A little pool in an enclosed and enchanted garden, such as this one, is an inexhaustible source of wonder and magic. One evening, standing thus in a dream, I remembered that there was a typewritten description of the place framed and posted near the pool. I descended the outer staircase and with the aid of a match I read the thing through. I reread the paragraph about the garden, as though it contained some magic incantation. Here it is:

> "A rectangular formal garden to the east of the house is enclosed by a clipped bamboo hedge and is bordered by walks of hand-shaped brick, at the four corners of which are marble statues of the Four Seasons which were once in the gardens of the old Hester plantation. The center of the grass rectangle has a clump of old Camellia trees planted when the house was built. The signed marble sundial is inscribed with the French adage—'Abundance is the Daughter of Economy and Work', and is dated 1827."

A heavy mist had descended. I walked cautiously in my bare feet for the old bricks were slippery with moss. As I got to the far corner of the rectangle the light of the moon broke full and clear on the serene face of the goddess there enshrined. I leaned over impulsively and kissed the marble lips. It was a strange sensation. I went to each of them in turn and kissed their cold, chaste lips. Then I strolled back to the trellised garden house which lies on the banks of the Bayou Teche. The scene before my eyes was that of a Chinese painting. Sky and water had become one: the whole world was floating in a nebular mist. It was indescribably beautiful and bewitching. I could scarcely believe that I was in America. In a moment or so a river boat loomed up, her colored lights scattering the dense mist into a frayed kaleidoscope of ribboned light. The deep fog horn sounded and was echoed by the hooting of invisible owls. To the left the draw-bridge slowly raised its broken span, the soft edges illumined by fulgurant lights of red and green. Slowly, like a white bird, the river boat glided past my vision, and in her wake the mist closed in, bearing down the sky, a fistful of frightened stars, the heavy wet limbs of the moss-covered trees, the density of night, and watery, smothered sounds. I went back to bed and lay there not just wide awake but super-conscious, alive in every tip and pore of my being. The portrait of an ancestor stared at me from the wall—a Manchu portrait, with the dress folded and pressed in the frame. I could hear Weeks Hall's booming voice saying to me: "I should like to do a garden which would not be a seed-catalogue by daylight, but strange, sculptural blossoms by night, things hanging in trees and moving like metronomes, transparent plastics in geometrical shapes, silhouettes lit by lights and changing with the changing hours. A garden is a show—why not make one enormous garden, one big, changing show?" I lay there wondering about those several thousand letters and documents which he had exhumed from the garret and stored in the Archives at Baton Rouge. What a story they would make! And the garret itself—that enormous room on the third floor with the forty trunks! Forty trunks, with the hair still intact on the bear-skin hides. Containing enormous hat boxes for the tall hats of the fifties, a stereoscope of mahogany and pictures for it taken in the sixties, fencing foils, shotgun cases, an old telescope, early side-saddles, dog baskets, linen dancing cloths with rings to fit over the carpets in the drawing room, banjos, guitars, zithers. Doll trunks too, and a doll house replica of the great house itself. All smelling dry and lightly fragrant. The smell of age, not of dust.

A strange place, the attic, with twelve huge closets and the ceiling slanting throughout the length of the house. Strange house. To get to any room you had to walk through every other room of the house. Nine doors leading outside—

more than one finds in most public buildings. Both staircases originally built on the outside—a somewhat mad idea. No central hall. A row of three identical double wooden doors placed in the dead center of the grave façade on the ground floor.

And the strange Mr. Persac, the intinerant painter who left a brace of microscopically done wash drawings in black enamel gilt frames on the walls of the reception room where we held our nightly pow-wows. Up and down the country, especially the Teche region, he wandered, just a few years before the War between the States. Making pictures of the great houses and living on the fat of the land. An honest painter who, when the task got beyond his powers, would cut out a figure from a magazine and paste it on the picture. Thus in one of his masterpieces the child standing by the garden gate has disappeared—but the balloon which she held in her hand is still visible. I adore the work of these travelling artists. How infinitely more agreeable and enriching than the life of the present day artist! How much more genuine and congenial their work than the pretentious efforts of our contemporaries! Think of the simple lunch that was served them in the old plantation days. I cull a menu at random from one of Lyle Saxon's books on old Louisiana: "a slice of bread and butter spread with marmalade or guava jelly, accompanied by a slab of jujube paste and washed down with lemonade or orange-flower syrup or tamarind juice." Think of his joy if he had the good fortune to be invited to a ball. I give a description of one culled from the same book:

> ". . . Gorgeous costumes of real lace . . . jewels, plumes. The staircase was garlanded in roses for full three flights. Vases on mantels and brackets filled with fragrant flowers . . . and gentlemen sampling Scotch or Irish whiskey . . . About midnight supper was announced and the hostess led the way to the dining room. On the menu, the cold meats, salads, salamis,

galantines quaking in jellied seclusion, and an infinite variety of *à las*, were served from side tables, leaving the huge expanse of carved oak besilvered, belinened and belaced, for flowers trailing from the tall silver *épergne* in the center to the corsage bouquet at each place; fruits, cakes in pyramids or layers or only solid deliciousness, iced and ornamented; custards, pies, jellies, creams, Charlotte Russes or home-concocted sponge cake spread with raspberry jam encircling a veritable Mont Blanc of whipped cream dotted with red cherry stars; towers of nougat or caramel, sherbets and ice creams served in little baskets woven of candied orange peel and topped with sugared rose leaves or violets . . . Various wines in cut glass decanters, each with its name carved in the silver grapeleaf suspended from its neck; iced champagne deftly poured by the waiters into gold-traced or Bohemian glasses . . . Illuminating the whole were wax candles in crystal chandeliers, and on the table, in silver candelabra . . . More dancing followed supper and at dawn when the guests were leaving a plate of hot gumbo, a cup of strong black coffee and enchanting memories sustained them on the long drive to their abodes."*

* * *

I feel like doing a little passacaglia now about things automotive. Ever since I decided to sell the car she's been running beautifully. The damned thing behaves like a flirtatious woman.

Back in Albuquerque, where I met that automotive expert Hugh Dutter, everything was going wrong with her. Sometimes I think it was all the fault of the tail wind that swept me along through Oklahoma and the Texas panhandle. Did I mention the episode with the drunk who tried to run

---

* Courtesy of Miss Louise Butler.

me into a ditch? He almost had me convinced that I had lost my generator. I was a bit ashamed, of course, to ask people if my generator were gone, as he said, but every time I had a chance to open up a conversation with a garage man I would work him round to the subject of generators, hoping first of all that he would show me where the damned thing was hidden, and second that he would tell me whether or not a car could function without one. I had just a vague idea that the generator had something to do with the battery. Perhaps it hasn't, but that's my notion of it still.

The thing I enjoy about visiting garage men is that one contradicts the other. It's very much as in medicine, or the field of criticism in literature. Just when you believe you have the answer you find that you're mistaken. A little man will tinker with your machinery for an hour and blushingly ask you for a dime, and whether he's done the correct thing or not the car runs, whereas the big service stations will lay her up in dry dock for a few days, break her down into molecules and atoms, and then like as not she'll run a few miles and collapse.

There's one thing I'd like to advise any one thinking of making a trans-continental journey: see that you have a jack, a monkey wrench and a jimmy. You'll probably find that the wrench won't fit the nuts but that doesn't matter; while you're pretending to fiddle around with it some one will stop and lend you a helping hand. I had to get stuck in the middle of a swamp in Louisiana before I realized that I had no tools. It took me a half hour to realize that if there were any they would be hidden under the front seat. And if a man promises you that he will stop at the next town and send some one to haul you don't believe him. Ask the next man and the next man and the next man. Keep a steady relay going or you'll sit by the roadside till doomsday. And never say that you have no tools—it sounds suspicious, as though you had stolen the car. Say you lost them, or that they were stolen from you in Chicago. Another thing—if you've just had your front wheels packed don't take it for granted that the wheels are on tight. Stop at the next station and ask to have the lugs tightened, then you'll be sure your front wheel won't roll off in the middle of the night. Take it for granted that nobody, not even a genius, can guarantee that your car won't fall apart five minutes after he's examined it. A car is even more delicate than a Swiss watch. And a lot more diabolical, if you know what I mean.

If you don't know much about cars it's only natural to want to take it to a big service station when something goes wrong. A great mistake, of course, but it's better to learn by experience than by hearsay. How are you to know that the little man who looks like a putterer may be a wizard?

Anyway, you go to the service station. And immediately you come smack up against a man dressed in a butcher's smock, a man with a pad in his hand and a pencil behind his ear, looking very professional and alert, a man who never fully assures you that the car will be perfect when they get through with it but who intimates that the service will be impeccable, of the very highest calibre, and that sort of thing. They all have something of the surgeon about them, these entrepreneurs of the automobile industry. You see, they seem to imply, you've come to us only at the last ditch; we can't perform miracles, but we've had twenty or thirty years' experience and can furnish the best of references. And, just as with the surgeon, you have the feeling when you entrust the car to his immaculate hands, that he is going to telephone you in the middle of the night, after the engine has been taken apart and the bearings are lying all about, and tell you that there's something even more drastically wrong with the car than he had at first suspected. Something serious, what! It starts with a case of bad lungs and ends up with a removal of the appendix, gall bladder, liver and testicles. The bill is always indisputably correct and of a figure no less than formidable. Everything is itemized, except the quality of the foreman's brains. Instinctively you put it safely away in order to produce it at the next hospital when the car breaks down again; you want to be able to prove that you knew what was wrong with the car all along.

After you've had a few experiences of this sort you get wary, that is if you're slow to catch on, as I am. After you stay in a town a while and get acquainted, feel that you are among friends, you throw out a feeler; you learn that just around the corner from the big service station there's a little fellow (his place is always in the rear of some other place and therefore hard to find) who's a wizard at fixing things and asks some ridiculously low sum for his services. They'll tell you that he treats *everybody* that way, even those with "foreign" license plates.

Well, that's exactly what happened to me in Albuquerque, thanks to the friendship I struck up with Dr. Peters who is a great surgeon and a *bon vivant* as well. One day, not having anything better to do—one of those days when you call up telephone numbers or else go to have your teeth cleaned—one day, as I say, in the midst of a downpour I decided to consult the master mind, the painless Parker of the automotive world: Hugh Dutter. There was nothing very seriously wrong—just a constant high fever. The men at the service station didn't attach much importance to it—they attributed it to the altitude, the age of the car and so on. I suppose there was nothing more that they could repair or replace. But when on a cold, rainy day a car runs a temperature of 170 to 180 there must be something wrong, so I reasoned. If she was running that high at 5,000 feet what would she run at 7,000 or 10,000?

I stood in the doorway of the repair shop for almost an hour waiting for Dutter to return. He had gone to have a bite with some friends, never dreaming that there would be any customers waiting for him in such a downpour. His assistant, who was from Kansas, regaled me with stories about fording flooded streams back in Kansas. He spoke as though people had nothing better to do when it rained than practice these dangerous manoeuvres with their tin Lizzies. Once he said a bus got caught in the head waters of a creek, keeled over, was washed downstream and never found again. He liked rain—it made him homesick.

Presently Dutter arrived. I had to wait until he went to a shelf and arranged some accessories. After I had sheepishly explained my troubles he leisurely scratched his head and without even looking in the direction of the engine he said: "Well, there could be a lot of reasons for her heating up on you that way. Have you had your radiator boiled out?"

I told him I had—back in Johnson City, Tennessee.

"How long ago was that?" he said.

"Just a few months back."

"I see. I thought you were going to say a few years ago."

The car was still standing outside in the rain. "Don't you want to look her over?" I said, fearing that he might lose interest in the case.

"You might bring her in," he said. "No harm in taking a look. Nine times out of ten it's the radiator. Maybe they didn't do a good job for you back in Cleveland."

"Johnson City!" I corrected.

"Well, wherever it was." He ordered his assistant to drive her in.

I could see he wasn't very enthusiastic about the job: it wasn't as though I had brought him a bursting gall bladder or a pair of elephantine legs. I thought to myself—better leave him alone with it for a while; maybe when he begins to putter around he'll work up a little interest. So I excused myself and went off to get a bite.

"I'll be back soon," I said.

"That's all right, don't hurry," he answered. "It may take hours to find out what's wrong with her."

I had a Chop Suey and on the way back I loitered a bit in order to give him time to arrive at a correct diagnosis. To kill a little time I stopped in at the Chamber of Commerce and inquired about the condition of the roads going to Mesa Verde. I learned that in New Mexico you can tell nothing about the condition of the roads by consulting the map. For one thing the road map doesn't say how much you may be obliged to pay if you get stuck in deep clay and have to be hauled fifty or seventy-five miles. And between gravel and graded roads there's a world of difference. At the Automobile Club in New York I remember the fellow taking a greasy red pencil and tracing a route for me backwards while answering two telephones and cashing a check.

"Mesa Verde won't be officially open until about the middle of May," said the fellow. "I wouldn't risk it yet. If we get a warm rain there's no telling what will happen."

I decided to go to Arizona, unless I had an attack of chilblains. I was a little disappointed though to miss seeing Shiprock and Aztec.

When I got back to the garage I found Dutter bending over the engine; he had his ear to the motor, like a doctor examining a weak lung. From the vital parts there dangled an electric bulb attached to a long wire. The electric bulb always reassures me. It means business. Anyway, he was down in the guts of the thing and getting somewhere—so it looked.

"Found out what's wrong yet?" I ventured to inquire timidly.

"No," he said, burying his wrist in a mess of intricate

whirring thingamajigs which looked like the authentic automotive part of the automobile. It was the first time I had ever seen what makes a car go. It was rather beautiful, in a mechanical way. Reminded me of a steam calliope playing Chopin in a tub of grease.

"She wasn't timing right," said Dutter, twisting his neck around to look at me but, like the skilful surgeon, still operating with his deft right hand. "I knew that much before I even looked at her. That'll heat a car up quicker'n anything." And he began explaining to me from deep down in the bowels of the car how the timing worked. As I remember it now an eight cylinder car fires 2,3,5,7 with one cam and 3,4,6,8 with the other. I may be wrong on the figures but the word cam is what interested me. It's a beautiful word and when he tried to point it out to me I liked it still better—the cam. It has a down-to-earth quality about it, like piston and gear. Even an ignoramus like myself knows that piston, just from the sound of the word, means something that has to do with the driving force, that it's intimately connected with the locomotion of the vehicle. I still have to see a piston per se, but I believe in pistons even though I should never have the chance to see one cold and isolate.

The timing occupied him for quite a while. He explained what a difference a quarter of a degree could make. He was working on the carburetor, if I am not mistaken. I accepted this explanation, as I had the others, unquestioningly. Meanwhile I was getting acquainted with the fly-wheel and some other more or less essential organs of the mysterious mechanism. Most everything about a car, I should say in passing, is more or less essential. All but the nuts underneath the chassis; they can get loose and fall out, like old teeth, without serious damage. I'm not speaking now of the universal—that's another matter. But all those rusty nuts which you see dropping off when the car's jacked up on the hoist—actually they mean very little. At worst the running board may drop off, but once you know your running board is off there's no great harm done.

Apropos of something or other he suddenly asked me at what temperature the thermostat was set. I couldn't tell him. I had heard a lot about thermostats, and I knew there was one in the car somewhere, but just where, and just what it looked like, I didn't know. I evaded all references to the subject as skilfully as I could. Again I was ashamed not to know where and what this piece of apparatus was. Starting out from New York, after receiving a brief explanation about the functioning or non-functioning of the thermostat, I had expected the shutters of the hood to fly open automatically when the heat gauge read 180 or 190. To me thermostat meant something like a cuckoo in a cuckoo clock. My eye was constantly on the gauge, waiting for it to hit 180. Rattner, my then side-kick, used to get a bit irritated watching me watch the gauge. Several times we went off the road because of this obsession on my part. But I always expected that some time or other an invisible man would release the trap and the cuckoo would fly out and then bango! the shutters would open up, the air circulate between the legs, and the motor begin to purr like a musical cat. Of course the damned shutters never did fly open. And when the gauge did finally hit 190 the next thing I knew was that the radiator was boiling over and the nearest town was forty miles away.

Well, after the timing had been corrected, the points adjusted, the carburetor calibrated, the accelerator exhilarated, all the nuts, bolts and screws carefully restored to their proper positions, Dutter invited me to accompany him on a test flight. He decided to drive her up through Tijeras Canyon where there was a big grade. He set out at fifty miles an hour, which worried me a bit because the mechanic at the big service station had said to drive her slow for the next thousand miles until she loosened up a bit. The gauge moved slowly up to 180, and once we were properly in the pass, it swung to 190 and kept on rising.

"I don't think she'll boil," he said, lighting himself a cigarette with a parlor match. "Up here the principle is never to worry until she boils over. Cars act temperamental up here, just like people. It could be weather, it could be scales in the engine box . . . it could be a lot of things. And it mightn't be anything more than altitude. The Buicks never did make big enough radiators for the size of the car." I found this sort of talk rather cheering. More like a good French doctor. The American physician always says immediately—"Better have an X-ray taken; better pull out all your back teeth; better get an artificial leg." He's got you all cut up and bleeding before he's even looked at your throat. If you've got a simple case of worms he finds that you've been suffering from hereditary constriction of the corneal phylactery since childhood. You get drunk and decide to keep the worms or whatever ails you.

Dutter went on to talk in his calm, matter of fact way about new and old Buicks, about too much compression and too little space, about buying whole parts instead of a part of a part, as with the Chevrolet or the Dodge. Not that the Buick wasn't a good car—oh no, it was a damned good car, but like every car it had its weak points too. He talked about boiling over several times on his way from Espanola to Santa Fe. I had boiled over there myself, so I listened sympathetically. I remember getting near the top of the hill and then turning round to coast down in order to get a fresh start. And then suddenly it was dark and there were no clear crystal springs anywhere in sight. And then the lizards began whispering to one another and you could hear them whispering for miles around, so still it was and so utterly desolate.

Coming back Dutter got talking about parts and parts of parts, rather intricate for me, especially when he began comparing Pontiac parts with parts of parts belonging to the Plymouth or the Dodge. The Dodge was a fine car, he thought, but speaking for himself he preferred the old Studebaker. "Why don't you get yourself a nice old Studebaker?" I asked. He looked at me peculiarly. I gathered that the Studebaker must have been taken off the market years ago. And then, almost immediately afterwards, I began talking about Lancias and Pierce Arrows. I wasn't sure whether they made them any more either, but I knew they had always enjoyed a good reputation. I wanted to show him that I was willing to talk cars, if that was the game. He glossed over these remarks however in order to launch into a technical explanation of how cores were casted and molded, how you tested them with an ice pick to see if they were too thick or too thin. This over he went into an excursus about the transmission and the differential, a subject so abstruse that I hadn't the faintest notion what he was getting at. The gauge, I observed, was climbing down towards 170. I thought to myself how pleasant it would be to hire a man like Dutter to accompany me the rest of the way. Even if the car broke down utterly it would be instructive and entertaining to hear him talk about the parts. I could understand how people became attached to their cars, knowing all the parts intimately, as they undoubtedly do.

When we got back to the laboratory he went inside for a thermometer. Then he took the cap off the radiator and stuck the thermometer in the boiling radiator. At intervals he made a reading—comparative readings such as a theologian might do with the Bible. There was a seventeen degree difference, it developed, between the reading of the gauge and the thermometer reading. The difference was in my favor, he said. I didn't understand precisely what he meant by this remark, but I made a mental note of it. The car looked pathetically human with the thermometer sticking out of its throat. It looked like it had quinsy or the mumps.

I heard him mumbling to himself about scales and what a delicate operation that was. The word hydrochloric acid popped up. "Never do that till the very last," he said solemnly.

"Do what?" I asked, but he didn't hear me, I guess.

"Can't tell what will happen to her when the acid hits her," he mumbled between his teeth.

"Now I tell you," he went on, when he had satisfied himself that there was nothing seriously wrong, "I'm going to block that thermostat open a little more with a piece of wood—and put in a new fan belt. We'll give her an eight pound pull to begin with and after she's gone about four hundred miles you can test her yourself and see if she's slipping." He scratched his head and ruminated a bit "If I were you," he continued, "I'd go back to that service station and ask them to loosen the tappets a little. It says .0010 thousandth on the engine but up here you can ride her at .0008 thousandth—until you hear that funny little noise, that clickety-click-click, you know—like little bracelets. I tried to catch that noise before when she was cold but I couldn't get it. I always like to listen for that little noise—then I know she's not too tight. You see, you've got a hot blue flame in there and when your valves are screwed down too tight that flame just burns them up in no time. That can heat a car up too! Just remember—*the tappets!*"

We had a friendly little chat about the slaughter going on in Europe, to wind up the transaction, and then I shook hands with him. "I don't think you'll have any more trouble," he said. "But just to make sure why you come back here after they loosen the tappets and I'll see how she sounds. Got a nice little car there. She ought to last you another twenty thousand miles—*at least.*"

I went back to the big service station and had the tappets attended to. They were most gracious about it, I must say. No charge for their services this time. Rather strange, I thought. Just as I was pulling out the floorwalker in the butcher's smock informed me with diabolical suavity that, no matter what any one may have told me, the pretty little noise I was looking for had nothing to do with the tightness or looseness of the valves. It was something else which caused that. "We don't believe in loosening them too much," he said. "But you wanted it that way, so we obliged you."

I couldn't pretend to contradict him, not having the knowledge of Hugh Dutter to fortify my argument, so I decided to have the car washed and greased and find out in a roundabout way what the devil he meant.

When I came back for the car the manager came over and politely informed me that there was one other very important thing I ought to have done before leaving. "What's that?" I said.

"Grease the clutch."

How much would that be, I wanted to know. He said it was a thirty minute job—not over a dollar.

"O.K.," I said. "Grease the clutch. Grease everything you can lay hands on."

I took a thirty minute stroll around the block, stopping at a tavern, and when I got back the boy informed me that the clutch didn't need greasing.

"What the hell is this?" I said. "What did he tell me to have it greased for?"

"He tells everybody that," said the boy, grinning.

As I was backing out he asked me slyly if she het up much on me.

"A little," I said.

"Well, don't pay any attention to it," he said. "Just wait till she boils. It's a mighty smooth running car, that

Buick. Prettiest little ole car I ever did see. See us again sometime."

Well, there it is. If you've ever served in the coast artillery you know what it's like to take the azimuth. First you take a course in higher trigonometry, including differential calculus and all the logarithms. When you put the shell in the breech be sure to remove all your fingers before locking the breech. A car is the same way. It's like a horse, in short. What brings on the heat is fuss and bother. Feed him properly, water him well, coax him along when he's weary and he'll die for you. The automobile was invented in order for us to learn how to be patient and gentle with one another. It doesn't matter about the parts, or even about the parts of parts, nor what model or what year it is, so long as you treat her right. What a car appreciates is responsiveness. A loose differential may or may not cause friction and no car, not even a Rolls Royce, will run without a universal, but everything else being equal it's not the pressure or lack of pressure in the exhaust pipe which matters—it's the way you handle her, the pleasant little word now and then, the spirit of forbearance and forgiveness. Do unto others as you would have them do by you is the basic principle of automotive engineering. Henry Ford understood these things from the very beginning. That's why he paid universal wages. He was calibrating the exchequer in order to make the steep grades. There's just one thing to remember about driving any automotive apparatus and that is this: when the car begins to act as though it had the blind staggers it's time to get out and put a bullet through its head. We American people have always been kind to animals and other creatures of the earth. It's in our blood. Be kind to your Buick or your Studebaker. God gave us these blessings in order to enrich the automobile manufacturers. He did not mean for us to lose our tempers easily. If that's clear we can go on to Gallup and trade her in for a spavined mule. . . .

8. Domestic Misery

The forties and fifties will make up the effective end of Miller's literary career. Almost seventy by 1960, The Rosy Crucifixion *finally done, he will write relatively little thereafter and begin to enjoy some of the honors which are due. With the open publication in America of* Tropic of Cancer, Capricorn *and* Black Spring *during the sixties, he begins at last to have something like a comfortable income, and his first love, an old love, returns. Now he would rather do watercolors than write. As he says to Jonathan Cott in an interview in* Rolling Stone,

> I've tried to model myself on the Chinese sages. And they were happy, gay men. I've heard that the old men in China before the Revolution used to sit out on river boats and converse, drink tea, smoke and just enjoy talking about philosophy or literature. They always invited girls to come and drink with them. And then they'd go and fly a kite afterwards, a real kite. I think that's admirable. . . . We flew kites in Big Sur, but there we had big winds in the canyons with birds being lifted by the updrafts. The kites got torn and smashed.*

There has, evidently, been a mellowing. A writer with a tongue like a 400 horsepower motor may dream of silence at the end of his career. In My Life and Times, *a book of inter-*

---

* Reflections of a Cosmic Tourist," *Rolling Stone* (February 27, 1975), pp. 38–46, 57.

views with Bradley Smith, published around his eightieth birthday, he will remark somewhat less happily:

> . . . the way I spend most of my time is not at all the way I would like to spend it. It's because I am still a man with a conscience—which I am sorry about. I am a man who has a regard for his obligations and duties, and these are the things I've been fighting against most of my life. I want to say fuck it all, fuck you all, get out of my life. That's how I feel. I would like, I've repeated it again and again, as far as possible to do nothing, and I mean absolutely nothing. Vegetate almost. Of course it isn't vegetating in the usual sense, but to me it means inactivity, it means a disregard for what people think is important. My emphasis in the last twenty years is in moving from doing to being. I am more interested in being than in doing.
>
> *My Life and Times*

Maybe that is the reasonable dream of any man who spends his life trying to interpret being. Jean-Paul Sartre, now near to totally blind at seventy, remarks that his serious writing is of necessity finished since he doubts if he can shift all those old habits of revision which depend upon looking at what he has written in preceding paragraphs and pages. A little later, Sartre states (not necessarily making the connection) that he does sleep exceptionally well these days. The inside of the soul of a hard-working writer has to be as full of corrosion as a rusty boiler—it is some oil in the essence of quiet time they may look to find before they die.

We are passing, however, too quickly over a period of Miller's life in which he has his last and most profound metamorphosis. If these changes evolve over ten and then close to twenty years—through the first two decades, indeed, after his return to America, it is still necessary to see that he came to live a little at last in the reverberations of the emotions of other people, a sentimental piece of applause for certain if applied to any writer but Miller. He is no ordinary ogre, however; in his beginnings, too many tender sentiments were grown in upon themselves. The fact that Henry Miller is ready to weep over the death of his father, or, for a period, raise his children alone (in all the near insanity of a sixty-year-old man trying to keep up with a six-year-old girl and a three-year-old boy while still obliged to write for a living) is equal in the stimulation it gives our sense of human possibility to the interest we would feel if we learned that Florence Nightingale was—in her closet—an orgy queen. In his remarkable short novel the Devil in Paradise (which takes up the last hundred pages of Big Sur) Miller even descends into the most agonizing of the conformities—he comes, once in his life, to the end of his own generosity and finally turns a man out of his house. His generosity has been abused—so he is smaller, meaner, more cautious, and in pain at the shrinking of his dimensions (like all of us) yet not without a half-admitted pleasure (like all of us) that he has been cold enough and hard enough to reject another soul. While these are typical comedies of behavior for any average man who will proceed precisely out of the logic of his average life to weep over the death of parents, worry about his children, and come to distrust friends, Miller's psyche is more comparable to a hand grenade which exploded in childhood. Pieces of his humanity have been floating down ever since. It is not even too fanciful to see one effort across the length of his work—a disrupted man slowly ingathering the scattered, strewn and dissipated fragments of a lost vision. He will find more than we might expect in the years he lives on the California coast. The wise record he offers in Big Sur and the Oranges of Hieronymus Bosch offers its worth in proportion to how we develop our sense of how much each piece of Miller's philosophy has cost the most unregenerate surrealist of them all.

From

Sunday After the War

I arrived at the dock in practically the same condition in which I had left, that is, penniless. I had been away exactly ten years. It seemed much longer, more like twenty or thirty. What sustained me more than anything else during my residence abroad was the belief that I would never be obliged to return to America.

I had of course kept up a correspondence with the family during this period; it was not a very fulsome correspondence and I am sure it gave them very little idea of what my life really was like. Towards the end of my stay in Paris I received a letter informing me of my father's illness; the nature of it was such that I entertained little hope of finding him alive on my return.

What plagued me all the time I was away, and with renewed force as I was crossing the ocean, was the realization that I could give them no help. In the fifteen years which had elapsed since I began my career I had not only proved incapable of supporting myself by my efforts but I had substantially increased my debts. I was not only penniless, as when I left, but I was further in the hole, so that actually my position was far worse than on leaving the country. All I had to my credit were a few books which more than likely will never be published in this country, at least not as they were written. The few gifts which I had brought with me I was obliged to leave at the Customs because I lacked the money to pay the necessary duty.

As we were going through the immigration formalities the officer asked me jokingly if I were *the* Henry Miller, to which I replied in the same vein that the one he meant was dead. He knew that, of course. Asked as to what I had been doing in Europe all that time I said—"enjoying myself"—an answer which had the double merit of being true and of forestalling further questions.

Almost the first words out of my mother's mouth, after we had greeted each other, were: "Can't you write something like *Gone With the Wind* and make a little money?" I had to confess I couldn't. I seem to be congenitally incapable of writing a best-seller. At Boston, where we first put in, I remember my astonishment on wandering through the railway station when I saw the staggering heaps of books and magazines for sale. (It was my first glimpse of America and I was rather dazzled and bewildered.) *Gone With the Wind* was all over the place, apparently, in a cheap movie edition which looked more interesting to me, accustomed to the paper-covered books of France, than the original format. I wondered vaguely how many millions of dollars had been put in circulation by this book. I noticed that there were other women writers whose works were displayed among the best-sellers. They all seemed to be huge tomes capable of satisfying the most voracious reader. It seemed perfectly natural to me that the women writers of America should occupy such a prominent place. America is essentially a woman's country—why shouldn't the leading novelists be women?

How I had dreaded this moment of returning to the bosom of my family! The thought of walking down this street again had always been a nightmare to me. If any one had told me when in Greece that two months hence I would be doing this I would have told him he was crazy. And yet, when I was informed at the American Consulate in Athens that I would be obliged to return to America I made no effort to resist. I accepted their unwarranted interference as if I were obeying the voice of Fate. Deep down, I suppose, was the realization that I had left something unfinished in America. Moreover, when the summons came I must confess that I was morally and spiritually stronger than I had ever been in my life. "If needs be," I said to myself, "I can go back to America," much as one would say, "I feel strong enough to face anything now!"

Nevertheless, once back in New York it took me several weeks to prepare myself for the ordeal. I had, of course, written my folks that I was on my way. They very naturally expected me to telephone them immediately on my arrival. It was cruel not to do so but I was so intent on easing my own pain that I postponed communicating with them for a week or more. Finally, I wrote them from Virginia, where I had fled almost at once, unable to bear the sight of my native city. What I was hoping for above all, in trying to gain a little time, was a sudden turn of fortune, the advent of a few hundred dollars from a publisher or editor, some little sum with which to save my face. Well, nothing turned up. The one person whom I had vaguely counted on failed me. I mean my American publisher. He hadn't even been willing to assist me in getting back to America, so I learned. He feared that if he sent me the passage money I would squander it on drink or in some other foolish way. He probably means well and he certainly writes well about honoring the artist in our midst, giving him food and drink and that sort of thing. "*Welcome home, Henry Miller. . . .*" I often thought of that phrase of his which he inserted in the preface of my book as I turned about in the rat trap. It's easy to write such things, but to substantiate words with deeds is quite another matter.

It was towards evening when I set out to visit the folks. I came up out of the new Eighth Avenue subway and, though I knew the neighborhood well, immediately proceeded to lose my bearings. Not that the neighborhood had changed much; if anything it was I who had changed. I had changed so completely that I couldn't find my way any more in the old surroundings. I suppose too that getting lost was a last unconscious effort to avoid the ordeal.

As I came down the block where the house stands it seemed to me as if nothing had changed. I was infuriated, in fact, to think that this street which I loathe so much had been so impervious to the march of time. I forget. . . . There was one important change. On the corner where the German grocery store had been, and where I had been horsewhipped as a boy, there now stood a funeral parlor. A rather significant transformation! But what was even more striking is the fact that the undertaker had originally been a neighbor of ours—in the old 14th Ward which we had left years ago. I recognized the name at once. It gave me a creepy feeling, passing his place. Had he divined that we would shortly be in need of his services?

As I approached the gate I saw my father sitting in the armchair by the window. The sight of him sitting there, waiting for me, gave me a terrible pang. It was as though he had been sitting there waiting all these years. I felt at once like a criminal, like a murderer.

It was my sister who opened the iron gate. She had altered considerably, had shrunk and withered like a Chinese nut. My mother and father were standing at the threshold to greet me. They had aged terribly. For the space of a moment I had the uncomfortable sensation of gazing at two mummies who had been removed from the vault and galvanized into a semblance of life. We embraced one another and then we stood apart in silence for another fleeting moment during which I comprehended in a flash the appalling tragedy of their life and of my own life and of every animate creature's on earth. In that moment all the strength which I had accumulated to fortify myself was undone; I was emptied of everything but an overwhelming compassion. When suddenly my mother said, "Well, Henry, how do we look to you?" I let out a groan followed by the most heart-rending sobs. I wept as I had never wept before. My father, to conceal his own feelings, withdrew to the kitchen. I hadn't removed my coat and my hat was still in my hand. In the blinding flood of tears everything was swimming before my eyes. "God Almighty!" I thought to myself, "what have I done? Nothing I thought to accomplish justifies this. I should have remained, I should have sacrificed myself for them. Perhaps there is still time. Perhaps I can do something to prove that I am not utterly selfish. . . ." My mother meanwhile said nothing. Nobody uttered a word. I stood there in the middle of the room with my overcoat on and my hat in my hand and I wept until there were no more tears left. When I had collected myself a bit I dried my eyes and looked about the room. It was the same immaculate place, showing not the least sign of wear or tear, glowing a little brighter, if anything, than before. Or did I imagine it because of my guilt? At any rate, I thanked God, it did not seem poverty-stricken as I had feared it might look. It was the same modest, humble place it had always been. It was like a polished mausoleum in which their misery and suffering had been kept brightly burning.

The table was set; we were to eat in a few moments. It seemed natural that it should be thus, though I hadn't the slightest desire to eat. In the past the great emotional scenes which I had witnessed in the bosom of the family were nearly always associated with the table. We pass easily from sorrow to gluttony.

We sat down in our accustomed places, looking somewhat more cheerful, if not actually merry, than we had a few moments ago. The storm had passed; there would only be slight and distant reverberations henceforth. I had hardly taken the spoon in my hand when they all began to talk at once. They had been waiting for this moment a long time; they wanted to pour out in a few minutes all that had been accumulating for ten years. Never have I felt so willing to listen. Had they poured it out for twenty-four hours on end I would have sat patiently, without a murmur, without a sign of restlessness, until the last word had been uttered. Now at last they had me and could tell me everything. They were so eager to begin, so beside themselves with joy, that it all came out in a babble. It was almost as if they feared that I would run off again and stay away another ten years.

It was about time for the war news and so they turned the radio on, thinking that I would be interested. In the midst of the babble and confusion, boats going down, ammunition works blasted, and the same smooth dentifricial voice switching from calamities to razor blades without a change of intonation or inflection, my mother interrupted the hubbub to tell me that they had been thinking about my homecoming and had planned that I should share a bed with my father. She said she would sleep with my sister in the little room where I had slept as a boy. That brought on another choking fit. I told them there was no need to worry about such things, that I had already found a place to stay and that everything was jake. I tried to tell them jokingly that I was now a celebrity, but it didn't sound very convincing either to them or to myself.

"Of course," said my mother, ignoring what I had just said, "it may be a little inconvenient for you; Father has to get up now and then during the night—but you'll get used to it. I don't hear him any more."

I looked at my father. "Yes," he said, "since the operation, the last one, I'm lucky if I get three or four hours' sleep." He drew aside his chair and pulled up the leg of his trousers to show me the bag which was strapped to his leg. "That's what I have to wear now," he said. "I can't urinate any more the natural way. It's a nuisance, but what can you do? They did the best they could for me." And he went on hurriedly to tell me of how good the doctor had been to him, though he was a perfect stranger and a Jew to boot. "Yes," he added, "they took me to the Jewish hospital. And I must say I couldn't have had better treatment anywhere."

I wondered how that had come about—the Jewish hospital—because my mother had always been scared to death of anything remotely connected with the Jews. The explanation was quite simple. They had outlived the family doctor and all the other doctors in the neighborhood whom they once knew. At the last moment some one had recommended the Jewish doctor, and since he was not only a specialist but a surgeon they had acquiesced. To their astonishment he had proved to be not only a good doctor but an entirely kind and sympathetic person. "He treated me as if he were my own son," said my father. Even my mother had to admit that they couldn't have found a better man. What seemed to impress them most about the hospital, I was amazed to learn, was the wonderful grub which they served there. One could eat à la carte apparently—and as much as one cared to. But the nurses were not Jewish, they wanted me to know. They were Scandinavian for the most part. The Jews don't like such jobs, they explained. "You know, they never like to do the dirty work," said my mother.

In the midst of the narrative, hardly able to wait for my mother to finish, my father suddenly recalled that he had made a note of some questions he wished to put to me. He asked my sister to get the slip of paper for him. Whereupon, to my surprise, my sister calmly told him to wait, that she hadn't finished her meal yet. With that he gave me a look, as much as to say—"you see what I have to put up with here!" I got up and found the piece of paper on which he had listed the questions. My father put on his spectacles and began to read.

"Oh, first of all," he exclaimed, "what pier did you dock at?"

I told him.

"That's what I thought," he said. "*Now*, what was the grub like on board the boat? Was it American cooking or Greek?"

The other questions were in a similar vein. Had we received the wireless news every day? Did I have to share my cabin with others? Did we sight any wrecks? And then this—which took me completely by surprise: "*What is the Parthenon?*"

I explained briefly what the Parthenon was.

"Well, that's all right," he said, as though to say—"no need to go into that any further." "I only asked," he added, looking up over the top of his spectacles, "because Mother said she thought it was a park. I knew it wasn't a park. How old did you say it was again?" He paused a moment to hmmn. "The place must be full of old relics," he added. Well, anyway, it must have been very interesting in Greece, that's what he thought. As for himself he had always wanted to see Italy—and London. He asked about Savile Row where the merchant tailors have their shops. "You say the tailors (meaning the workmen on the bench) are all English? No Jews or Italians, eh?" "No," I said, "they all seemed to be English, from their looks anyway." "That's queer," he reflected. "Must be a strange place, London."

He moved over to the armchair near the window. "I can't sit here very long," he said, "it sinks down too low. In a moment I'll change to the hard chair. You see, with all this harness on it gets pretty uncomfortable at times, especially when it's warm." As he talked he kept pressing the long tube which ran down his leg. "You see, it's getting gritty again. Just like sand inside. You'd never think that you pass off all that solid matter in your urine, would you? It's the damndest thing. I take all the medicines he prescribes religiously, but the damned stuff *will* accumulate. That's my condition, I suppose. When it gets too thick I have to go to the doctor and let him irrigate me. About once a month, that is. *And does that hurt!* Well, we won't talk about that now. Some times it's worse than other times. There was one time I thought I couldn't stand it any more—they must have heard me for blocks around. If everything goes well I can stretch the visits to five or six weeks. It's five dollars a crack, you know."

I ventured to suggest that it might be better if he went oftener instead of trying to stretch it out.

"That's just what I say," he responded promptly. "But Mother says we have to economize—there's nothing coming in any more, you know. Of course she doesn't have to stand the pain."

I looked at my mother inquiringly. She was irritated that my father should have put it thus. "You can't run to the doctor every time you have a little pain," she said scoldingly, as if to rebuke him for having brought up the subject. "I've told him time and again that's his condition."

By condition she meant that he would have to endure his suffering until . . . well, if she had to put it baldly she would say—*until the end*. He was lucky to be alive, after all he had gone through. "If it weren't for that old bag, for that awful leakage," she ruminated aloud, "Father would be all right. You see what an appetite he has—and what a color!"

"Yes," my sister put in, "he eats more than any of us. We do all the work; he has it easy."

My father gave me another look. My mother, catching his mute appeal, tried to pass it over lightly with a little joke, one of those crude jokes which the family were fond of. "Look at him," she said with a slightly hysterical laugh, "hasn't he a good color? Why, he's as tough as an old rooster. You couldn't kill him off with an axe!"

It was impossible for me to laugh at this. But my sister, who had learned to take her cue from my mother, suddenly grew apoplectic with indignation. "Look at us," she exclaimed, rolling her head from side to side. "Look how thin we got! Seventy times a day I climbed the stairs when Father was in bed! Everybody tells me how bad I look, that I must take care of myself. We don't even have a chance to go to the movies. I haven't been to New York for over a year."

"And I have a cinch of it, is that it?" my father put in pepperily. "Well, I wish I could change places with you, that's all I want to say."

"Come now," said my mother, addressing my father as if he were a petulant child, "you know you shouldn't talk like that. We're doing our best, you know that."

"Yes," said my father, his tone getting more caustic, "and what about that cranberry juice I'm supposed to drink every day?"

With this my mother and sister turned on him savagely. How could he talk that way, they wanted to know, when they had been working themselves to the bone nursing and tending him? They turned to me. I must try to understand, they explained, that it was difficult sometimes to get out of the house, even to go as far as the corner.

"Couldn't you use the phone?" I asked.

The phone had been disconnected long ago, they told me. Another of my mother's economies, it seemed.

"But supposing something happened during the night?" I ventured to say.

"That's just what I tell them," my father put in. "That was Mother's idea, shutting off the phone. I never approved of it."

"The things you say!" said my mother, trying to silence him with a frowning grimace. She turned to me, as if I were the very seat of reason. "All the neighbors have phones," she said. "Why, they won't even let me pay for a call—but of course I do in some other way. And then there's Teves up at the corner. . . ."

"You mean the undertaker?" I said.

"Yes," said my father. "You see, when the weather permits I often take a stroll as far as the corner. If Teves is there he brings a camp chair out for me—and if I want to make a call why I use his phone. He never charges me for it. He's been very decent, I must say that." And then he went on to explain to me how nice it was to be able to sit up there at the corner and watch the promenade. There was more life there, he reflected almost wistfully. "You know, one gets sick of seeing the same faces all the time, isn't that so?"

"I hope you're not sick of us!" said my mother reproachfully.

"You know that's not what I mean," replied my father, obviously a little weary of this sort of exchange.

As I got up to change my seat I noticed a pile of old newspapers on the rocker. "What are you doing with those?" I asked.

"Don't touch them!" screamed my sister. "Those are for me!"

My father quickly explained that my sister had taken to reading the papers since my absence. "It's good for her," he said, "it takes her mind off things. She's a little slow, though . . . always about a month behind."

"I am not," said my sister tartly. "I'm only two weeks behind. If we didn't have so much work to do I'd be up to date. The minister says. . . ."

"All right, you win," said my father, trying to shut her up. "You can't say a word in this house without stepping on someone's toes."

There was a Vox-Pop program due over the radio any minute. They wanted to know if I had ever heard it, but before I could say yes or no my sister put in her oar—she wanted to listen to the choir singing carols. "Perhaps he'd like to hear some more war news," said my mother. She said it as though, having just come from Europe, I had a special proprietary interest in the grand carnage.

"Have you ever heard Raymond Gram Swing?" asked my father.

I was about to tell him I hadn't when my sister informed us that he wasn't on this evening.

"How about Gabriel Heatter then?" said my father.

"He's no good," said my sister, "he's a Jew."

"What's that got to do with it?" said my father.

"I like Kaltenborn," said my sister. "He has such a beautiful voice."

"Personally," said my father, "I prefer Raymond Swing. He's very impartial. He always begins—'Good *Evening!*' Never 'Ladies and gentlemen' or 'My friends,' as President Roosevelt says. You'll see. . . ."

This conversation was like a victrola record out of the past. Suddenly the whole American scene, as it is portrayed over the radio, came flooding back—chewing gum, furniture polish, can openers, mineral waters, laxatives, ointments, corn cures, liver pills, insurance policies; the crooners with their eunuchlike voices; the comedians with their stale jokes; the puzzlers with their inane questions (how many matches in a cord of wood?) ; the Ford Sunday evening hour, the Bulova watch business, the xylophones, the quartets, the bugle calls, the roosters crowing, the canaries warbling, the chimes bringing tears, the songs of yesterday, the news fresh from the griddle, the facts, the facts, the facts. . . . Here it was again, the same old stuff, and as I was soon to discover, more stupefying and stultifying than ever. A man named Fadiman, whom I was later to see in the movies with a quartet of well-informed nitwits, had organized some kind of puzzle committee—*Information Please*, I think it was called. This apparently was the *coup de grâce* of the evening's entertainment and befuddlement. This was real education, so they informed me. I squirmed in my seat and tried to assume an air of genuine interest.

It was a relief when they shut the bloody thing off and settled down to telling me about their friends and neighbors, about the accidents and illnesses of which seemingly there was no end. Surely I remembered Mrs. Froehlich? Well, all of a sudden—she was the picture of health, mind you!—she was taken to the hospital to be operated on. Cancer of the bladder it was. Lasted only two months. And just before she died—"she doesn't know it," said my father, absent-mindedly using the present tense—her husband met with an accident. Ran into a tree and had his head taken off—just as clean as a razor. The undertakers had sewn it back on, of course—wonderful job they made of it too. Nobody would have been able to tell it, seeing him lying there in the coffin. Marvelous what they can do nowadays, the old man reflected aloud. Anyway, that's how it was with Mrs. Froehlich. Nobody would have thought that those two would pass on so quickly. They were only in their fifties. . . .

Listening to their recital I got the impression that the whole neighborhood was crippled and riddled with malignant diseases. Everybody with whom they had any dealings, friend, relative, neighbor, butcher, letter-carrier, gas inspector, every one without exception carried about with him perpetually a little flower which grew out of his own body and which was named after one or the other of the familiar maladies, such as rheumatism, arthritis, pneumonia, cancer, dropsy, anemia, dysentery, meningitis, epilepsy, hernia, encephalitis, megalomania, chilblains, dyspepsia and so on and so forth. Those who weren't crippled, diseased or insane were out of work and living on relief. Those who could use their legs were on line at the movies waiting for the doors to be thrown open. I was reminded in a mild way of *Voyage au Bout de la Nuit*. The difference between these two worlds otherwise so similar lay in the standard of living; even those on relief were living under conditions which would have seemed luxurious to that suburban working class whom Céline writes about. In Brooklyn, so it seemed to me, they were dying of malnutrition of the soul. They lived on as vegetable tissue, flabby, sleep-drugged, disease-ridden carcasses with just enough intelligence to enable them to buy oil burners, radios, automobiles, newspapers, tickets for the cinema. One whom I had known as a ballplayer when I was a boy was now a retired policeman who spent his evenings writing in old Gothic. He had composed the Lord's Prayer in this script on a small piece of cardboard, so they were telling me, and when it was finished he discovered that he had omitted a word. So he was doing it over again, had been at it over a month already. He lived with his sister, an old maid, in a lugubrious big house which they had inherited from their parents. They didn't want any tenants—it was too much bother. They never went anywhere, never visited anybody, never had any company. The sister was a gossip who sometimes took three hours to get from the house to the corner drug store. It was said that they would leave their money to the Old Folks' Home when they died.

My father seemed to know every one for blocks around. He also knew who came home late at night because, sitting in the parlor at the front window all hours of the night waiting for the water to flow, he got a slant on things such as he'd never had before. What amazed him apparently was the number of young women who came home alone at all hours of the night, some of them tight as a pigskin. People no longer had to get up early to go to work, at least not in this neighborhood. When he was a boy, he remarked, work began at daylight and lasted till ten in the evening. At eight-thirty, while these good for nothings were still turning over in bed, he was already having a second breakfast, meaning some pumpernickel sandwiches and a pitcher of beer.

The recital was interrupted because the bag was beginning to fill up. In the kitchen my father emptied the contents of the bag into an old beer pitcher, examined it to see if the urine looked cloudy or sandy, and then emptied it in the toilet. His whole attention, since the advent of the bag, was concentrated on the quality and flow of his urine. "People say hello, how are you getting on, and then biffo! they forget about you," he said, as he came back and resumed his place by the window. It was a random remark, apropos of nothing as far as I can remember, but what he meant evidently was that others *could* forget whereas he couldn't. At night, on going to bed, he had always the comforting thought that in an hour or two he would be obliged to get up and catch the urine before it began to leak out of the hole which the doctor had drilled in his stomach. There were rags lying about everywhere, ready to catch the overflow, and newspapers, in order to prevent the bedding and furniture from being ruined by the endless flow. Sometimes it would take hours for the urine to begin flowing and at other times the bag would have to be emptied two or three times in quick succession; now and then it would come out in the natural way also, as well as from the tube and the wound itself. It was a humiliating sort of malady as well as a painful one.

Out of a clear sky my mother, in an obviously false natural voice, suddenly requested me to accompany her upstairs, saying she wanted to show me some of the improvements which had been made during my absence. We no sooner got to the landing than she began explaining to me in muffled tones that my father's condition was incurable. "He'll never get well," she said, "it's . . . ," and she mentioned that word which has come to be synonymous with modern civilization, the word which holds the same terror for the man of today as did leprosy for the men of old. It was no surprise to me, I must say. If anything, I was amazed that it was only that and nothing more. What bothered me more than anything was the loud voice in which she was whispering to me, for the doors were all open and my father could easily have heard what she was saying had he tried. I made her walk me through the rooms and tell me in a natural voice about the various renovations, about the thermostat, for instance, which was hanging on the wall under my grandfather's portrait. That fortunately brought up the subject of the new oil burner, thus precipitating a hurried visit of inspection to the cellar.

The appearance of the cellar was a complete surprise. It had been denuded, the coal bins removed, the shelves taken out, the walls whitewashed. Like some medieval object used by alchemists, there stood the oil burner, neat, immaculate, silent, except for a spasmodic ticking whose rhythm was unpredictable. From the reverence with which my mother spoke of it I gathered that the oil burner was quite the most important object in the house. I gazed at it in fascination and astonishment. No more coal or wood, no ashes to haul, no coal gas, no watching, no fussing, no fuming, no dirt, no smoke; temperature always the same, one for day and one for night; the little instrument on the parlor wall regulated its functioning automatically. It was as though a magician had secreted himself in the walls of the house, a new electrodynamic, super-heterodyne god of the hearth. The cellar, which had once been a frightening place filled with unknown treasures, had now become bright and habitable; one could serve lunch down there on the concrete floor. With the installation of the oil burner a good part of my boyhood was wiped out. Above all I missed the shelves where the wine bottles covered with cobwebs had been kept. There was no more wine, no more champagne, not even a case of beer. Nothing but the oil burner—and that peculiar, unnaturally rhythmed ticking which however muffled always gave me a start.

As we climbed the stairs I observed another sacred object also ticking in a mechanically epileptic way—the refrigerator. I hadn't seen a refrigerator since I left America and of course those I had known then were long since outmoded. In France I hadn't even used an ice-box, such as we had been accustomed to at home. I bought only as much as was required for the current meal; what was perishable perished, whatever turned sour turned sour, that was all. Nobody I knew in Paris owned a refrigerator; nobody I knew ever thought of refrigerators. As for Greece, where coal was at a premium, the cooking was done on charcoal stoves. And, if one had any culinary instincts, the meals could be just as palatable, just as delicious and nourishing as anywhere else. I was reminded of Greece and the charcoal stoves because I had suddenly become aware that the old coal stove in the kitchen was missing, its place taken now by a shining white enameled gas range, another indispensable, just-as-cheap and equally sacred object as the oil burner and the refrigerator. I began to wonder if my mother had become a little daffy during my absence. Was everybody installing these new conveniences? I inquired casually. Most everybody, was the answer, including some who couldn't afford to do so. The Gothic maniac and his sister hadn't, to be sure, but then they were eccentric—they never bought anything unless they had to. My mother, I couldn't deny, had the good excuse that they were getting old and that these little innovations meant a great saving of labor. I was glad, in fact, that they had been able to provide for themselves so well. At the same time, however, I couldn't help but think of the old ones in Europe; they had not only managed to do without these comforts but, so it seemed to me, they remained far healthier, saner and more joyous than the old ones in America. America has comforts; Europe has other things which make all these comforts seem quite unimportant.

During the conversation which ensued my father brought up the subject of the tailor shop which he hadn't set foot in for over three years. He complained that he never heard a word from his former partner. "He's too miserly to spend a nickel on a telephone call," he said. "I know there was an order from So-and-so for a couple of suits; that was about six months ago. I haven't heard a word about it since." I naturally volunteered to pay a visit to the shop one day and inquire about things. "Of course," he said, "he doesn't have to worry any more whether things go or not. His daughter is a movie star now, you know." It was possible too, he went on to say, that the client had gone off on a cruise; he was always knocking about somewhere in his yacht. "By the time he comes in again he'll have either gained a few pounds or lost a few, and then everything will have to be altered. It may be a year before he's ready to take the clothes."

I learned that there were now about a dozen customers left on the books. No new ones forthcoming, of course. It was like the passing of the buffaloes. The man with the yacht who had ordered two precious suits of clothes, for which he was in no apparent hurry, used formerly to order a dozen at a time, to say nothing of cutaways, overcoats, dinner jackets, and so on. Nearly all the great merchant tailors of the past were either out of business, in bankruptcy, or about to give up. The great English woolen houses which had once served them were now shrunk to insignificant size. Though we have more millionaires than ever, fewer men seem inclined to pay two hundred dollars for an ordinary sack suit. Curious, what!

It was not only pathetic, it was ludicrous, to hear him talking about those two suits which, by the way, I was to remember to ask his partner not to leave hanging on the rack by the front window because they would be faded by the time the man called for a fitting. They had become mythical, legendary—the two suits ordered by a millionaire in the year '37 or '38 just prior to a short cruise in the Mediterranean. If all went well why possibly two years hence there would be ten or fifteen dollars accruing to the old man as his share of the transaction. Wonderful state of affairs! Somehow the two legendary suits belonged with the oil burner and the frigidaire—part and parcel of the same system of luxurious waste. Meantime, just to take a random shot, the fumes from the copper smelting plant at Ducktown, Tennessee, had rendered absolutely deathlike and desolate the whole region for fifty miles around. (To see this region is to have a premonition of the fate of still another planet—our Earth—should the human experiment fail. Here Nature resembles the raw backside of a sick chimpanzee.) The president of the plant, undisturbed by the devastation, to say nothing of the premature deaths in the mines, may possibly be getting ready to order a hunting jacket on his coming trip to New York. Or he may have a son who is preparing to enter the Army as a brigadier-general for whom he will put in an order for the appropriate outfit when the time comes. That disease which boss tailors acquire, just like other people, won't be such a terrifying thing to the president of Copper Hill, should it strike him down, because with trained nurses to irrigate him every few hours and a specialist to summon by taxi when he has a little pain, he can have quite a tolerable time of it—perhaps not as much rich food as he is used to having, but plenty of good things just the same, including a game of cards every night or a visit to the cinema in his wheel chair.

As for my father, he has his little pleasure too every month or so, when he is given a joy ride to the doctor's office. I was a little annoyed that my father should be so grateful to his friend for acting as a chauffeur once a month. And when my mother began to lay it on about the kindness of the neighbors—letting her telephone free of charge and that sort of thing—I was about ready to explode. "What the devil," I remarked, "it's no great favor they're doing. A nigger would do as much for you—more maybe. That's the least one can do for a friend."

My mother looked aggrieved. She begged me not to talk that way. And in the next breath she went on to say how good the people next door were to her, how they left the morning paper for them at the window every evening. And another neighbor down the block was thoughtful enough to save the old rags which accumulated. Real Christians, I must say. Generous souls, what!

"And the Helsingers?" I said, referring to their old friends who were now millionaires. "Don't they do anything for you?"

"Well," my father began, "you know what a stinker he always was. . . ."

"How can you talk that way!" exclaimed my mother.

"I'm only telling the truth," said the old man innocently.

They had been very kind and thoughtful too, my mother tried to say. The proof of it was that they had remembered on their last visit—eight months ago—to bring a jar of preserves from their country estate.

"So that's it!" I broke out, always enraged by the very mention of their name. "So that's the best they can do, is it?"

"They have their own troubles," said my mother reprovingly. "You know Mr. Helsinger is going blind."

"Good," I said bitterly. "I hope he grows deaf and dumb too—and paralyzed to boot."

Even my father thought this a bit too vehement. "Still," he said, "I can't say that I ever knew him to do a generous deed. He was always close, even from the beginning. But he's losing it all now—the boy is going through it fast."

"That's fine," I said. "I hope he loses every penny of it before he croaks. I hope he dies in want—and in pain and agony."

Here my sister suddenly popped up. "You shouldn't talk that way," she said, "you'll be punished for it. Pastor Liederkranz says we must only speak good of one another." And with the mention of the pastor's name she began to ramble on about Greece which his holiness, the Episcopal cheese of the diocese, had visited last year during his vacation.

"And what have they done for you all?" (meaning the church) I asked, turning to my father and mother.

"We never belonged to any church, you know," said my mother softly.

"Well, *she* belongs, doesn't she?" I said, nodding in my sister's direction. "Isn't that enough for them?"

"They have their own to take care of."

"*Their own!*" I said sneeringly. "That's a good excuse."

"He's right," said my father. "They could have done *something.* You take the Lutheran Church—we're not members of that either, but they send us things just the same, don't they. And they come and visit us, too. How do you explain that?" and he turned on my mother rather savagely, as if to show that he was a bit fed up with her continuous whitewashing of this one and that.

At this juncture my sister, who always became alert when the church was involved, reminded us that a new parish house was being built—there would be new pews installed too, we shouldn't forget that either. "That costs something!" she snarled.

"All right, you win!" yelled my father. I had to laugh. I had never realized before what an obstinate, tenacious creature my sister could be. Half-witted though she was, she seemed to realize that she needn't let my father bulldoze her any longer. She could even be cruel, in her witless way. "No, I won't get any cigarettes for you," she would say to the old man. "You smoke too much. We don't smoke and we're not sick."

The great problem, the old man confided to me when we were alone for a few minutes, was to be able to have a quarter in his pocket at all times—"in case anything should happen," as he put it. "They mean well," he said, "but they don't understand. They think I ought to cut out the cigarettes, for instance. By God, I have to do something to while away the time, don't I? Of course it means fifteen cents a day, but. . . ."

I begged him not to say any more about it. "I'll see that you have cigarettes at least," I said, and with that I fished out a couple of dollars and blushingly thrust the money in his hand.

"Are you sure you can spare it?" said my father, quickly hiding it away. He leaned forward and whispered: "Better not let them know you gave me anything—they'll take it away from me. They say I don't need any money."

I felt wretched and exasperated.

"Understand," he went on, "I don't mean to complain. But it's like the doctor business. Mother wants me to delay the visits as long as possible. It's not right, you know. If I wait too long the pains get unbearable. When I tell her that she says—'*it's your condition.*' Half the time I don't dare tell her I'm in pain; I don't want to annoy her. But I do think if I went a little oftener it would ease things up a bit, don't you?"

I was so choked with rage and mortification I could scarcely answer him. It seemed to me that he was being slowly tortured and humiliated; they behaved as if he had committed a crime by becoming ill. Worse, it was as if my mother, knowing that he would never get well, looked upon each day that he remained alive as so much unnecessary expense. She delighted in depriving herself of things, in order to impress my father with the need of economizing. Actually the only economy he could practice would be to die. That's how it looked to me, though I dare say if I had put it to my mother that way she would have been horrified. She was working herself to the bone, no doubt about that. And she had my sister working the treadmill too. But it was all stupid—unnecessary labor for the most part. They *created* work for themselves. When any one remarked how pale and haggard they looked they would reply with alacrity—"Well, some one has to keep going. We can't all afford to be ill." As though to imply that being ill was a sinful luxury.

As I say, there was a blend of stupidity, criminality and hypocrisy in the atmosphere. By the time I was ready to take leave my throat was sore from repressing my emotions. The climax came when, just as I was about to slip into my overcoat, my mother in a tearful voice came rushing up to me and, holding me by the arm, said: "Oh Henry, there's a thread on your coat!" A thread, by Jesus! That was the sort of thing she would give attention to! The way she uttered the word thread was as if she had spied a leprous hand sticking out of my coat pocket. All her tenderness came out in removing that little white thread from my sleeve. Incredible—and disgusting! I embraced them in turn rapidly and fled out of the house. In the street I allowed the tears to flow freely. I sobbed and wept unrestrainedly all the way to the elevated station. As I entered the train, as we passed the names of familiar stations, all of them recalling some old wound or humiliation, I began enacting in my mind the scene I had just been through, began by describing it as if I were seated before the typewriter with a fresh piece of paper in the roller. "Jesus, don't forget that about the head that was sewn on," I would say to myself, the tears streaming down my face and blinding me. "*Don't forget this . . . don't forget that.*" I was conscious that everybody's eyes were focused on me, but still I continued to weep and to write. When I got to bed the sobbing broke out again. I must have gone on sobbing in my sleep for in the early morning I heard some one rapping on the wall and awoke to find my face wet with tears. The outburst continued intermittently for about thirty-six hours; any little thing served to make me break out afresh. It was a complete purge which left me exhausted and refreshed at the same time.

From **Big Sur**

As a father I've also been somewhat of a mother, because not having a job like other honest citizens—writing is only a pastime!—I was always within earshot, always within reach, when the kids got out of hand. As a father who was also unhappily married, I had often to act as arbiter when there should have been no need for an arbiter. Whatever decisions I made, they were wrong, and they were subsequently used against me. At least, so it seemed to me.

One of the minor aspects of this tragicomic dilemma was the fact that my wife believed that she was protecting *me*. Protecting me, I mean to say, from the annoyances which children are prone to inflict upon fathers who have nothing more important to do than write books. Since she did everything by the book, and to the extreme, the protection she was offering me usually worked more harm than good. Or so I regarded it. (I know I didn't always see straight!)

Anyway, it went something like this. . . . No matter what happened, they were not to disturb me at work. If they fell and hurt themselves, they were not to make a fuss about it. If they had to weep or scream, they were to do it out of earshot. (It never occurred to her, I suppose, that I would have felt much better if they had come and wept on my shoulder.) Whatever it was they wanted, they were to wait until I was ready to give them my attention. If, in spite of all injunctions, they knocked at my studio door—and they did, of course!—

they were made to feel that they were guilty of committing a small crime. And, if I were foolish enough to open the door and give them a moment's attention, then I was abetting the crime. Worse, I was guilty of sabotage. If I took a breather, and profited by it to see what the kids were up to, then I was guilty of encouraging them to expect things of me which they had no right to expect.

By midafternoon I usually had but one thought—to get as far away from the house as possible, and take the kids with me. Often we would return home exhausted. And when children get exhausted they are not the most amenable creatures in the world.

It was an endless circle. *Punkt!*

When the separation came about I made a forlorn and desperate effort to be a father *and* mother. The girl had just started school, but the boy, her junior by three years, was too young to attend school. What he needed was a nurse or a governess. Now and then a neighbor—and here I think especially of that kind soul, Dorothy Herbert—came and lent a hand. In a short time I realized that there was nothing to do but to entrust the boy to his mother's care, which I did, with the understanding that she would return him to me as soon as I found someone capable of providing him with the proper care and attention.

Shortly thereafter an attractive-looking woman knocked at the door and said she had been told that I was looking for someone to take care of my children. She had two children of her own, about the same age as ours, and she had separated from her husband. All she wanted was room and board in exchange for her services. As she expressed it, she didn't care what was demanded of her, if only she might live in Big Sur.

Her arrival coincided with the arrival of my wife and boy, who had come to celebrate the girl's birthday. What a stroke of fortune, I thought, as I explained the situation. To my astonishment my wife agreed that the young woman seemed suitable for the task, and after a few tears, consented to leave the boy in my care.

It was a hectic day. From miles around the kids had come to celebrate and jubilate. Some of them brought their parents along.

I forgot to say that a few days previous to this event my friend Walker Winslow had installed himself in the studio above. He had driven all the way from Topeka with his left hand, having cracked his right shoulder blade some weeks before. Knowing of my plight, Walker had volunteered his services as cook and part-time "governess," hoping, no doubt, that he would find a few hours a day in which to work in peace and quiet. (He had received a commission from a big publisher to do a book on the founder of the Menninger Foundation, where he had been staying.*) He also looked forward, no doubt, to repeating the pleasant experiences we had shared while at Anderson Creek.

In the course of the merrymaking the young woman, Ivy was her name, discreetly withdrew from sight. She was shy and somewhat embarrassed, knowing no one present and having no particular role to fill. Strolling about by her lonesome she ran into Walker.

As Walker related it to me afterwards, Ivy was on the point of leaving then and there. She was depressed, confused, and thoroughly ill at ease. However, after a cup of coffee and a quiet chat in the studio, he had succeeded in restoring her self-confidence. Walker is easy to talk to, and women particularly find him very understanding, very comforting.

Later that day he took me aside to explain that I might have difficulties with Ivy, that she was emotionally disturbed because of her own unhappy life, and somewhat intimidated

---

* *The Menninger Story* (New York: Doubleday & Co., Inc., 1956).

by the responsibility she was assuming. The situation was aggravated, for her, by the fact that she would be obliged to leave her own two children in her husband's care.

"I felt I ought to tell you this," he said. Then he added: "But I think she deserves a tryout. She means well, I know that."

Walker was of the opinion that if the arrangement didn't work out well he and I should be able to look after the children. I could take care of Tony in the morning and he in the afternoon. He would do all the cooking and the dishwashing too. But it would be better if Ivy proved equal to the task.

Ivy lasted just about twelve hours. She quit cold, giving as her reason that my kids were "impossible." My wife, of course, had already left and I was in no hurry to inform her of the turn of events. Walker had to drive Ivy and her two youngsters to town and rush home to prepare the evening meal.

After dinner we had a short talk. "Are you sure you want to keep the children now?" he asked. I told him I felt up to it, if he would carry out his end of the bargain.

The very next day the fun began. To devote a whole morning to a three-year-old boy full of piss and vinegar is a job for someone with six hands and three pairs of legs. No matter what we decided to play, the jig lasted only a few minutes. Every toy in the place had been taken out, used, and thrown aside in less than an hour. If I suggested that we go for a walk he was too tired. There was an old tricycle he liked to ride, but before the morning was out a wheel had come off and, though I sweated blood, I simply could not make it stay on again. I tried playing ball but his co-ordination wasn't good enough; I almost had to stand on top of him and put the ball in his hands. I got out his building blocks too—several bushel baskets full—and tried, as they say, to have him do something "constructive," but his interest in this pastime lay exclusively in kicking the house, or the bridge, apart after I had built it. That was fun! I tied all his choo-choo cars together, added a few tin cans and other noise-makers to them, and ran about like a zany while he sat and watched me. This bored the shit out of him in no time.

At intervals Walker showed up to see how we were making out. Finally—it couldn't have been later than ten o'clock, if that late—he said: "Go up and work a while. I'll take over. You need a break."

More to recover myself than to work, I reluctantly obeyed. There I sat, in my den, poring over the pages I had just finished, but too dead to squeeze out another line. What I wanted, early as it was, was a nap! I could hear Tony shouting and screaming, shrieking and wailing. Poor Walker!

When Val arrived, after school, the difficulties increased. It was nothing but fight, fight, fight. Even if it were nothing more than a rock which one of them had picked up, the other one immediately claimed it. *It's mine, I saw it first! You did not! I did too see it first. Caca pipi head, caca pipi head!* (Their favorite expression.) It now demanded the full time of the two of us to handle the situation. By dinnertime we were always pooped out.

It was the same old story every day. No improvements, no progress. An absolute standstill. Walker, being an early riser, managed to get some work done before breakfast. He was up at five, regular as a clock. After he had made himself a pot of strong coffee he would sit down to the machine. When he wrote, he wrote fast. He did everything fast. As for me, I would remain in bed till the last horn, hoping to store up an extra supply of nervous energy. (I didn't know, in those days, about "rose hips," nor about calcium and phosphorus tablets, nor about tiger's milk.) As for getting any writing done I dismissed the idea once and for all. Even a writer has first of all to be, and to feel like, a human being. My problem was—to survive. Always I nourished the illusion that someone would turn up to rescue me, someone who loved children and knew how to handle them. Whatever I needed usually came my way, when sorely pressed. Why not the perfect governess? In my dreams I always pictured my savior in the guise of a Hindu, Javanese or Mexican, a woman of the people, simple, not too intelligent, but definitely possessed of that one great prerequisite: *patience*.

Evenings, after the kids had been put to bed, poor Walker would endeavor to engage me in talk. It was hopeless. I had only one thought in mind—to get to bed as soon as possible. Every day I would say to myself: "It can't go on this way forever. *Courage*, you poor imbecile!" Every night, on climbing into bed, I would repeat: "Another day! Patience, patience!"

One day, after he had been to town to fetch supplies, Walker quietly announced that he had looked up Ivy. "Just wanted to see how she was getting along." I thought it was very kind of Walker to do that. Just like him, of course. The sort of man who looks after every one who is in trouble. And always getting himself into trouble.

What I didn't know, until after the next trip to town, was that he and Ivy had become close friends. Or, as he put it: "Ivy seems to have a yen for me." In the interim Ivy's problems had taken a new twist. Having no means of support, she had been obliged to surrender her children to her husband. She was supposed to be quite cut up about this.

I had made the mistake of telling Walker that I never wanted to see Ivy again. She had left me in the lurch after a half-hearted effort and, like the elephant, I found it hard to forgive her. If her own children were well behaved, I said, it was only because their mother was a cold, ruthless bitch.

Walker defended her as best as he could, assuring me

that I would change my mind once I got to know her. "She has her troubles too," he said. "Don't forget that." But I was thoroughly unimpressed.

Winter had set in and with it the rains. Ivy showed up unannounced one afternoon and remained a few days. She made no effort to help with the children, or even with the cooking and cleaning. Knowing that I disliked her, she kept out of bounds. Occasionally she would pop in toward dark to sit by the little stove and poke the fire. For some reason she had fallen in love with this stove, so much so that she kept it clean and polished.

How the two of them managed in the studio above was beyond me. It was altogether without conveniences of any kind; there wasn't even a sink in it. The wood-stove, which I found somewhere, smoked continually. The floor was of cement and over it, to keep his feet dry, Walker had strewn some filthy, discarded rugs, potato sacks and torn sheets. The sliding door, which used to be the entrance (when it was a garage), gaped at both ends, thus providing an unwelcome circulation of air. Overhead, between the plaster-boards and the roofing, the squirrels and the rats made merry night and day. What was particularly exacerbating was the sound of nuts rolling back and forth up there. Not only did the roof leak but the windows too. When it rained a pool of water collected on the floor in no time. Hardly a "love nest," I must say.

Ivy had hardly returned to town when the rains came down in earnest. Never have I seen it rain as it did that winter. For days on end it deluged us, like a punishment from above. During this period it was impossible for Val to go to school; the school was about ten miles away and the road from our house to the highway was virtually unnavigable. This meant that I had to keep the two of them indoors—and keep them happy.

We worked at it in relays, Walker and I. When it came nap time I lay down with them. I hoped by doing so to replenish my powers for the second half of the day. What a delusion! All we did at nap time was to toss to and fro. When I thought "we" had enough, I would tell them to scram—and that they would do, like kittens scrambling out of a sack. Usually I was more exhausted after the nap than I had been before. The hours that lay ahead moved like lead.

The room in which all the shenanigans went on was of ordinary size and fortunately not too cluttered with furniture. The main obstructions were the bed, the table and the little stove. I say "obstructions" because to make their joy unconfined I had given them permission to use their bikes indoors. The bikes were brought into play whenever they grew tired of games. To clear the deck (from front door to back door) for the races the floor had first to be cleared of all obstacles. Everything was thrown on the bed and the table. The table was piled with chairs, toys, tools and implements, and the bed with games, bugles, swords, rubber dolls, balls, klaxons, building blocks, rifles and toy soldiers. The rugs I rolled up and shoved against the big French windows where the rain water always collected. In the middle of the room, where the bed and the stove faced each other, there was always danger of traffic congestion. From whichever end of the room they began the racing they always collided between the stove and the bed. Naturally they engaged in the usual abusive arguments which traffic snarls provoke.

They could keep it up for an hour or more at a time, the bike races. I had no place to sit or lie, so I stood first in one spot, then another, like a referee at a boxing match. Now children who are having fun hate to see a grownup idling his time away. It didn't take them long to suggest that, since I had chosen to stand and watch, I might as well be a traffic cop. I was provided with a club, a rifle and a diminutive bobby's hat which someone had made Tony a gift of. Oh yes, and a whistle! My job was to wait till they rode a few paces, blow the whistle, put my hand up—vertically or horizontally—and then blow again. Sometimes the change of pace was so abrupt that one of us would accidentally get conked with a club or a rifle butt. As to whether they were genuine accidents was always a matter of hot dispute.

From the bike performance we generally moved into the clown and tumbling act. At this point Walker would be summoned. Walker was a good head taller than I, and when he put them on his shoulders and started trotting and bucking they were in seventh heaven. When Walker had had enough of it, I would get down on the floor and engage them in the snake act. This meant squirming and struggling, with one on top and the other below, until someone got flattened. It had no other purpose than to use up energy quickly. To get a breather, I would suggest we roll dice or shoot marbles. We played dice for pennies, for chips, for buttons and for matches. They were on the way to becoming real good crapshooters, I must say. When that gig was up, Walker or I would play the clown.

The act they loved the most was an imitation of Red Skelton advertising some famous brand of beer and getting drunk in the process. Red Skelton had been to the house some months before and he had put on this skit as the crowning touch to a long and most hilarious afternoon. The kids had not forgotten it. Never would. Nor I either. . . . To do it properly, one has to have a suit of old clothes and a battered slouch hat, preferably a size too big. The reason is simple. Aside from the beer which one has to guzzle, and which must trickle freely over one's chin, throat and chest, there comes a fall at the end which, taken on a floor slippery with beer and pieces of bread and cheese, plays havoc with one's clothes. (Oddly enough, what my kids remember most vividly about that afternoon when Skelton came is the fact that he himself, he, the great Red Skelton, had insisted on mopping up the mess he made!) Anyway, as all television fans know, it's a sloppy, goofy, hiccoughing, sidesplitting performance. Anything goes, so long as you keep on guzzling, spilling the beer, sticking bread into your eyes and ears, and rocking back and forth on your heels. Sometimes I actually felt drunk after giving one of these imitations. The kids would get even drunker. Just watching, I mean. At the end we would all be flopping around like double-jointed crowbars. If I happened now and then to slide under the bed, I would lie there as long as possible, to recuperate.

Then dinner. Time for a general cleanup. Had a visitor walked in at this hour he would have thought himself in a lunatic asylum. For one thing, we had to work fast. Because, when Walker starts cooking, he cooks like lightning. Every evening he would cook a full course meal, beginning with soup and salad and including meat, potatoes, gravy, vegetables, biscuits and pie or custard pudding.

Of course everyone was famished by dinner time. What objects we had failed to allocate during the cleaning up period we left on the floor—for later. Later meant after the kids had retired for the night, when, so to speak, there was nothing more to do. It was only a half-hour's work, this mopping up. A pleasant fillip to a gruelling day. Bending, stooping, sorting, wiping, disentangling, arranging and rearranging—child's play, you might say. I used to think how lucky I was that we had no pets to take care of, no livestock in the house, no bird cages to clean out.

A word about the meals. . . . To me they were delicious. Every day I blessed Walker for being the excellent cook he was. Not the kids, however! Hungry though they were, it was not the sort of cooking they had been used to. One didn't like gravy, the other didn't like fat. "I *hate* Brussels sprouts," Tony would say. "I can't eat macaroni any more, it makes me vomit." This from Val. It took days to discover, by the trial and error system, what they did like, what they would eat. Even pie and puddings were no longer to their taste. They wanted jello.

Walker was not only at his wit's end but plumb disgusted. From a chef he had been reduced to a short-order cook. I did nothing but apologize for their behavior throughout the meal. Often I was driven to assume the ridiculous role of the anxious parent who feels that his only recourse is to plead with the child, beg it to try this, taste that—just a weeny, teeny little bit! Spearing a piece of juicy roast pork with a succulent rim of fat around it, spearing it from Tony's plate, I would hold it a few inches from my mouth a moment, admire it, examine it, make clucking sounds with tongue and palate, dribble a bit into the bargain, then, just before gobbling it, say: "Ooooooh! How delicious! Ooooooh! you don't know what you're missing!" All to no effect, naturally.

"It stinks!" he would say. Or, "It makes me puke!"

And then with a sigh, the sigh of a weary *grande dame*, Val would push her plate aside and in a languid, bored tone inquire what the nature of the dessert might be this evening.

"Jello, my dear!" I would say, putting all the venom and sarcasm into my voice that I could command.

"*Jello?* I'm sick of that stuff."

"O.K. How about frogs' nests then? Or a bowl of rusty nails with sliced cucumbers on the side? Listen, kid, tomorrow we're having pea soup with finnan haddie and smoked oysters. And you're going to like it!"

"Oh yeah?"

"Yes, and don't throw that crust of bread to the birds either! We're serving it up for breakfast tomorrow morning, sprinkled with honey, mustard and garlic sauce. I know you *love* mustard. Did I ever tell you, my finicky little sweetheart, that when bread gets old enough, moldy enough, it breeds worms? And out of little worms come tapeworms. You know what I'm talking about, don't you?" (Brief pause, to observe effect.) "Do you remember that restaurant I once told you about . . . on the rue de la Gaîeté . . . where I used to go for snails? It was a smelly old place but everything tasted good there. If you didn't like the food, they threw you out on your. . . ."

"Oh, Daddy, cut it out! We don't want to listen to that stuff."

From Tony: "Daddy, you're not talking right. You don't mean it, do you?"

"I do too mean it, Tony me boy. I'm just working into it. You kids talk puke and vomit; I talk snails and turtle soup. Get me?"

Val, sort of haughtily: "We don't like that kind of talk, Daddy. Mommy never talks that way. . . ."

"That's what's the matter . . ." I check myself just in time. (Ahoy, mate! Up with the jib!) "What was I saying now? Oh yeah, about the mock turtle. There are three kinds of turtle, you know: the mock, the hard shell, and the Ojibway. . . ."

"Daddy, you're drunk!"

"I am not drunk neither!" (I sure would like to have been.) "No, I'm just feeling feisty. That's a new one for you. Wrap it up, it's yours for the asking."

"Aw, *shit!*" says Tony.

(Now where in the world could he have picked up a word like that?)

"You mean caca, don't you, son? Or *manure?*"

"I said *shit,*" says Tony.

"And I say caca-pipi head!"

"And I say you're goofy," says Val.

"Good, now we can start all over again. But how about a piece of pie first . . . with some nice Yogurt smeared over it? I say now, did you ever have a go at limburger? No? Well, you've got a treat in store for you. . . . Walker, why don't you bring us home some limburger next time you go to town? Or Liederkranz . . . the soft, runny kind. . . . Now if you'll all join me in a piece of pie I'll have another cut of salami and a swig of Haig and Haig. How's that?"

(Delivering this little spiel, a most bizarre thought entered my head. What if, when the divorce proceedings came up, I were to hand the judge a stenographic copy of these post-prandial *divertissements?* Wouldn't that be a stunner?)

A lull. I'm holding my head in my hands, doing my damndest to keep my eyes open. Walker's already washing the dishes, scraping the pans. I ought to make an effort to toss the garbage, but I'm glued to the chair. I look at the kids. They have that groggy look of a pug trying to fall into a clinch after a swift one in the guts.

"You gotta read us a story, Daddy."

"The hell I do."

"You promised."

"I did not neither."

"If you don't read us a story we won't go to sleep."

"*Ich gebibble.*"

To jerk them out of it I make a reference to the frying pan. "How would you like me to conk you with *that?*"

A few more pippa passes and I've got them as far as the bathroom. I've cajoled them into washing their faces, but not into brushing their teeth.

What an ordeal that was—getting them to brush their teeth! I'd sooner drink a pint of Sloan's Liniment than go through that routine again. And, despite all the bloody fussing and fuming at the wash basin, today they've got cavities galore. The wonder is that I, the taskmaster, haven't got chronic laryngitis, what with all the coaxing, pleading, wheedling and threatening I indulged in.

One fine day Walker lost his temper. The incident made a deep impression on me. I had never believed it possible for Walker to say so much as a cross word. He was always calm, amiable, yielding, and as for patience, well, he had the patience of a saint. With dangerous psychopaths Walker could hold his own. As an attendant in lunatic asylums he had kept things under control without ever resorting to strap, club or truncheon.

But the kids had found his Achilles heel.

It was in the middle of a long, exasperating morning when he exploded. I was indoors puttering around when he called me out. "You've got to do something," he yelled, his face red as a beet. "These kids are completely out of hand."

I didn't even ask what they had done. I knew that he had taken more than his share right from the start. I didn't even try to apologize. I felt thoroughly humiliated, and absolutely desperate. To see Walker in such a state was the last straw.

That evening, after the kids were out of the way, he talked to me quietly and soberly. He made it clear that I was not only punishing myself but the kids as well. He talked not only as a friend but also as an analyst might talk to a patient. In the course of his talk he opened my eyes to a twist in the situation which I had been blind to. He said that I should endeavor to find out—for my own good—whether my desire to keep the children was based on love for them and concern for their welfare or on a hidden desire to punish my wife.

"You're not getting anywhere this way," he said. He spoke so gently and reasonably. "I came here to help you. If you insist on going through with it, I won't desert you. But how long can you hold out? You're a bundle of nerves now. Frankly, Henry, you're licked—but you won't admit it to yourself."

Walker's words had their effect. I slept on it, thought it over another twenty-four hours, then announced the decision.

"Walker," I said, "I'm throwing in the sponge. You're right. I'll send her a wire to come and fetch them."

She came immediately. Relieved as I was, I was nevertheless heartbroken. And with the dull ache came exhaustion and loss of spirits. The place now seemed like a morgue to me. A dozen times a night I would wake with a start, thinking they were calling me. There is no emptiness like the emptiness of a home which your children have flown. It was worse than death. And yet it had to be.

Did it, though? Did I really try hard enough? Couldn't I have been more flexible, more ingenious, more inventive, more this, more that? I made myself the most bitter accusations. I was a fool to have listened to Walker, wise and well meaning though he had been. He had caught me in a moment of weakness. Another day and I would have had the courage and the will to resist his suggestion. Though I couldn't deny the truth of his words, I would nevertheless say to myself: "But he's not a *father!* He doesn't know what it means to be a father."

Wherever I strayed I stumbled over something that they had dropped and forgotten. There were toys everywhere, despite all that my wife had carted with her. And tops and marbles. And spoons and dishes. Each little object brought the tears to my eyes. With each passing hour I wondered aloud what they were doing. Did they like their new school? (Tony was being put in a nursery school.) Had they found new playmates? Did they fight as much as ever, or were they too despondent now to think of fighting? Every day I had the impulse to go down the road and telephone them, but I resisted the urge for fear of upsetting them. I tried to resume the writing, but I had no thoughts except for them. If I took a walk, hoping to shake off my black thoughts, I was reminded at every turn of some little incident, some escapade, we had shared together.

Yes, I missed them. I missed them like sin. I missed them the more for all the difficulties we had gone through together. Now there was only Walker. And what good was I to Walker, or he to me? I wanted to be alone with my grief, my bereavement. I wanted to go up into the hills and bellow like a wounded bull. I had been a husband, I had been a father, I had been a mother—and a governess and a playmate and a fool and an idiot. Now I was nothing, not even a clown. As for being a writer, I wanted no more of it. What could I possibly say that would be of interest or of value to anyone? The mainspring was broken, the clock had stopped. If only a miracle would happen! But I couldn't think of any solution that would have the remedial virtues of a miracle. I would have to learn to live again as if nothing had happened. But if you love your children you can't learn to live that way.

You wouldn't *want* to live that way.

Life, however, says: "*You must!*"

I went back to the bathroom, as I had the morning they left, and I wept like a madman. I wept and sobbed and screamed and cursed. I carried on like that until there wasn't another drop of anguish left in me. Until I was like a crumpled, empty sack.

9. Portraits

Let us finish with some of his best writing. Good portraits are to be found in all his books, but nowhere perhaps as in the best pages of The Rosy Crucifixion do his characters come alive so extravagantly. They are his friends and not so ordinary in any way—his vision for what is exceptional is ready to deal with what is best or worst in any living human, although like Dickens he is at his best with the worst. Some of Miller's characters are so vivid that favorable comparisons can be made to any novelist. It has already been suggested that he is better than Thomas Wolfe, and Balzac's name has been invoked. So, too, is it natural to speak of Dickens, indeed there is intense resemblance in Miller's instinct for the bizarre detail which becomes the center of the man. As in Dickens, his eccentrics levitate themselves quickly into great eccentrics, prodigious and twisted men, vulpine, intellectually raddled, prodigies of vanity so swollen on their unique misconceptions that they stagger under spiritual elephantiasis, yet finally, incongruously, in company with Dickens' creations, a novelistic heat comes off, hot as over-compressed humanity.

Of course, they are also figures in a gallery. It is a little like looking at the busts of a hundred doges in the Ducal Palace at Venice. What character in those faces. One could get lost in study except that they are not attached to our own history. Similarly, Miller's narrative is rarely connected for long to the splendid characters he offers us. Like life, it is his friends (rather than villains) who pop into his book, pop out, we listen to them talk—they can talk!—and if they have a novelistic flaw it is that they rattle afterward in memory like idler gears loose in a clock. Of course Miller is not so much making a clock as suggesting it is more interesting to break one. Then you can titillate your eyes over the new mix of sprung works and connective details still intact. That is more like life, more like a garbage can with a fresh-cooked meal inside.

At bottom, we can suspect that Miller hated to obey the narrative line of the novel. It is as if he would be conforming then to all the demands of the machine, of the American machine. So, deliberately or instinctively, he violates our natural desire for narrative. Does the story get too interesting? —make the reader pay his way! And Miller will give us a forty-page rant on the necessity to be generous and free, the same speech he has given a dozen times already in all the oppressiveness of that total German spirit he also carries in himself. There will be nuggets buried, of course, in the forty pages. The best of Miller is often hidden in the congelations of his prose—there are usually phrase-filled treasures in the hard-packed clay of his worst give-my-cancer-to-the-reader rhetoric, and memorable free-flight poesies of surrealism. But no narrative line. Fuck you, programmed American reader, for getting interested in my narrative, Miller is invariably saying. He cannot, however, keep himself from celebrating a good character, and so his best portraits give every promise they will live on so long as print remains a nutrient of culture.

Let us remember that he did this work under what may have been the most severe if subtle trial of his life, for The Rosy Crucifixion was done into the drift of a long depression. Five years after his return to America, his career had fixed him in an irksome mold—no better in reputation than Dirty Writer and/or Eccentric, he lived on as king of a very *small literary duchy (Big Sur, no less!) and was newly and unhappily married for the third time, miserably married we recognize by his text.*

> Every day of my life I was fighting a corpse, a ghost, a cancer that had taken possession of my mind and that ravaged me more than any bodily affliction possibly could. Every day I had to meet and battle anew with the person I had chosen as a mate, chosen as one who would appreciate "the good life" and share it with me. And from the very beginning it had been nothing but hell—hell and torment. To make it worse, the neighbors regarded her as a model creature—so spry, so lively, so generous, so warm. Such a good little mother, such an excellent housewife, such a perfect hostess! It's not easy to live with a man thirty years older, a writer to boot, and especially a writer like Henry Miller. Everyone knew that. Everyone could see that she was doing her utmost. She had courage, that girl!
>
> And hadn't I made a failure of it before? Several times, in fact? Could any woman on earth possibly get along with a man like me? That's how most of our arguments ended, on that note. What to answer? There was no answer. Convicted, sentenced, condemned to rehearse the situation over and over, until one or the other should fall apart, dissolve like a rotting corpse.
>
> Not a day of peace, not a day of happiness, unless on my own. The moment she opened her mouth—*war!*
>
> *Big Sur*

Feeling all the suppressed self-doubt of a man of sixty when his romance with a young wife has failed and their days are loaded with acrimony, there has to be a faint but daily horror in reliving one's past achievements while knowing considerably less of glory in one's present than early success has promised. It is the time when writer's wings begin to flutter. The unhappy end of Hemingway and Fitzgerald will go on living in the mind of American writers for a century or more. Of course, not all writers lose so much nor so dramatically, but few do not feel the ghost which rests in the long depression that comes to every writer when he loses the confidence that his talent will continue to expand.

Miller held on through continuing poverty, and the scalding attrition of mutual marital dislike, held on for all those lonely years in Big Sur, and continued to forge his values, elaborating his sense of measure for life, and ended a long way from where he had begun, for we sense in all the quiet work of Reunion in Brooklyn, *the* Devil in Paradise *and the pages from* Big Sur, *as well as in the mellow presence of the following portraits written in this period, that we are hearing the tone of that rare writer who ends as a skilled moral craftsman. Hemingway, with his clear sense of masculine growth and deterioration, spoke more than once of how it might be necessary to sacrifice a piece of one's talent in the act of becoming a man, but it may have been Henry Miller, of all people, who took the advice.*

From "Conrad Moricand" (Big Sur)

It was Anaïs Nin who introduced me to Conrad Moricand. She brought him to my studio in the Villa Seurat one day in the fall of 1936. My first impressions were not altogether favorable. The man seemed somber, didactic, opinionated, self-centered. A fatalistic quality pervaded his whole being.

It was late afternoon when he arrived, and after chatting a while, we went to eat in a little restaurant on the Avenue d'Orleans. The way he surveyed the menu told me at once that he was finicky. Throughout the meal he talked incessantly, without its spoiling his enjoyment of the food. But it was the kind of talk that does not go with food, the kind that makes food indigestible.

There was an odor about him which I could not help but be aware of. It was a mélange of bay rum, wet ashes and *tabac gris*, tinctured with a dash of some elusive, elegant perfume. Later these would resolve themselves into one unmistakable scent—the aroma of death.

I had already been introduced to astrologic circles before meeting Moricand. And in Eduardo Sanchez, a cousin of Anaïs Nin, I had found a man of immense erudition, who, on the advice of his analyst, had taken up astrology therapeutically, so to speak. Eduardo often reminded me of the earthworm, one of God's most useful creatures, it is said. His powers of ingestion and digestion were stupendous. Like the worm, his labors were primarily for the benefit of others, not himself. At the time Eduardo was engrossed in a study of the Pluto-Neptune-Uranus conjunctions. He had delved deep into history, metaphysics and biography in search of material to corroborate his intuitions. And finally he had begun work on the great theme: Apocatastasis.

With Moricand I entered new waters. Moricand was not only an astrologer and a scholar steeped in the hermetic philosophies, but an occultist. In appearance there was something of the mage about him. Rather tall, well built, broad shouldered, heavy and slow in his movements, he might have been taken for a descendant of the American Indian family. He liked to think, he later confided, that there was a connection between the name Moricand and Mohican. In moments of sorrow there was something slightly ludicrous about his expression, as if he were consciously identifying himself with the last of the Mohicans. It was in such moments that his square head with its high cheek bones, his stolidity and impassivity, gave him the look of anguished granite.

Inwardly he was a disturbed being, a man of nerves, caprices and stubborn will. Accustomed to a set routine, he lived the disciplined life of a hermit or ascetic. It was difficult to tell whether he had adapted himself to this mode of life or accepted it against the grain. He never spoke of the kind of life he would have liked to lead. He behaved as one who, already buffeted and battered, had resigned himself to his fate. As one who could assimilate punishment better than good fortune. There was a strong feminine streak in him which was not without charm but which he exploited to his own detriment. He was an incurable dandy living the life of a beggar. And living wholly in the past!

Perhaps the closest description I can give of him at the outset of our acquaintance is that of a Stoic dragging his tomb about with him. Yet he was a man of many sides, as I gradually came to discover. He had tender skin, was extremely susceptible, particularly to disturbing emanations, and could be as fickle and emotional as a girl of sixteen. Though he was basically not fair-minded, he did his utmost to be fair, to be impartial, to be just. And to be loyal, though by nature I felt that he was essentially treacherous. In fact, it was this undefinable treachery which I was first aware of in him, though I had nothing on which to base my feelings. I remember that I deliberately banished the thought from my mind, replacing it with the vague notion that here was an intelligence which was suspect.

What I looked like to him in those early days is a matter of conjecture on my part. He did not know my writings except for a few fragments which had appeared in translation in French revues. He, of course, knew my date of birth and had presented me with my horoscope shortly after I became acquainted with him. (If I am not mistaken, it was he who detected the error in my hour of birth which I had given as midnight instead of noon.)

All our intercourse was in French, in which I was none too fluent. A great pity, because he was not only a born conversationalist but a man who had an ear for language, a man who spoke French like a poet. Above all, a man who loved subtleties and nuances! It was a dual pleasure I enjoyed whenever we came together—the pleasure of receiving instruction (not only in astrology) and the pleasure of listening to a musician, for he used the language much as a musician would use his instrument. In addition there was the thrill of listening to personal anecdotes about celebrities whom I knew only through books.

In brief, I was an ideal listener. And for a man who loves to talk, for a monologist especially, what greater pleasure could there be for him than in having an attentive, eager, appreciative listener?

I also knew how to put questions. Fruitful questions.

All in all, I must have been a strange animal in his eyes. An expatriate from Brooklyn, a francophile, a vagabond, a writer only at the beginning of his career, naive, enthusiastic, absorbent as a sponge, interested in everything and seemingly rudderless. Such is the image I retain of myself at this period. Above all, I was gregarious. (He was anything but.) And a Capricorn, though not of the same decan. In age we were but a few years apart.

Apparently I was something of a stimulant to him. My native optimism and recklessness complemented his ingrained pessimism and cautiousness. I was frank and outspoken, he judicious and reserved. My tendency was to exfoliate in all directions; he, on the other hand, had narrowed his interests and focused on them with his whole being. He had all the reason and logic of the French, whereas I often contradicted myself and flew off at tangents.

What we had in common was the basic nature of the Capricorn. In his *Miroir d'Astrologie** he has summed up succinctly and discriminatingly these common factors to be found in the Capricorn type. Under "*Analogies*" he puts it thus, to give a few fragments:

"Philosophers. Inquisitors. Sorcerers. Hermits. Gravediggers. Beggars.

"Profundity. Solitude. Anguish.

"Chasms. Caverns. Abandoned places."

Here are a few Capricorns of varying types which he gives: "Dante, Michelangelo, Dostoevsky, El Greco, Schopenhauer. Tolstoy, Cézanne, Edgar Allan Poe, Maxim Gorky. . . ."

Let me add a few of the more common qualities they possess, according to Moricand.

* Paris: Au Sans Pareil, 1928.

"Grave, taciturn, closed. Love solitude, all that is mysterious, are contemplative.

"They are sad and heavy.

"They are born old.

"They see the bad before the good. The weakness in everything leaps immediately to their eyes.

"Penitence, regrets, perpetual remorse.

"Cling to the remembrance of injuries done them.

"Seldom or never laugh; when they do, it is a sardonic laugh.

"Profound but heavy. Burgeon slowly and with difficulty. Obstinate and persevering. Indefatigable workers. Take advantage of everything to amass or progress.

"Insatiable for knowledge. Undertake longwinded projects. Given to the study of complicated and abstract things.

"Live on several levels at once. Can hold several thoughts at one and the same time.

"They illumine only the abysses."

There are the three decans or divisions to each house. For the first decan—I was born the 26th of December—he gives this:

"Very patient and tenacious. Capable of anything in order to succeed. Arrive by dint of perseverance, but step by step. . . . Tendency to exaggerate the importance of earthly life. Avaricious of self. Constant in their affections and in their hatreds. Have a high opinion of themselves."

I quote these observations for several reasons. The reader will discover, each in his own way, the importance which may or may not be attached to them.

But to get on. . . . When I first met him, Moricand was living—*existing* would be better—in a very modest hotel called the Hotel Modial in the rue Notre Dame de Lorette. He had but recently weathered a great crisis—the loss of his fortune. Completely destitute, and with no ability or concern for practical affairs, he was leading a hand-to-mouth existence. For breakfast he had his coffee and croissants in his room, and often he had the same for dinner too, with no lunch in between.

Anaïs was a godsend. She aided him with modest sums as best she could. But there were others, quite a few indeed, whom she likewise felt compelled to aid. What Moricand never suspected was that, in presenting him to me, Anaïs hoped to unload some of her burden. She did it gently, tactfully, discreetly, as she did all things. But she was definitely finished with him.

Anaïs knew quite well that I was unable to support him, unless morally, but she also knew that I was ingenious and resourceful, that I had all manner of friends and acquaintances, and that if I was sufficiently interested I would probably find a way to help him, at least temporarily.

She was not far wrong in this surmise.

Naturally, from my standpoint, the first and most important thing was to see that the poor devil ate more regularly, and more abundantly. I hadn't the means to guarantee him three meals a day, but I could and did throw a meal into him now and then. Sometimes I invited him out to lunch or dinner; more often I invited him to my quarters where I would cook as bountiful and delicious a meal as possible. Half-starved as he was most of the time, it was small wonder that by the end of the meal he was usually drunk. Drunk not with wine, though he drank copiously, but with food, food which his impoverished organism was unable to assimilate in such quantities. The ironic thing was—and how well I understood it!—that by the time he had walked home he was hungry all over again. Poor Moricand! How very, very familiar to me was this ludicrous aspect of his tribulations! Walking on an empty stomach, walking on a full stomach, walking to digest a meal, walking in search of a meal, walking because it is the only recreation one's pocketbook permits, as Balzac discovered when he came to Paris. Walking to lay the ghost. Walking instead of weeping. Walking in the vain and desperate hope of meeting a friendly face. Walking, walking, walking. . . . But why go into it? Let's dismiss it with the label—"ambulatory paranoia."

To be sure, Moricand's tribulations were without number. Like Job, he was afflicted in every way. Altogether devoid of the latter's faith, he nevertheless displayed remarkable fortitude. Perhaps all the more remarkable in that it was without foundation. He did his best to keep face. Rarely did he break down, in my presence at least. When he did, when tears got the better of him, it was more than I could bear. It left me speechless and impotent. It was a special kind of anguish he experienced, the anguish of a man who is incapable of understanding why he of all men should be singled out for punishment. He led me to believe, always indirectly, that never had he done his fellow-man an injury with intent and deliberation. On the contrary, he had always tried to be of help. He liked to believe, and I have no doubt he was sincere, that he harbored no evil thoughts, bore no one any ill will. It is true, for example, that he never spoke ill of the man who was responsible for his comedown in the world. He attributed this misfortune entirely to the fact that he was too trusting. As though it were his own fault and not the fault of the one who had taken advantage of his confidence.

Using what little wits I possessed, for I was scarcely more capable than he in practical matters, I finally hit upon the idea of asking my friends to have Moricand do their horoscopes for a modest fee. I believe I suggested a hundred francs as a fee, but it may only have been fifty. One could then get a very decent meal for from twelve to fifteen francs. As for Moricand's room rent, it could not have been more than three hundred francs per month, possibly less.

All went well until I exhausted my list of friends and acquaintances. Then, not to let Moricand down, I began inventing people. That is to say, I would give him the name, sex, date, hour and place of birth of individuals who did not exist. I paid for these horoscopes out of my own pocket, naturally. According to Moricand, who had not the least suspicion of the turn things had taken, these imaginary subjects comprised an astounding variety of characters. Occasionally, faced with a most incongruous chart, he would express a desire to meet the subject, or would press me for intimate details which of course I would offer with the ease and nonchalance of one who knew whereof he spoke.

When it came to reading personalities, Moricand impressed one as possessing certain powers of divination. His sixth sense, as he called it, served him well in interpreting a chart. But often he had no need of a chart, no need of date, places, and so on. Never shall I forget the banquet given by the group sponsoring the revue *Volontés* which was directed by Georges Pelorson. Eugene Jolas and I were the only Americans in the group, the rest were all French. There must have been about twenty of us at table that evening. The food was excellent and the wine and liqueurs plentiful. Moricand sat opposite me. On one side of him sat Jolas and on the other, I believe, Raymond Queneau. Every one was in excellent spirits, the conversation running high.

With Moricand in our midst, it was inevitable that sooner or later the subject of astrology must come up for discussion. There he was, Moricand, cool as a cucumber, and filling his breadbasket to the best of his ability. Lying in wait, as it were, for the jeers and derision which he doubtless anticipated.

And then it came—an innocent question by an unsuspecting nobody. Immediately a sort of mild insanity pervaded the atmosphere. Questions were being hurled from all directions. It was as if a fanatic had suddenly been uncovered—or worse, a lunatic. Jolas, who was a little under the weather by now and consequently more aggressive than usual, insisted that Moricand give demonstrable proofs. He challenged Moricand to single out the various zodiacal types seated about him. Now Moricand had undoubtedly made such classification in his head during the course of his conversation with this one and that. He could not help doing so by virtue of his calling. It was everyday routine with him, when talking to an individual, to observe the person's manner of speech, his gestures, his tics and idiosyncrasies, his mental and physical build, and so on. He was acute enough, adept enough, to distinguish and classify the more pronounced types present at the table. So, addressing himself to one after another whom he had singled out, he named them: Leo, Taurus, Libra, Virgo, Scorpio, Capricorn, and so on. Then, turning to Jolas, he quietly informed him that he believed he could tell him the year and day of his birth, perhaps the hour too. So saying, he took a good pause, raised his head slightly, as if studying the look of the heavens on the appointed day, then gave the exact date and, after a further pause, the approximate hour. He had hit it right on the nose. Jolas, who was dumbfounded, was still catching his breath as Moricand went on to relate some of the more intimate details of his past, facts which not even Jolas' close friends were aware of. He told him what he liked and what he disliked; he told him what maladies he had suffered from and was likely to suffer from in the future; he told him all manner of things which only a mind-reader could possibly divulge. If I am not mistaken, he even told him the location of a birthmark. (A shot in the dark like this was a trump card that Moricand loved to play when he had things well in hand. It was like putting his signature to a horoscope.)

That was one occasion when he ran true to form. There were others, some of them more eerie, more disturbing. Whenever it happened it was a good act. Far better than a spiritualistic séance.

Thinking of these performances, my mind always reverts to the room he occupied on the top floor of his hotel. There was no elevator service, naturally. One had to climb the five or six flights to the attic. Once inside, the world outside was completely forgotten. It was an irregular shaped room, large enough to pace up and down in, and furnished entirely with what belongings Moricand had managed to salvage from the wreck. The first impression one had, on entering, was that of orderliness. Everything was in place, but exactly in place. A few millimeters this way or that in the disposal of a chair, an *objet d'art*, a paper knife, and the effect would have been lost—in Moricand's mind, at least. Even the arrangement of his writing table revealed this obsession with order. Nowhere at any time was there ever any trace of dust or dirt. All was immaculate.

He was the same about his own person. He always appeared in clean, starched linen, coat and pants pressed (he probably pressed them himself), shoes polished, cravat arranged just so and to match his shirt of course, hat, overcoat, rubbers and suchlike neatly arranged in the clothes closet. One of the most vivid remembrances he had of his experiences in the First World War—he had served in the Foreign Legion—was of the filth which he had been obliged to endure. He once recounted to me at great length how he had stripped and washed himself from head to toe with wet snow (in the trenches) after a night in which one of his comrades had vomited all over him. I had the impression that he would far rather have suffered a bullet wound than an ordeal of this nature.

What sticks in my crop about this period, when he was so desperately poor and miserable, is the air of elegance and fastidiousness which clung to him. He always seemed more like a stockbroker weathering a bad period than a man utterly without resources. The clothes he wore, all of excellent cut as well as of the best material, would obviously last another ten years, considering the care and attention he gave them. Even had they been patched, he would still have looked the well-dressed gentleman. Unlike myself, it never occurred to him to pawn or sell his clothes in order to eat. He had need of his good clothes. He had to preserve a front were he to maintain even interrupted relations with *le monde*. Even for ordinary correspondence he employed good stationery. Slightly perfumed too. His handwriting, which was distinctive, was also invested with the traits I have underlined. His letters, like his manuscripts and his astrological portraits, bore the stamp of a royal emissary, of a man who weighed every word carefully and would vouch for his opinions with his life.

One of the objects in this den he inhabited I shall never forget as long as I live. The dresser. Towards the end of an evening, usually a long one, I would edge toward this dresser, wait for a propitious moment when his glance was averted, and deftly slip a fifty- or hundred-franc note under the statuette which stood on top of the dresser. I had to repeat this performance over and over because it would have embarrassed him, to say the least, had I handed him the money or sent it to him in the mail. I always had the feeling, on leaving, that he would give me just time enough to reach the nearest Métro station, then duck out and buy himself a *choucroute garnie* at a nearby *brasserie*.

I must also say that I had to be very careful about expressing a liking for anything he possessed, for if I did he would thrust it on me in the manner of a Spaniard. It made no difference whether I admired a cravat he was wearing or a walking stick, of which he still had a number. It was thus I inadvertently acquired a beautiful cane which Moïse Kisling had once given him. On one occasion it demanded all my powers of persuasion to prevent him from giving me his only pair of gold cuff links. Why he was still wearing starched cuffs and cuff links I never dared ask him. He would probably have answered that he had no other kind of shirts.

On the wall by the window, where he had arranged his writing table caticornered, there was always pinned up two or three charts of subjects whose horoscopes he was studying. He kept them there at his elbow just as a chess player keeps a board handy on which he has a problem arranged. He believed in allowing time for his interpretations to simmer. His own chart hung beside the others in a special niche.

He regarded it at frequent intervals, much as a mariner would a barometer. He was always waiting for an "opening." In a chart, he told me, death manifested itself when all the exits were blocked. It was difficult, he averred, to detect the advent of death in advance. It was much easier to see it after a person had died; then everything became crystal clear, dramatic from a graphic standpoint.

What I recall most vividly are the red and blue pencil marks he employed to indicate the progress or regression of the span of chance in his chart. It was like watching the movement of a pendulum, a slow moving pendulum which only a man of infinite patience would bother to follow. If it swung a little this way, he was almost jubilant; if it swung a little the other way, he was depressed. What he expected of an "opening" I still do not know, since he was never prepared to make any apparent effort to improve his situation. Perhaps he expected no more than a breather. All he could possibly hope for, given his temperament, was a windfall. Certainly nothing in the way of a job could have meant anything to him. His one and only desire was to continue his researches.

Seemingly, he had reconciled himself to his limitations. He was not a man of action, not a brilliant writer who might some day hope to liberate himself by the pen, nor was he flexible and yielding enough to beg his way. He was simply Moricand, the personality so clearly revealed by the chart which he himself had drawn up. A "subject" with a bad Saturn, among other things. A sad wizard who in moments of desperation would endeavor to extract a thin ray of promise from his star Regulus. In short, a victim doomed to live a dolorous, circumscribed life.

"We all get a break some time or other," I used to say to him. "It can't rain all the time! And what about that saying—'It's an ill wind that blows no one some good'?"

If he was in a mood to listen I might even go further and say: "Why don't you forget the stars for a while? Why not take a vacation and act *as if* fortune were yours? Who knows what might happen? You might meet a man in the street, an utter stranger, who would be the means of opening these doors you regard as locked. There is such a thing as grace too. It could happen, you know, if you were in the right mood, if you were prepared to let something happen. And if you forgot what was written in the sky."

To a speech of this sort he would give me one of those strange looks which signified many things. He would even throw me a smile, one of those tender, wistful smiles which an indulgent parent gives a child who poses an impossible problem. Nor would he rush to offer the answer which he had ever at his disposal and which, no doubt, he was weary of stating when thus cornered. In the pause which followed he gave the impression that he was first testing his own convictions, that he was rapidly surveying (for the thousandth time) all that he had ever said or thought about the subject, that he was even giving himself an injection of doubt, widening and deepening the problem, giving it dimensions which neither I nor anyone else could imagine, before slowly, ponderously, coldly and logically formulating the opening phrases of his defense.

"*Mon vieux*," I can hear him saying, "one must understand what is meant by chance. The universe operates according to law, and these laws obtain as much for man's destiny as for the birth and movements of the planets." Leaning back in his comfortable swivel chair, veering slightly round to focus better on his chart, he would add: "Look at *that!*" He meant the peculiar and particular impasse in which he was fixed at the moment. Then, extracting my chart from the portfolio which he always kept handy, he would beg me to examine it with him. "The only chance for me at this moment," he would say most solemnly, "is *you*. There *you* are!" And he would indicate how and where I fitted into the picture. "You and that angel, Anaïs. Without you two I would be a goner!"

"But why don't you look at it more positively?" I would exclaim. "If we are there, Anaïs and I, if we are all that you credit us with being, why don't you put all your faith and trust in us? Why don't you let us help you to free yourself? There are no limits to what one person can do for another, is that not so?"

Of course he had an answer to that. His great failing was that he had an answer for everything. He did not deny the power of faith. What he would say quite simply was that he was a man to whom faith had been denied. It was there in the chart, the absence of faith. What could one do? What he failed to add was that he had chosen the path of knowledge, and that in doing so he had clipped his own wings.

From "Karen Lundgren" (Plexus)

It was Maxie Schnadig who had introduced me, some years ago, to Karen Lundgren. Whatever brought these two together I can't possibly imagine. They had nothing whatever in common, nothing.

Karen Lundgren was a Swede who had been educated at Oxford, where he had made something of a stir due to his athletic prowess and his rare scholarship. He was a giant with curly blond hair, soft-spoken and excessively polite. He possessed the combined instincts of the ant, the bee and the beaver. Thorough, systematic, tenacious as a bulldog, whatever he engaged in he pursued to the limit. He played just as hard as he worked. Work, however, was his passion. He could work standing up, sitting down, or lying in bed. And, like all hard workers, at bottom he was lazy as sin. Whenever he set out to do something he had first to devise ways and means of doing it with the least effort. Needless to say, these short cuts of his entailed much time and labor. But it made him feel good to sweat his balls off devising short cuts. Efficiency, moreover, was his middle name. He was nothing but a walking, talking, labor-saving device.

No matter how simple a project might be, Karen could make it complicated. I had had a good dose of his eccentricity while serving as his apprentice in a bureau of anthropological research some years previously. He had initiated me into the absurd complexities of a decimal system for filing which made our Dewey system seem like child's play. With Karen's system we were able to index anything under the sun, from a pair of white wool socks to hemorrhoids.

As I say, it was some years since I last saw Karen. I had always regarded him as a freak, having respect neither for his vaunted intelligence nor for his athletic prowess. Dull and laborious, those were his chief characteristics. Now and then, to be sure, he indulged in a hearty laugh. He laughed too heartily, I might say, and always at the wrong time or for the wrong reason. This ability to laugh he cultivated, just as he had once cultivated his muscles. He had a mania to be all things to all men. He had the mania, but no flair.

I give this thumbnail sketch because it happens that once again I'm working with him, working *for* him. Mona too. We're all living together on the beach at Far Rockaway, in a shack which he has erected himself. To be exact, the house isn't quite finished. Hence our presence in it. We work without compensation, content to room and board with Karen and his wife. There's much yet to be done. Too much. Work begins from the moment I open my eyes until I drop from fatigue.

To go back a pace. . . . Running into Karen on the street was something of a godsend for us. We were literally without a cent when he happened along. Stanley, you see, had told us one evening, just as he was setting forth to work, that he was fed up with us. We were to pack our things and get out immediately. He would help us pack and see us to the subway. No words. Of course I had been expecting something of the sort to happen any day. I wasn't the least bit angry with him. On the contrary, I was rather amused.

At the subway entrance he handed over the valises, put a dime in my hand for carfare, and without shaking hands turned abruptly and stalked off. Not even a good-bye. We of course got into the subway, not knowing what else to do, and began riding. We rode back and forth two or three times trying to decide what the next step would be. Finally we got out at Sheridan Square. We had hardly walked a few steps when, to my astonishment, I saw Karen Lundgren approaching. He seemed unusually pleased to have found me again. What was I doing? Had we had dinner yet? And so on.

We accompanied him to his town flat, as he called it, and while his wife prepared the meal we unburdened ourselves. He was even more delighted to hear of our circumstances. "I've got just the thing for you, Henry," he said, with his insensitive cheerfulness. And he began at once to explain the nature of his work, which sounded like higher mathematics to me, meanwhile plying us with cocktails and caviar sandwiches. He had taken it for granted, when he began his discourse, that I would give assent to his project. To make things more interesting I pretended that I would have to think it over, that I had other things in mind. That of course only stimulated him more.

"Stay with us overnight," he begged, "and let me know what you think in the morning."

He had explained, to be sure, that in addition to acting as his secretary and amanuensis, I might have to give him a hand with the house-building. I had warned him frankly that I wasn't much good with my hands, but he had waved this aside as unimportant. It would be fun, after working with one's brain, to devote a few hours to more menial tasks. Recreation, he called it. And then there was the beach: we would be able to swim, toss the ball around, perhaps even do a bit of canoeing. In passing he made mention of his library, his collection of records, his chess set, as if to say that we would have all the luxuries of a first-class club.

In the morning I said yes, naturally. Mona was enthusiastic. She was not only willing, but eager, to help Karen's wife do the dirty work. "O.K.," I said, "no harm in trying it."

We went by train to Far Rockaway. All during the ride Karen talked incessantly about his work. I gathered that he was engaged in writing a book on statistics. According to him, it was a unique contribution to the subject. The data he had amassed was enormous, so enormous in fact that I was terrified before I had even moved a finger. In his customary way he had equipped himself with all manner of devices, machines which he assured me I would catch on to in no time. One of them was the dictaphone. He had found it more convenient, he explained, to dictate to the machine, which was impersonal, than to a secretary. There would be times, of course, when he might feel impelled to dictate direct, in which case I could take it down on the typewriter. "You needn't worry about the spelling," he added. My spirits dropped, I must say, when I learned of the dictaphone. However, I said nothing, just smiled and let him roll on from one thing to another.

What he had omitted to tell us about was the mosquitoes.

There was a little storeroom, just big enough to accommodate a creaky bed, which he indicated as our sleeping quarters. The moment I saw the netting over the bed I knew what we were in for. It began at once, the first night. Neither of us slept a wink. Karen tried to laugh it off by urging us to loaf for a day or two until we got adjusted. Fine, I thought. Mighty decent of him, I thought. An Oxford gentleman, what! But we didn't sleep the second night either, even though we had greased ourselves all over, like Channel swimmers. The third night we burned Chinese punk and incense. Towards dawn, utterly worn out, our nerves frazzled, we dozed off. As soon as the sun came up we plunged into the surf.

It was after we had breakfast that morning that Karen intimated we ought to begin work in earnest. His wife took

Mona aside to explain *her* duties. It took Karen almost the whole morning to explain the mechanism of the various machines he found invaluable for his work. There was a veritable mountain of records piled up which I was to transcribe on the typewriter. As for the charts and diagrams, the rulers, compasses and triangles, the slide rules, the filing system, and the thousand and one details which I was to familiarize myself with, that could wait a few days. I was to make a dent in the heap of records and then, if there were still enough light, I was to assist him on the roof.

I'll never forget that first day with the bloody dictaphone. I thought I would go mad. It was like operating a sewing machine, a switchboard and a victrola all at once. I had to use simultaneously hands, feet, ears and eyes. If I had been just a bit more versatile I could have swept out the room at the same time. Of course the first ten pages made absolutely no sense. I not only wrote the wrong things, I missed whole sentences and began others in the middle or near the end. I wish I had preserved a copy of that first day's work—it would have been something to put beside the cold-blooded nonsense of Gertrude Stein. Even if I had transcribed correctly, the words would have made little sense to me. The whole terminology, not to speak of his plodding, wooden style, was foreign to me. I might just as well have written down telephone numbers.

Karen, like a man who is accustomed to training animals, a man of infinite patience and perseverance, pretended that I hadn't done bad at all. He even tried to joke a bit, reading over some of the screwy sentences. "It will take a little time," he said, "but you'll get on to it." And then, to add a little sauce: "I'm really ashamed of myself for asking you to do this kind of work, Henry. You don't know how much I appreciate your assistance. I don't know what I would have done if you hadn't come along." He would have talked much the same way if he were giving me lessons in jujitsu, of which he was supposedly a master. I could well visualize him picking me up, after spinning me twenty feet through the air, and saying solicitously: "Sorry, old man, but you'll get the hang of it after a few days. Just couldn't help it, you know. Are you hurt much?"

What I wanted more than anything was a good drink. But Karen rarely drank. When he wanted relaxation he employed his energies at a different kind of work. To work was his passion. He worked while he slept. I mean it seriously. On falling off he would set himself a problem which his unconscious was to solve during the night.

The best I could wheedle out of him was a coke. Even this I couldn't enjoy in peace, for while I leisurely sipped it he was busy explaining to me the next day's problems. What bothered me more than anything was his way of explaining things. He was one of those idiots who believe that diagrams make things easier to comprehend. For me, anything in the way of a chart or a diagram means hopeless confusion. I have to stand on my head to read the simplest plans. I tried to tell him this but he insisted that I had been miseducated, that if I would just be patient I would soon learn to read charts and diagrams with ease—and enjoyment. "It's like mathematics," he told me.

"But I detest mathematics," I protested.

"One shouldn't say a thing like that, Henry. How can one detest something useful? Mathematics is only another instrument to serve us." And here he expatiated *ad nauseam* on the wonders and the benefits of a science in which I had not the slightest interest. But I was always a good listener. And I had discovered already, in the space of just a few days, that one way of reducing the working time was to involve him in just such lengthy discussions. The fact that I listened so good-naturedly made him feel that he was really seducing me. Now and then I would throw in a question, in order to put off for a few more minutes the inevitable return to the grindstone. Of course, nothing he told me about mathematics made the least impression on me. It went in one ear and out the other.

"You see," he would say, with all the seriousness of the fatuous ones, "it's not nearly as complicated as you imagined. I'll make a mathematician of you in no time."

Meanwhile Mona was getting her education in the kitchen. All day long I heard the dishes rattling. I wondered what in hell they were up to in there. It sounded like a spring cleaning. When we got to bed I learned that Lotta, Karen's wife, had allowed the dirty dishes to accumulate for a week. She didn't like housework, apparently. She was an artist. Karen never complained. He wanted her to be an artist—that is, after she had done the chores and assisted him in every possible way. He himself never set foot in the kitchen. He never noticed the condition of the plates or the cutlery, no more than he noticed what sort of food was being served him. He ate without relish, to stoke the furnace, and when he was through he pushed the dishes aside and began figuring on the tablecloth, or if there were no tablecloth, on the bare boards. He did everything leisurely, and with painful deliberation, which in itself was enough to drive me frantic. Wherever he worked there was dirt, disorder and a clutter of non-essentials. If he reached for something he had first to remove a dozen obstructions. If the knife he grabbed were dirty he would slowly and deliberately wipe it clean with the tablecloth, or with his handkerchief. Always without fuss or emotion. Always bearing down, pressing onward, like a glacier in its relentless advance. Sometimes there were three cigarettes burning at once at his elbow. He never stopped smoking, not even in bed. The butts piled up like sheep droppings. His wife was also an inveterate smoker, a chain smoker.

Cigarettes were one thing we had a plentiful supply of. *Food*, that was another matter. Food was doled out scantily and in the most unappetizing fashion. Mona, of course, had offered to relieve Lotta of the burden of cooking, but Lotta had refused to hear of it. We soon discovered why. She was stingy. She feared that Mona might prepare succulent, bounteous repasts. She was damned right about that! To take over the kitchen and stage a feast was the one thought uppermost in our minds. We kept praying that they would go to town for a few days and let us take over. Then at last we would enjoy a good meal.

"What I would like," Mona would say, "is a good roast of beef."

"Give me chicken—or a fine roast duck."

"I'd like to have sweet potatoes for a change."

"Suits me, honey, only make some rich gravy to go with them."

Like badminton it was. We shuffled the phantom food back and forth like two starved peacocks. If only they would breeze! God, but we were sick of looking at sardine tins, cans of sliced pineapple, bags of potato chips. The two of them nibbled away like mice the whole damned day. Never a hint of wine, never a drop of whisky. Nothing but coke and sarsaparilla.

I can't say that Karen was stingy. No, he was insensitive, unobservant. When I informed him one day that we were not getting enough to eat he professed to be appalled. "What would you like?" he asked. And at once he got up from his work, borrowed a car from a neighbor, and whisked us off to town where we went from one store to another ordering provisions. It was typical of him to react in this way. Always to extremes. By going to extremes he intended, quite unconsciously, I believe, to make you slightly disgusted with yourself. "Food? Is that all you want?" he seemed to say. "That's easy, we'll buy heaps of it, enough to choke a horse." There was a further implication in his exaggerated willingness to please you. "Food? why that's a mere trifle. Of course we can get you food. I thought you had deeper worries."

His wife, of course, was dismayed when she saw the load of provisions we brought back with us. I had asked Karen not to say anything to his wife about our hunger. He pretended, therefore, that he was laying in a supply against a rainy day. "The larder was getting low," he explained. But when he added that Mona would like to fix a meal for us at dinner time her face dropped. For an instant there passed over her countenance that horrified look of the miser whose hoard is menaced. Once again Karen stepped into the breach. "I thought, darling, that you would enjoy having someone else cook the meal for a change. Mona is an excellent cook, it appears. We're going to have filet mignon this evening—how does that sound to you?" Lotta, of course, had to feign delight.

We made the dinner an event. In addition to fried onions and mashed potatoes we had succotash, beets and Brussels sprouts, with celery, stuffed olives and radishes on the side. We washed this down with red and white wine, the best obtainable. There were three kinds of cheese, followed by strawberries and rich cream. For a change we had some excellent coffee, which I prepared myself. Good, strong coffee with a bit of chicory in it. All that lacked was a good liqueur and Havana cigars.

Karen enjoyed the meal immensely. He acted like a different man. He joked, told stories, laughed until his sides ached, and never once referred to his work. Toward the end of the meal he even tried to sing.

"Not bad, eh?" I said.

"Henry, we ought to do this oftener," he responded. He looked to Lotta for approval. She gave him a thin, bleak smile which caused her face to crack. It was obvious that she was desperately trying to reckon the cost of the spread.

Suddenly Karen pushed his chair back and rose from the table. I thought he was going to bring his charts and diagrams to the table. Instead he went into the next room and returned in a jiffy with a book. He waved it before my eyes.

"Ever read this, Henry?" he demanded.

I looked at the title. "No," I said. "Never heard of it."

Karen passed the book to his wife and begged her to read us a morsel. I expected something dismal, and instinctively poured out some more wine.

Lotta solemnly turned the pages, looking for one of her favorite passages.

"Read anywhere," said Karen. "It's good through and through."

Lotta stopped fumbling with the pages and looked up. Her expression changed suddenly. For the first time I saw her countenance illuminated. Even her voice had altered. She had become a *diseuse.*

"It's chapter three," she began, "from *The Crock of Gold,* by James Stephens."

"And a darling of a book it is!" Karen broke in gleefully. With this he pushed his chair back a bit and put his big feet on the arm of the easy chair nearby. "Now you're going to hear something, you two."

Lotta began: "It's a dialogue between the Philosopher and a farmer called Meehawl MacMurrachu. The two have just greeted one another." She begins reading.

" 'Where is the other one?' said he (the farmer) .

" 'Ah!' said the Philosopher.

" 'He might be outside, maybe?'

" 'He might indeed,' said the Philosopher gravely.

" 'Well, it doesn't matter,' said the visitor, 'for you have enough knowledge by yourself to stock a shop. The reason I came here today was to ask your honored advice about my wife's washing board. She only had it a couple of years, and the last time she used it was when she washed out my Sunday shirt and her black shirt with the red things on it—you know the one?'

" 'I do not,' said the Philosopher.

" 'Well, anyhow, the washboard is gone, and my wife says it was either taken by the fairies or by Bessie Hannigan—you know Bessie Hannigan? She has whiskers like a goat and a lame leg!'

" 'I do not,' said the Philosopher.

" 'No matter,' said Meehawl MacMurrachu. 'She didn't take it, because my wife got her out yesterday and kept her talking for two hours while I went through everything in her bit of a house—the washboard wasn't there.'

" 'It wouldn't be,' said the Philosopher.

" 'Maybe your honor could tell a body where it is then?'

" 'Maybe I could,' said the Philosopher; 'are you listening?'

" 'I am,' said Meehawl MacMurrachu.

"The Philosopher drew his chair closer to the visitor until their knees were jammed together. He laid both his hands on Meehawl MacMurrachu's knees. . . .

" 'Washing is an extraordinary custom,' said he. 'We are washed both on coming into the world and on going out of it, and we take no pleasure from the first washing nor any profit from the last.'

" 'True for you, sir,' said Meehawl MacMurrachu.

" 'Many people consider that scourings supplementary to these are only due to habit. Now, habit is continuity of action, it is a most detestable thing and is very difficult to get away from. A proverb will run where a writ will not, and the follies of our forefathers are of greater importance to us than is the well-being of our posterity.' "

At this point Karen interrupted his wife to ask if we liked the passage.

"I do indeed," I said. "Let her continue!"

"Continue!" said Karen, settling still deeper into his chair.

Lotta read on. She had an excellent voice and could handle the brogue expertly. The dialogue got funnier and funnier. Karen began to titter and then to laugh like a hyena. The tears were rolling down his face.

"Do be careful, Karen," begged his wife, putting the book down for a moment. "I'm afraid you'll get the hiccups."

"I don't care," said Karen, "it's worth getting the hiccups."

"But you remember, the last time it happened we had to call a doctor."

"Just the same," said Karen. "I'd like to hear the end of it." And again he exploded into peals of laughter. It was frightening to hear him laugh. He had no control whatever. I wondered to myself if he could weep just as bravely. It would be something to unnerve one.

Lotta waited for him to subside, then resumed her reading.

" 'Did you ever hear, sir, about the fish that Paudeen MacLaughlin caught in the policeman's hat?'

" 'I did not,' said the Philosopher. 'The first person who washed was possibly a person seeking a cheap notoriety. Any fool can wash himself, but every wise man knows that it is an unnecessary labor, for nature will quickly reduce him to a natural and healthy dirtiness again. We should seek, therefore, not how to make ourselves clean, but how to attain a more unique and splendid dirtiness, and perhaps the accumulated layers of matter might, by ordinary geologic compulsion, become incorporated with the human cuticle and so render clothing unnecessary. . . .'

" 'About that washboard,' said Meehawl, 'I was just going to say. . . .'

" 'It doesn't matter,' said the Philosopher. 'In its proper place I. . . .' "

Here Lotta had to close the book. Karen was laughing, if it could be called that, with such uncontrollable violence that his eyes were popping out of his head. I thought he would throw a fit.

"Darling, darling!" came Lotta's anxious voice, registering a concern I hadn't believed her capable of. "Please, darling, calm yourself!"

Karen continued to be rocked by spasms which now sounded more like sobs. I got up and thumped him violently on the back. At once the commotion subsided. He looked up at me gratefully. Then he coughed and wheezed and blew his nose vigorously, wiping the tears away with his coat sleeve.

"Next time, Henry, use a mallet," he sputtered. "Or a sledge hammer."

"That I will," I said.

He began to titter again.

"Please don't!" begged Lotta. "He's had enough for one evening."

"It was indeed a wonderful evening," said Mona. "I'm beginning to like it here. And how wonderfully you read," she said, addressing Lotta.

"I used to be on the stage," said Lotta modestly.

"I thought so," said Mona. "So was I once."

Lotta arched her eyebrows. "*You were?*" There was a tinge of sarcasm in her voice.

"Why yes," said Mona, unruffled, "I played with the Theatre Guild."

"Hear, hear!" said Karen, relapsing into his Oxford manner.

"What's so strange about that?" I demanded to know. "Didn't you think she had any talent?"

"Why, Henry," said Karen, clasping my arm, "you *are* a sensitive brute, aren't you? I was congratulating myself on our good luck. We'll all take turns reading some night. I was on the stage once myself, you know."

"And I was once a trapeze artist," I countered.

"*Really!*" This from Lotta and Karen simultaneously.

"Didn't I ever tell you? I thought you knew."

For some strange reason this innocent lie impressed them. If I had said I had been a cabinet minister once it could not have produced as telling an effect. It was amazing how limited was their sense of humor. Naturally I expatiated at length on my virtuosity. Mona chimed in now and then to help me out. They listened as if spellbound.

When I had finished Karen soberly remarked: "Among other things, Henry, you're not a bad storyteller. You must tell us some more yarns like that when we're in the mood."

The next day, as if to make up for the grand splurge, Karen was determined to tackle the roof. It had to be shingled and then coated with tar. And I who could never drive a nail straight was to do the job—under his directions. Fortunately it took some time to find the right ladder, the proper nails, the hammer and saw and a dozen other tools which he thought might come in handy. What followed was straight out of Laurel and Hardy. First of all I insisted on finding a pair of old gloves so as not to get any splinters in my hands. I made it clear as a Euclidian theorem that with splinters in my fingers I would be unable to type and being unable to type would mean no dictaphone work. After that I insisted on finding a pair of sneakers so as not to slip and break my neck.

Karen nodded approval in dead seriousness. He was the type who, in order to get the maximum amount of work out of you, would carry you to the toilet if necessary and wipe your ass for you. It was clear by this time that I would need a lot of assistance to fix the roof. Mona was to stand by in case anything fell to the ground; she was also to fetch us some ice-cold lemonade at intervals. Karen, of course, had already drawn several diagrams explaining how the shingles were to be adjusted one to another. Naturally I profited not at all from these explanations. I had only one thought in mind—to start hammering away like a demon and let the chips fall where they would.

In order to limber up I suggested that I first practice walking along the ridgepole. Karen, still nodding approval, wanted to lend me an umbrella, but at this Mona laughed so heartily that he abandoned the idea. I scurried up the ladder as nimbly as a cat, hoisted myself up to the ridgepole and began my tightrope exercises. Lotta looked on with suppressed fright, her mind busy, doubtless, computing hospital expenses in thc event I should slip and break a leg. It was a scorcher of a day, the flies out in swarms and biting like fury. I had on a huge Mexican hat much too big for me which kept falling over my eyes. When I descended I took the notion to change into my swimming trunks. Karen thought he would do likewise. This consumed a little more time.

Finally there was nothing left but to begin. I climbed up the ladder with the hammer under my arm clutching a keg of nails. It was getting on towards noon. Karen had rigged up a platform on wheels from which he unloaded the shingles and gave directions. He looked like a Carthaginian setting the defenses of the city in order. The women stood below, clucking away like hens, all set to catch me if I fell.

I got the first shingle set and picked up the hammer to drive the first nail home. I missed it by an inch or two and the shingle went flying homeward like a kite. I was so surprised, so stunned, that the hammer fell out of my hands and the keg of nails tumbled to the ground. Karen, unperturbed, gave orders to remain where I was, the women would gather up the hammer and nails. It was Lotta who ran to the kitchen to get the hammer. When she returned I learned that I had broken the teapot and a few plates. Mona was scrambling for the nails, picking them up so fast that they fell out of her hand before she could get them in the keg.

"Easy, easy!" shouted Karen. "All right up there, Henry? Steady now!"

With this I got the giggles. The situation reminded me all too vividly of those dreadful occasions in the past when my mother and sister would aid me in putting up the awnings—parlor floor front. Nobody except an awning maker has any idea how complicated an awning can be. There are not only the rods and flaps, the bolts and screws, the pulleys and cords, there are a hundred perplexing difficulties which arise after you have mounted the ladder and anchored yourself gingerly on the edge of the double window. Somehow there always seemed to be a gale blowing when my mother decided to put up the awnings. Holding the flapping awning with one hand and the hammer with the other, my mother would then endeavor to pass the various things which were needed and which my sister had handed to her. To keep a tight grip with my legs and not permit the awning to carry me aloft was a feat in itself. My arms would grow tired before I had driven in the first screw. I would have to disentangle the damned contraption and jump down for a breathing spell. All the time my mother would be mumbling and groaning—"It's so simple, I could put them up myself in a few minutes if I didn't have the rheumatism." Recommencing, she would be obliged to explain to me all over again which part went outside and which inside. For me it was like doing something backwards.

Once in position again, the hammer would fall from my hands, and I would sit there wrestling with the belly of the awning while my sister ran below and fetched it. It would take at least an hour to put up one awning. At this point I could invariably say—"Why not leave the other ones till tomorrow?" Whereupon my mother would fly into a rage, horrified by the thought of what the neighbors would think seeing only one awning in place. Sometimes, at this point, I would suggest that we call upon a neighbor to finish the job, offering to pay him handsomely out of my own pocket. But this would enrage her even more. It was a sin, in her opinion, to pay out money for work which one could do oneself. By the time we finished I always had a few bruises. "Serves you right," my mother would say. "You ought to be ashamed of yourself. You're as helpless as your father."

Sitting astride the ridgepole, laughing quietly to myself, I congratulated myself that we were doing something other than dictaphone work. I knew that by evening my back would be so sunburned that I would be unable to work on the morrow. I would have to lie on my belly all day. Fine. It would give me a chance to read something interesting. I was growing stupid listening to nothing but statistical abracadabra. I realized that Karen would try to find something "light" for me to do while lying on my belly, but I knew how to discourage such attempts.

Well, we began again, slowly and deliberately this time. The way I worked over one nail would have driven any normal person crazy. But Karen was anything but a normal individual. From his Carthaginian tower he continued to shower me with directions and encouragements. Why he didn't put the shingles up himself and let me pass them to him I couldn't understand. But he was happy only when directing. Even when it was a simple thing he had to do he could somehow break it up into a multitude of component parts which would necessitate the co-operation of several individuals. It never mattered to him how long it took to complete a job; all that mattered was that it be done his way, i.e., the longest and the most complicated way. This was what he called "efficiency." He had learned it in Germany while studying how to make organs. (*Why organs?* So that he could appreciate music better.)

I had only put up a few shingles when the signal came for lunch. It was a cold lunch made of the odds and ends from yesterday's banquet. "A salad," Lotta called it. Happily there were a few bottles of beer to make it palatable. We even had a few grapes. I ate them slowly, one by one, stretching the minutes out. Already my back looked raw. Mona wanted me to put a shirt on. I assured them that I tanned quickly. Wouldn't think of donning a shirt. Karen, who wasn't altogether a fool, suggested that we lay off the roof work for the afternoon and tackle something "light." He began explaining that he had made some complicated charts which had to be corrected and remade.

"No, let's get on with the roof," I urged. "I'm just getting the hang of it."

As this sounded plausible and logical to him, Karen voted to tackle the roof again. Once more we clambered up the ladder, did a little preliminary footwork on the ridgepole, and settled down to hammering nails. In a short time the sweat was pouring off me like rain. The more I perspired the more the flies buzzed and bit. My back felt like a raw steak. I accelerated my rhythm perceptibly.

"Good work, Hank!" yelled Karen. "We ought to be through in a day or two at this rate."

He had no more than got the words out of his mouth when a shingle flew skyward and caught him over the eye. It made a gash from which the blood trickled into his eye.

"Oh darling, are you hurt?" cried Lotta.

"It's nothing," he said. "Carry on, Henry."

"I'll get some iodine," yelled Lotta, trotting off into the house.

Quite unintentionally I let the hammer fall from my hand. It fell through a hole in the sheathing right on Lotta's skull. She gave a shriek as if a shark had bitten her, and with that Karen scrambled down from his perch.

It was time to call a halt. Lotta had to be put to bed with a cold compress on her head. Karen had a big patch of court plaster over his left eye. He never uttered a word of complaint.

"I guess you'll have to make the dinner again tonight," he said to Mona. It seemed to me that there was a secret note of pleasure in his voice. Mona and I had difficulty restraining our jubilation. We waited a while before broaching the subject of the menu.

"Fix anything you like," said Karen.

"How about lamb chops?" I put in. "Some lamb chops with French peas, some noodles and maybe artichokes too —how does it sound?"

Karen thought it would be excellent. "You don't mind, do you?" he asked Mona.

"Not at all," she said. "It's a pleasure."

Then, as if it were quite an afterthought, she added: "Didn't we bring some Riesling yesterday? I think a bottle of Riesling would go well with the chops."

"Just the thing," said Karen.

I took a shower and got into my pajamas. The prospect of enjoying another good meal revived me. I was ready to sit down and do a bit of dictaphone work to show my appreciation.

"I think you'd better rest up," said Karen. "You'll feel a little muscle-bound tomorrow."

"What about those charts?" I said. "I'd really like to do something, you know. I'm sorry I was so damned awkward."

"Tut tut," said Karen. "You've done a good day's work. Take it easy till dinner time."

"All right, if you insist. O.K."

I opened a bottle of beer and plunked myself in the easy chair.

Thus it went *au bord de la mer.* Great sand spits, with an increasing surf which pounded in one's ears at night like the hammering of a stupendous toccata. Now and then sandstorms. The sand seeped in everywhere, even through the glass panes, it seemed.

We were all good swimmers; we bobbed up and down in the heavy surf like otters. Karen, always seeking to improve matters, made use of an inflated rubber mattress. After he had taken a siesta on the bosom of the deep, he would swim out a mile or two and give us all a good fright.

Evenings he enjoyed playing games. He played in dead earnest always, whether it was pinochle, cribbage, checkers, casino, whist, fan-tan, dominoes, euchre or backgammon. I don't believe there was a game with which he was not conversant. Part of his general education, don't you know. The rounded individual. He could play hopscotch or tiddlywinks with the same furious zeal and adroitness. Once, when I went to town with him, I suggested that we drop into a pool parlor and play a game of pool. He asked me if I wanted to shoot first. Without thinking I said, "No, you go ahead." He did. He cleaned up the table four times before I had a chance to use the cue. When it finally came my turn I suggested that we go home. "Next time you shoot first," he said, intimating that that would be a break for me. It never occurred to him, that just because he was a shark, it would have been sporting to miss a shot occasionally. To play ping-pong with him was hopeless; only Bill Tilden could have returned his serves. The only game in which I might have stood a chance to break even was craps, but I never liked rolling dice, it was boring.

One evening, after discussing some books on occultism, I reminded him of the time we had taken a trip up the Hudson on an excursion boat. "You remember how we pushed the ouija board around?" His face lit up. Of course he did. He would like to try it again if I were willing. He'd improvise a board.

We sat up that night till two in the morning pushing the damned thingamajig around. We must have made a lot of connections in the astral realm, judging by the time which elapsed. As usual it was I who summoned the eccentric figures—Jacob Boehme, Swedenborg, Paracelsus, Nostradamus, Claude Saint-Martin, Ignatius Loyola, the Marquis de Sade and such like. Karen made notes of the messages we received. Said he would dictate them to the dictaphone the next day. To be filed under 1.352-Cz 240. (18), which was the exact index for material derived from the departed spirits by means of the ouija board on such and such an evening in the region of the Rockaways. It was weeks later when I decocted this particular record. I had forgotten all about the incident. Suddenly, in Karen's serious voice I began getting these crazy messages from the blue. . . . "Eating well. Time hangs heavy. Coronary divertissements tomorrow. Paracelsus." I began to shake with laughter. So the idiot really was filing this stuff away! I was curious to know what else he might have tucked away under this classification. I went to the card files first. There were at least fifty cross references indicated. Each one was battier than the previous one. I got out the folders and file boxes in which the papers were stored away. His notes and jottings were scribbled in a minute scrawl on odds and ends, often paper napkins, blotters, menus, tally cards. Sometimes it was nothing more than a phrase which a friend had dropped while conversing in the subway; sometimes it was an embryonic thought which had flitted through his head while taking a crap. Sometimes it was a page torn from a book—the title, author, publisher and place always carefully noted as well as the date when he had come across it. There were bibliographies in at least a dozen languages, including Chinese and Persian.

One curious chart interested me enormously; I intended to pump him about it one day but never did. As best I could make out, it represented a map of some singular region in limbo, the boundaries of which had been given in a seance with a medium. It looked like a geodetic survey of a bad dream. The names of the places were written in a language which nobody could possibly understand. But Karen had given a rough translation on separate sheets of paper. "*Notes*," it read: "The following translations of place names in the quaternary decan of Devachan were volunteered by de Quincey working through Madame X. Coleridge is said to have verified them before his death but the documents in which the testimony is given are temporarily lost." The singular thing about this shadowy sector of the beyond was this: in its confines, imaginary perhaps, were gathered the shades of such diverse and interesting personalities as Pythagoras, Heraclitus, Longinus, Virgil, Hermes Trismegistus, Apollonius of Tyana, Montezuma, Xenophon, Jan van Ruysbroeck, Nicolaus of Cusa, Meister Eckhart, St. Bernard of Clairvaux, Asoka, St. François de Sales, Fénelon, Chuang Tzu, Nostradamus, Saladin, the Pope Joanna, St. Vincent de Paul, Paracelsus, Malatesta, Origen, together with a coterie of women saints. One would like to know what had drawn this conglomeration of souls together. One would like to know what they discussed in the mysterious language of the departed. One would like to know if the great problems which had tormented them on earth had been finally resolved. One would like to know if they consorted together in divine harmony. Warriors, saints, mystics, sages, magicians, martyrs, kings, thaumaturgists. . . . What an assemblage! What would one not give to be with them just for a day!

As I say, for some mysterious reason I never brought this subject to Karen's attention. There was little, indeed, outside our work which I did discuss with him, first because of his great reserve, second because to introduce even a slight detail meant listening to an inexhaustible harangue, third because I was intimidated by the vast domain of knowledge which appeared to be his. I contented myself with browsing through his books, which embraced an enormous range of subject matter. He read Greek, Latin, Hebrew and Sanskrit with apparent ease, and was fluent in a dozen living tongues, including Russian, Turkish and Arabic. The titles of his books were alone sufficient to set my head spinning. What astounded me, however, was that so little of this vast store of learning seeped into our daily talk. Sometimes I had the feeling that he regarded me as a thorough ignoramus. Other times he embarrassed me by posing questions which only a Thomas Aquinas could cope with. Now and then he gave me the impression that he was just a child with an overdeveloped brain. He had little humor and almost no imagination. Outwardly he appeared to be a model husband, always ready to cater to his wife's whims, always alert to serve her, always solicitous and protective, at times positively chivalric. I couldn't help but wonder at times what it would be like to be married to this human adding machine. With Karen everything proceeded according to schedule. Intercourse too, no doubt. Perhaps he kept a secret file reminding him when intercourse was due, together with notes on the results—spiritual, moral, mental and physical.

From "Mr. Elfenbein" (Nexus)

At this point the doorbell rang. It was a neighbor who had heard that we were visiting the Essens and had come to make our acquaintance.

"This is Mr. Elfenbein," said Mrs. Essen. She didn't seem too delighted to see him.

With elbows bent and hands clasped Mr. Elfenbein came forward to greet us. His face was radiant, the perspiration was dripping from his brow.

"What a privilege!" he exclaimed, making a little bow, then clasping our hands and wringing them vigorously. "I have heard so much about you, I hope you will pardon the invasion. Do you speak Yiddish perhaps—or Russe?" He hunched his shoulders and moved his head from side to side, the eyes following like compass needles. He fixed me with a grin. "Mrs. Skolsky tells me you are fond of Cantor Sirota. . . ."

I felt like a bird released from its cage. I went up to Mr. Elfenbein and gave him a good hug.

"From Minsk or Pinsk?" I said.

"From the land of the Moabites," he replied.

He gave me a beamish look and stroked his beard. The boy put a glass of kümmel in his hand. There was a stray lock of hair on the crown of Mr. Elfenbein's baldish head; it stood up like a corkscrew. He drained the glass of kümmel and accepted a piece of fruit cake. Again he clasped his hands over his breast.

"Such a pleasure," he said, "to make the acquaintance of an intelligent Goy. A Goy who writes books and talks to the birds. Who reads the Russians and observes Yom Kippur. And has the sense to marry a girl from Bukovina . . . a Tzigane, no less. And an actress! *Where is that loafer, Sid? Is he drunk again?*" He looked around like a wise old owl about to hoot. "*Nun*, if a man studies all his life and then discovers that he is an idiot, is he right? The answer is Yes and No. We say in our village that a man must cultivate his own nonsense, not somebody else's. And in the *Cabala* it says . . . But we mustn't split hairs right away. From Minsk came the mink coats and from Pinsk nothing but misery. A Jew from the Corridor is a Jew whom the devil never touches. Moishe Echt was such a Jew. My cousin, in other words. Always in trouble with the rabbi. When winter came he locked himself in the granary. He was a harness maker. . . ."

He stopped abruptly and gave me a Satanic smile.

"In the Book of Job," I began.

"Make it Revelations," he said. "It's more ectoplasmic."

Mona began to giggle. Mrs. Essen discreetly withdrew. Only the boy remained. He was making signs behind Mr. Elfenbein's back, as if ringing a telephone attached to his temple.

"When you begin a new opus," Mr. Elfenbein was saying, "in what language do you pray first?"

"In the language of our fathers," I replied instanter. "Abraham, Isaac, Ezekiel, Nehemiah. . . ."

"And David and Solomon, and Ruth and Esther," he chimed in.

The boy now refilled Mr. Elfenbein's glass and again he drained it in one gulp.

"A fine young gangster he will grow to be," said Mr. Elfenbein, smacking his lips. "Already he knows nothing from nothing. A *malamed* he should be—if he had his wits. Do you remember in *Tried and Punished* . . . ?"

"You mean *Crime and Punishment*," said young Essen.

"In Russian it is *The Crime and Its Punishment.* Now take a back seat and don't make any faces behind my back. I know I'm *meshuggah,* but this gentleman doesn't. Let him find out for himself. Isn't that so, Mr. Gentleman?" He made a mock bow.

"When a Jew turns from his religion," he went on, thinking of Mrs. Essen, no doubt, "it's like fat turning to water. Better to become a Christian than one of these milk and water—." He cut himself short, mindful of the proprieties. "A Christian is a Jew with a crucifix in his hand. He can't forget that we killed him, Jesus, who was a Jew like any other Jew, only more fanatical. To read Tolstoy you don't have to be a Christian; a Jew understands him just as well. What was good about Tolstoy was that he finally got the courage to run away from his wife . . . and to give his money away. The lunatic is blessed; he doesn't care about money. Christians are only make-believe lunatics; they carry life insurance as well as beads and prayer books. A Jew doesn't walk about with the Psalms; he knows them by heart. Even when he's selling shoelaces he's humming a verse to himself. When the Gentile sings a hymn it sounds like he's making war. *Onward Christian Soldiers!* How does it go—? Marching as to war. Why as to? They're always making war—with a saber in one hand and a crucifix in the other."

Mona now rose to draw closer. Mr. Elfenbein extended his hands, as if to a dancing partner. He sized her up from head to toe, like an auctioneer. Then he said: "And what did you play in last, my rose of Sharon?"

"*The Green Cockatoo,*" she replied. (Tic-tac-toe.)

"And before that?"

"*The Goat Song, Liliom . . . Saint Joan.*"

"Stop!" He put up his hand. "*The Dybbuk* is better suited to your temperament. More gynecological. Now what was that play of Sudermann's? No matter. Ah yes . . . *Magda.* You're a Magda, not a Monna Vanna. I ask you, how would I look in *The God of Vengeance?* Am I a Schildkraut or a Ben Ami? Give me *Siberia* to play, not *The Servant in the House!*" He chucked her under the chin. "You remind me a little of Elissa Landi. Yes, with a touch of Nazimova perhaps. If you had more weight, you could be another Modjeska. *Hedda Gabler*, that's for *you.* My favorite is *The Wild Duck.* After that *The Playboy of the Western World.* But not in Yiddish, God forbid!"

The theater was his pet subject evidently. He had been an actor years ago, first in Rummeldumvitza or some hole like that, then at the Thalia on the Bowery. It was there he met Ben Ami. And somewhere else Blanche Yurka. He had also known Vesta Tilley, odd thing. And David Warfield. He thought *Androcles and the Lion* was a gem, but didn't care much for Shaw's other plays. He was very fond of Ben Jonson and Marlowe, and of Hasenclever and von Hoffmansthal.

"Beautiful women rarely make good actresses," he was saying. "There should always be a defect of some kind—a longish nose or the eyes a little misfocused. The best is to have an unusual voice. People always remember the voice. Pauline Lord's for example." He turned to Mona. "You have a good voice too. It has brown sugar in it and cloves and nutmeg. The worst is the American voice—no soul in it. Jacob Ben Ami had a marvelous voice . . . like good soup . . . never turned rancid. But he dragged it around like a tortoise. A woman should cultivate the voice above everything. She should also think more, about what the play means . . . not about her exquisite postillion . . . I mean *posterior.* Jewish actresses have too much flesh usually; when they walk across the stage they shake like jelly. But they have sorrow in their voices . . . *Sorge*. They don't have to imagine that a devil is pulling a breast off with hot pincers. Yes, sin and sorrow are the best ingredients. And a bit of *phantasmus*. Like in Webster or Marlowe. A shoemaker who talks to the Devil every time he goes to the water closet. Or falls in love with a beanstalk, as in Moldavia. The Irish plays are full of lunatics and drunkards, and the nonsense they talk is holy nonsense. The Irish are poets always, especially when they know nothing. They have been tortured too, maybe not as much as the Jews, but enough. No one likes to eat potatoes three times a day or use a pitchfork for a toothpick. Great actors, the Irish. Born chimpanzees. The British are too refined, too mentalized. A masculine race, but castrated. . . ."

A commotion was going on at the door. It was Sid Essen returning from his walk with a couple of mangy-looking cats he had rescued. His wife was trying to shoo them out.

"Elfenbein!" he shouted, waving his cap. "Greetings! How did *you* get here?"

"How *should* I get here? By my two feet, no?" He took a step forward. "Let me smell your breath!"

"Go 'way, go 'way! When have you seen me drunk?"

"When you are too happy—or not so happy."

"A great pal, Elfenbein," said Reb, slinging an arm around his shoulder affectionately. "The Yiddish King Lear, that's what he is . . . What's the matter, the glasses are empty."

"Like your mind," said Elfenbein. "Drink of the spirit. Like Moses. From the rock gushes water, from the bottle only foolishness. Shame on you, son of Zweifel, to be so thirsty."

The conversation became scattered. Mrs. Essen had got rid of the cats, cleaned up the mess they had made in the hallway, and was once again smoothing her hair back from her brow. A lady, every inch of her. No rancor, no recriminations. Gelid, in that super-refined, ethical-culturish way. She took a seat by the window, hoping no doubt that the conversation would take a more rational turn. She was fond of Mr. Elfenbein, but he distressed her with his Old World talk, his crazy grimaces, his stale jokes.

The Yiddish King Lear was now beyond all bridling. He had launched into a lengthy monologue on the Zend Avesta, with occasional sideswipes at the Book of Etiquette, Jewish presumably, though from the references he made to it it might as well have been Chinese. He had just finished saying that, according to Zoroaster, man had been chosen to continue the work of creation. Then he added: "Man is nothing unless he is a collaborator. God is not kept alive by prayers and injections. The Jew has forgotten all this—and the Gentile is a spiritual cripple."

A confused discussion followed these statements, much to Elfenbein's amusement. In the midst of it he began singing at the top of his lungs—"*Rumeinie, Rumeinie, Rumeinie . . . a mameligele . . . a pastramele . . . a karnatsele . . . un a gleizele wine, Aha!*"

"You see," he said, when the hubbub had subsided, "even in a liberal household it's dangerous to introduce ideas. Time was when such talk was music to one's ears. The Rabbi would take a hair and with a knife like a razor he would split it into a thousand hairs. Nobody had to agree with him; it was an exercise. It sharpened the mind and made us forget the terror. If the music played you needed no partner; you danced with Zov, Toft, Giml. Now when we argue we put bandages over our eyes. We go to see Tomashevsky and we weep like pigs. We don't know any more who is Pechorin or Aksakov. If on the stage a Jew visits a bordel—perhaps he lost his way—everyone blushes for the author. But a good Jew can sit in the slaughterhouse and think only of Jehovah. Once in

Bucuresti I saw a holy man finish a bottle of vodka all by himself, and then he talked for three hours without stopping. He talked of Satan. He made him so repulsive that I could smell him. When I left the café everything looked Satanic to me. I had to go to a public house, excuse me, to get rid of the sulphur. It glowed like a furnace in there; the women looked like pink angels. Even the Madame, who was really a vulture. Such a time I had that night! All because the *Tzaddik* had taken too much vodka.

"Yes, it's good to sin once in a while, but not to make a pig of yourself. Sin with eyes open. Drown yourself in the pleasures of the flesh, but hang on by a hair. The Bible is full of patriarchs who indulged the flesh but never lost sight of the one God. Our forefathers were men of spirit, but they had meat on their bones. One could take a concubine and still have respect for one's wife. After all, it was at the door of the temple that the harlot learned her trade. Yes, sin was real then, and Satan too. Now we have ethics, and our children become garment manufacturers, gangsters, concert performers. Soon they will be making trapeze artists of them and hockey players. . . ."

"Yes," said Reb from the depth of his armchair, "now we are less than nothing. Once we had pride. . . ."

Elfenbein cut in. "Now we have the Jew who talks like the Gentile, who says nothing matters but success. The Jew who sends his boy to a military academy so that he can learn how to kill his fellow Jew. The daughter he sends to Hollywood, to make a name for herself, as a Hungarian or Roumanian by showing her nakedness. Instead of great rabbis we have heavyweight prize fighters. We even have homosexuals now, *weh is mir*. Soon we will have Jewish Cossacks."

Like a refrain, Reb sighed: "The God of Abraham is no more."

"Let them show their nakedness," said Elfenbein, "but

not pretend that they are heathen. Let them remember their fathers who were peddlers and scholars and who fell like chaff under the heels of the hooligans."

On and on he went, leaping from subject to subject like a chamois in thin air. Names like Mordecai and Ahasuerus dropped from his lips, together with *Lady Windermere's Fan* and Sodom and Gomorrah. In one breath he expatiated on *The Shoemaker's Holiday* and the lost tribes of Israel. And always, like a summer complaint, he came back to the sickness of the Gentiles, which he likened unto *eine Arschkrankheit.* Egypt all over again, but without grandeur, without miracles. And this sickness was now in the brain. Maggots and poppy-seed. Even the Jews were looking forward to the day of resurrection. For them, he said, it would be like war without dum-dum bullets.

He was swept along by his own word, now. And drinking only seltzer water. The word bliss, which he had let fall, seemed to cause an explosion in his head. What was bliss? A long sleep in the fallopian tubes. Or—Huns without *Schrecklichkeit.* The Danube always blue, as in a Strauss waltz. Yes, he admitted, in the Pentateuch there was much nonsense written, but it had a logic. The Book of Numbers was not all horseradish. It had teleological excitement. As for circumcision, one might just as well talk about chopped spinach, for all the importance it had. The synagogues smelled of chemicals and roach powder. The Amalekites were the spiritual cockroaches of their time, like the Anabaptists of today. "No wonder," he exclaimed, giving us a frightening wink, "that everything is in a state of 'chassis.' How true were the words of the *Tzaddik* who said: 'Apart from Him there is nothing that is really clear.' "

Oof! He was getting winded, but there was more to come. He made a phosphorescent leap now from the depths of his trampoline. There were a few great souls whose names he had to mention: they belonged to another order. Barbusse, Tagore, Romain Rolland, Péguy, for example. The friends of humanity. Heroic souls, all of them. Even America was capable of producing a humanitarian soul, witness Eugene V. Debs. There are mice, he said, who wear the uniforms of field marshals and gods who move in our midst like beggars. The Bible swarmed with moral and spiritual giants. Who could compare to King David? Who was so magnificent, yet wise, as Solomon? The lion of Judah was still alive and snorting. No anesthetic could put this lion permanently to sleep. "We are coming," said he, to a time when even the heaviest artillery will be caught with spiders' webs and armies melt like snow. Ideas are crumbling, like old walls. The world shrinks, like the skin of a lichee nut, and men press together like wet sacks mildewed with fear. When the prophets give out the stones must speak. The patriarchs needed no megaphones. They stood still and waited for the Lord to appear unto them. Now we hop about like frogs, from one cesspool to another, and talk gibberish. Satan has stretched his net over the world and we leap out like fish ready for the frying pan. Man was set down in the midst of a garden, naked and dreamless. To each creature was given his place, his condition. *Know thy place!* was the commandment. Not "Know thyself!" The worm becomes a butterfly only when it becomes intoxicated with the splendor and magnificence of life.

"We have surrendered to despair. Ecstasy has given way to drunkenness. A man who is intoxicated with life sees visions, not snakes. He has no hangovers. Nowadays we have a bluebird in every home—corked and bottled. Sometimes it's called Old Kentucky, sometimes it's a license number—Vat 69. All poisonous, even when diluted."

He paused to squirt some seltzer water in his glass. Reb was sound asleep. He wore a look of absolute bliss, as if he had seen Mt. Sinai.

"There now," said Elfenbein, raising his glass, "let us drink to the wonders of the Western World. May they soon be no more! It's getting late and I have monopolized the floor. Next time we will discuss more ecumenical subjects. Maybe I will tell you about my Carmen Sylva days. I mean the café, not the Queen. Though I can say that I once slept in her palace . . . in the stable, that is. Remind me to tell you more about Jacob Ben Ami. He was much more than a voice. . . ."

As we were taking leave he asked if he could see us to our door. "With pleasure," I said.

Walking down the street he stopped to give vent to an inspiration. "May I suggest," he said, "that if you have not yet fixed on a title for your book that you call it *This Gentile World?* It would be most appropriate even if it makes no sense. Use a *nom de plume* like Boguslavsky—that will confuse the reader still more."

"I am not always so voluble," he added, "but you, the two of you, are the *Grenze* type, and for a derelict from Transylvania that is like an apéritif. I always wanted to write novels, foolish ones, like Dickens. The Mr. Pickwick kind. Instead I became a playboy. Well, I will say good night now. Elfenbein is my pseudonym; the real name would astonish you. Look up Deuteronomy, Chapter thirteen. 'If there arise among you a—'." He was seized with a violent fit of sneezing. "The Seltzer water!" he exclaimed. "Maybe I should go to a Turkish bath. It's time for another influenza epidemic. Good night now! *Onward as to war!* Don't forget the lion of Judah! You can see him in the movies, when the music starts up." He imitated the growl. "*That,*" he said, "is to show that he is still awake."

From "Cousin Julie" (Sexus)

. . . I was eating breakfast when I suddenly recalled that I had never canvased cousin Julie. Maude's cousin Julie. Julie was married now, just long enough, I figured, to want a change of rhythm. Julie would be my first call. I'd take it easy, pop in just a little before lunch, sell her a set of books, have a good meal, get my end in and then go to a movie.

Julie lived at the upper end of Manhattan in a wall-papered incubator. Her husband was a dope, as near as I could make out. That's to say he was a perfectly normal specimen who earned an honest living and voted the Republican or Democratic ticket according to mood. Julie was a good-natured slob who never read anything more disturbing than the Saturday Evening Post. She was just a piece of ass, with about enough intelligence to realize that after a fuck you have to take a douche and if that doesn't work then a darning needle. She had done it so often, the darning needle stunt, that she was an adept at it. She could bring on a haemorrhage even if it had been an immaculate conception. Her main idea was to enjoy herself like a drunken weasel and get it out of her system as quick as possible. She wouldn't flinch at using a chisel or a monkey wrench, if she thought either would do the trick.

I was a bit flabbergasted when she came to the door. I hadn't thought of the change a year or so can work in a female, nor had I thought how most females look at eleven in the morning when they are not expecting visitors. To be cruelly exact, she looked like a cold meat loaf that had been spattered with catsup and put back in the ice box. The Julie I had last seen was a dream by comparison. I had to make some rapid transpositions to adjust myself to the situation.

Naturally I was more in the mood to sell than to fuck. Before very long, however, I realized that to sell, I would have to fuck. Julie just couldn't understand what the hell had come over me—to walk in on her and try to dump a load of books on her. I couldn't tell her it would improve her mind because she had no mind, and she knew it and wasn't the least embarrassed to admit it.

She left me alone for a few minutes in order to primp herself up. I began reading the prospectus. I found it so interesting that I almost sold myself a set of books. I was reading a fragment about Coleridge, what a wonderful mind he had (and I had always thought him a bag of shit!), when I felt her coming towards me. It was so interesting, the passage, that I excused myself without looking up and continued reading. She knelt behind me, on the couch, and began reading over my shoulder. I felt her sloshy boobs joggling me but I was too intent on pursuing the ramifications of Coleridge's amazing mind to let her vegetable appendages disturb me.

Suddenly the beautifully bound prospectus went flying out of my hand.

"What are you reading that crap for?" she cried, swinging me around and holding me by the elbows. "I don't understand a word of it, and neither do you, I'll bet. What's the matter with you—can't you find yourself a job?"

A witless-shitless sort of grin slowly spread over her face. She looked like a Teutonic angel doing a real think. I got up, recovered the prospectus, and asked what about lunch.

"Jesus, I like your crust," said she. "What the hell do you think I am anyway?"

Here I had to pretend that I was only joking, but after putting my hand down her bosom and twiddling the nipple of her right teat a while, I deftly brought the conversation back to the subject of food.

"Listen, you've changed," she said. "I don't like the way you talk—or act." Here she firmly stuck her teat back, as if it were a ball of wet socks going into a laundry bag. "Listen, I'm a married woman, do you realize that? Do you know what Mike would do to you if he caught you acting this way?"

"You're a bit changed yourself," said I, rising to my feet and sniffing the air in search of provender. All I wanted now was food. I don't know why, but I had made up my mind that she would dish me up a good meal—that was the least she could do for me, lop-sided moron that she was.

The only way to get anything out of her was to handle her. I had to pretend to get passionate mauling the cheeks of her tumorous ass. And yet not too passionate, because that would mean a quick fuck and maybe no lunch. If the meal were good I might do a hit and run job—that's what I was thinking to myself, as I foozled around.

"Jesus Christ, all right, I'll get you a meal," she blurted out, reading my thoughts like a blind bookworm.

"Fine," I almost shouted. "What have you got?"

"Come and see for yourself," she answered, dragging me to the kitchen and opening the ice-box.

I saw ham, potato salad, sardines, cold beets, rice pudding, apple sauce, frankfurters, pickles, celery stalks, cream cheese and a special dish of puke with mayonnaise on it which I knew I didn't want.

"Let's bring it all out," I suggested. "And have you any beer?"

"Yeah, and I got mustard too," she snarled.

"Any bread?"

She gave me a look of clean disgust. I quickly yanked the things out of the ice-box and set them on the table.

"Better make some coffee too," I said.

"I suppose you'd like some whipped cream with it, wouldn't you? You know, I feel like poisoning you. Jesus, if you're hard up you could ask me to lend you some money . . . you oughtn't to come here and try to sell me a lot of crap. If you'd been a little nicer I'd have asked you out to lunch. I've got tickets for the theatre. We could have had a good time . . . I might even have bought the fool books. Mike isn't a bad guy. He'd have bought the books even if we had no intention of reading them. *If he thought you needed help.* . . . You walk in and treat me as if I were dirt. What did I ever do to you? I don't get it. Don't laugh! I'm serious. I don't know why I should take this from *you.* Who the hell do you think you are?"

She slammed a dish down in front of me. Then she turned on her heel and went to the kitchen. I was left there with all the food heaped up in front of me.

"Come, come, don't take it like that!" I said, shoveling a forkful into my mouth. "You know I didn't mean anything personal." (The word personal struck me as being highly incongruous, but I knew she'd like it.)

"Personal or not, I'm not joining you," she retorted. "You can eat your fill and get out. I'll make you some coffee. I don't want to ever see you again. You're disgusting."

I put the knife and fork down and went into the kitchen. The things were cold anyway, so it wouldn't matter if I did spend a few minutes soothing her feelings.

"I'm sorry, Julie," I said, trying to put my arm around her. She brushed me away angrily. "You see," and I began to put some feeling into my words, "Maude and I don't get along very well. We had a bad quarrel this morning. I must be out of sorts. . . ."

"Is that any reason to take it out on *me?*"

"No, it isn't. I don't know, I was desperate this morning. That's why I came to see *you*. And then, when I started in to work on you . . . to sell you the books . . . I felt ashamed of myself. I wouldn't have let you take the books even if you had pretended you wanted them. . . ."

"I know what's the matter with you," she said. "You were disappointed in my looks. *I've changed*, that's what's the matter. And you're a bad loser. You want to take it out on me—but it's your own fault. You've got a good-looking wife . . . why don't you stick to her? Everybody has quarrels—you're not the only two in the world. Do I run off to somebody else's husband when things go wrong? Where the hell would that get us? Mike's no angel to live with . . . nobody is, I guess. You act like a spoiled child. What do you think life is, *a wet dream?*"

This speech couldn't be laughed off. I had to beg her to sit down and eat with me, give me a chance to explain myself. Reluctantly she consented.

It was a long drawn-out story I unfolded, as I polished off one plate after another. She seemed so impressed by my sincerity that I began to toy with the idea of re-introducing the world's best literature. I had to skate very delicately because this time it would have to look as if I were doing *her* a favor. I was trying to jockey myself into the position of letting her help me. At the same time I was wondering if it were worth it, if perhaps it wouldn't be more pleasant to go to the matinee.

She was just getting back to normal, getting friendly and trusting. The coffee was excellent, and I had just finished the second cup when I felt a bowel movement coming on. I excused myself and went to the bathroom. There I enjoyed the luxury of a thorough evacuation. I pulled the chain and sat there a few moments, a bit dreamy and a bit lecherous too, when suddenly I realized that I was getting a sitz bath. I pulled the chain again. The water started to overflow between my legs on to the floor. I jumped up, dried my ass with a towel, buttoned my trousers and looked frantically up at the toilet box. I tried everything I could think of but the water kept rising and flowing over—and with it came one or two healthy turds and a mess of toilet paper.

In a panic I called Julie. Through a crack in the door I begged her to tell me what to do.

"Let me in, I'll fix it," said she.

"Tell *me*," I begged, "I'll do it. You can't come in yet."

"I can't explain," said Julie, "you'll have to let me in."

There was no help for it, I had to open the door. I was never more embarrassed in my life. The floor was one ungodly mess. Julie, however, went to work with dispatch, as though it were an everyday affair. In a jiffy the water had stopped running; it only remained to clean up the mess.

"Listen, you get out now," I begged. "Let me handle this. Have you got a dust-pan—and a mop?"

"*You* get out!" said she. "I'll take care of it." And with that she pushed me out and closed the door.

I waited on pins and needles for her to come out. Then a real funk took hold of me. There was only one thing to do—escape as fast as possible.

I fidgeted a few moments, listening first on one foot, then the other, not daring to make a peep. I knew I'd never be able to face her. I looked around, measured the distance to the door, listened intently for just a second, then grabbed my things and tiptoed out.

It was an elevator apartment, but I didn't wait for the elevator. I skipped down the stairs, three steps at a time, as though the devil himself were pursuing me.

From "McGregor and Tess" (Sexus)

. . . At noon, as I was leaving the office, I ran into MacGregor and his wife sporting a new car. We hadn't seen each other for months. He insisted on my having lunch with them. I tried to get out of it but couldn't. "What's the matter with you," he said, "you're not yourself. A woman again, I suppose. Jesus, when will you ever learn to take care of yourself?"

During the lunch he informed me that they had decided to take a ride out on Long Island, perhaps spend the night there somewhere. Why couldn't I come along? I said I had made a date with Ulric. "That's all right," he said, "bring your friend Ulric along. I haven't much use for him, but if it'll make you any happier, sure we'll pick him up, why not?" I tried to tell him that Ulric might not be so eager to join us. He wouldn't listen. "He'll come," he said, "you leave that to me. We'll go out to Montauk Point or Shelter Island and just lie around and take it easy—it'll do you good. As for that Jane you're worrying about, why forget it! If she likes you she'll come round by herself. Treat 'em rough, that's what I always say, eh Tess?" and with that he gave his wife a dig in the ribs that knocked the breath out of her.

Tess Molloy was what you'd call a good-natured Irish slob. She was about the homeliest woman I've ever seen, broad in the beam, pock-marked, her hair scant and stringy (she was getting bald), but jolly and indolent, always ready to fight at the drop of the hat. MacGregor had married her for purely practical reasons. They had never pretended to be in love with one another. There was scarcely even an animal affection between them since, as he had readily explained to me shortly after their marriage, sex didn't mean a thing to her. She didn't mind being diddled now and then, but she got no pleasure from it. "*Are you through?*" she would ask every now and then. If he took too long a time over it she would ask him to fetch her a drink or bring her something to eat. "I got so damned sore at her once that I brought her the newspaper to read. 'Now go ahead and read,' I says to her, and see that you don't miss the comic strip!' "

I thought we'd have a hard time persuading Ulric to come along. He had only met MacGregor a few times and each time he had shaken his head as though to say—"It beats me!" To my surprise Ulric greeted MacGregor quite cordially. He had just been promised a fat check for a new can of beans he was to do next week and he was in a mood to lay off work for a while. He had just been out to get himself a few bottles of liquor. There had been no phone call from Mara, of course. There wouldn't be any, not for a week or two, thought Ulric. *Have a drink!*

MacGregor was impressed by a magazine cover that Ulric had just finished. It was a picture of a man with a golf bag just setting out for the greens. MacGregor found it extremely life-like. "I didn't know you were that good," he said with his customary tactlessness. "What do you get for a job like that, if I may ask?" Ulric told him. His respect deepened. Meanwhile his wife had spied a water color which she liked. "Did *you* do that?" she asked. Ulric nodded. "I'd like to buy it," she said. "How much do you want for it?" Ulric said he would be glad to *give* it to her when it was finished. "*It's not finished yet, you mean?*" she screamed. "It looks finished to me. I don't care, I'll take it anyway, just as it is. Will you take twenty dollars for it?"

"Now listen, you fathead," said MacGregor, giving her a playful ox-like poke on the jaw which knocked the glass out of her hand, "the man says it ain't finished yet; what do you want to do, make a liar out of him?"

"I'm not saying it's finished," she said, "and I didn't call him a liar. I like it just as it is and I want to buy it."

"Well, buy it then, by Jesus, and get done with it!"

"No, really, I couldn't let you take it in that condition," said Ulric. "Besides, it's not good enough to sell—it's just a sketch."

"That doesn't matter," said Tess Molloy, "I want it. I'll give you thirty dollars for it."

"You just said twenty a minute ago," put in MacGregor. "What's the matter with you, are you nuts? Didn't you ever buy a picture before? Listen, Ulric, you'd better let her have it or else we'll never get started. I'd like to do a little fishing before the day's over, what do you say? Of course this bird"—indicating me with his thumb—"doesn't like fishing; he wants to sit and mope, dream about love, study the sky and that kind of crap. Come on, let's get going. Yeah, that's right, take a bottle along—we might want a swig of it before we get there."

Tess took the water color from the wall and left a twenty dollar bill on the desk.

"Better take it with you," warned MacGregor. "No telling who may break in while we're gone."

After we had gone a block or so it occurred to me that I ought to have left a note for Mara on the doorbell. "Oh, fuck that idea!" said MacGregor. "Give her something to worry about—they like that. *Eh Toots?*" and again he poked his wife in the ribs.

"If you poke me again like that," said she, "I'll wrap this bottle around your neck. I mean it too."

"*She means it,*" he said, glancing back at us with a bright nickel-plated sort of smile. "You can't prod her *too much,* can you Toots? Yep, she's got a good disposition—otherwise she'd never have stood me as long as she has, ain't that right, kid?"

"Oh, shut up! Look where you're driving. We don't want this car smashed up like the other one."

"*We* don't?" he yelled. "Jesus, I like that. And who, may I ask, ran into the milk truck on the Hempstead Turnpike in broad daylight?"

"Oh, forget it!"

They kept it up like that until way past Jamaica. Suddenly he quit pestering and nagging her and, looking through the mirror, he began talking to us about his conception of art and life. It was all right, he thought, to go in for that sort of thing—meaning pictures and all that humbug—provided one had the talent for it. A good artist was worth his money, that was his opinion. The proof was that he got it, if you noticed. Anybody who was any good always got recognition, that's what he wanted to say. Wasn't that so? Ulric said he thought so too. Not always, of course, but generally speaking. Of course, there were fellows like Gauguin, MacGregor went on, and Christ knows they were good artists, but then there was some strange quirk in them, something anti-social, if you wanted to call it that, which prevented them from being recognized immediately. You couldn't blame the public for that, could you? Some people were born unlucky, that's how he saw it. Now take himself, for instance. He wasn't an artist, to be sure, but then he wasn't a dud either. In his way he was as good as the next fellow, maybe just a little bit better. And yet, just to prove how uncertain everything could be, nothing he had put his hand to had turned out right. Sometimes a little shyster had gotten the better of him. And why? Because he, MacGregor, wouldn't stoop to doing certain things. There are things you just don't do, he insisted. No sir! and he banged the wheel emphatically. But that's the way they play the game, and they get away with it too. But not forever! Ah no!

"Now you take Maxfield Parrish," he continued. "I suppose he doesn't count, but just the same he gives 'em what they want. While a guy like Gauguin has to struggle for a crust of bread—and even when he's dead they spit in his eye. It's a queer game, art. I suppose it's like everything else—you do it because you like it, that's about the size of it, what? Now you take that bastard sitting alongside of you—yeah *you!*" he said, grinning at me through the mirror—"he thinks we ought to support him, nurse him along until he writes his masterpiece. He never thinks that he might look for a job meanwhile. Oh no, he wouldn't soil his lily-white hands that way. He's an *artist.* Well, maybe he is, for all I know. But he's got to prove it first, am I right? Did anybody support me because I thought I was a lawyer? It's all right to have dreams—we all like to dream—but somebody has to pay the rent."

We had just passed a duck farm. "Now that's what I'd like," said MacGregor. "I'd like nothing better than to settle down and raise ducks. Why don't I? Because I've got sense enough to know that I don't know anything about ducks. You can't just dream them up—you've got to raise them! Now Henry there, if he took it into his head to raise ducks, he'd just move out here and dream about it. First he'd ask me to lend him some money, of course. He's got that much sense, I must admit. He knows that you have to *buy* them before you can raise them. So, when he wants something, say a duck now, he just blandly says 'Give me some money, I want to buy a duck!' Now that's what I call impractical. That's dreaming. . . . *How did I get my money?* Did I pick it off a bush? When I tell him to get out and hustle for it he gets sore. He thinks I'm against him. Is that right—or am I slandering you?" and he gave me another nickel-plated grin through the mirror.

"It's O.K.," I said. "Don't take it to heart."

"*Take it to heart?* Do you hear that? Jesus, if you think I lay awake nights worrying about you, you're sadly mistaken. I'm trying to set you right, that's all. I'm trying to put a little sense into your thick head. Of course I know you don't want to raise ducks, but you must admit you do get some crazy notions now and then. Jesus, I hope you don't forget the time you tried to sell me a Jewish Encyclopaedia. Imagine, he wanted me to sign for a set so that he could get his commission, and then I was to return it after a while—just like that. I was to give them some cock-and-bull story which he had trumped up on the spur of the moment. That's the sort of genius he has for business. And me a lawyer? Can you see me signing my name to a phoney proposition like that? No, by Jesus, I'd have more respect for him if he had told me he wanted to raise ducks. I can understand a guy wanting to raise ducks. But to try and palm off a Jewish Encyclopaedia on your best friend—that's raw, to say nothing of it being illegal and untenable. *That's another thing*—he thinks the law is all rot. 'I don't believe in it,' he says, as if his believing or not believing made any difference. And as soon as he's in trouble he comes hot-footing it to me. 'Do something,' he says, 'you know how to handle these things.' It's just a game to him. He could live without law, so he thinks, but I'll be damned if he isn't in trouble all the time. And of course, as to paying me for my trouble, or just for the time I put in on him, that never enters his bean. I should do those little things for him out of friendship. You see what I mean?"

Nobody said anything.

We drove along in silence for a while. We passed more duck farms. I asked myself how long it would take to go crazy if one bought a duck and settled down on Long Island with it. Walt Whitman was born here somewhere. I no sooner thought of his name than, like buying the duck, I wanted to visit his birthplace.

"What about visiting Walt Whitman's birthplace?" I said aloud.

"*What?*" yelled MacGregor.

"Walt Whitman!" I yelled. "He was born somewhere on Long Island. Let's go there."

"Do you know where?" shouted MacGregor.

"No, but we could ask some one."

"Oh, the hell with that! I thought you knew where. These people out here wouldn't know who Walt Whitman was. I wouldn't have known myself only you talk about him so goddamn much. He was a bit queer, wasn't he? Didn't you tell me he was in love with a bus driver? Or was he a nigger lover? I can't remember any more."

"Maybe it was both," said Ulric, uncorking the bottle.

We were passing through a town. "Jesus, but I seem to know *this* place!" said MacGregor. "Where in hell are we?" He pulled up to the curb and hailed a pedestrian. "Hey, what's the name of this burg?" The man told him. "Can you beat that?" he said. "I thought I recognized the dump. Jesus, what a beautiful dose of clap I got here once! I wonder if I could find the house. I'd just like to drive by and see if that cute little bitch is sitting on the verandah. God, the prettiest little trick you ever laid eyes on—a little angel, you'd say. And could she fuck! One of those excitable little bitches, always in heat—you know, always throwing it up to you, rubbing it in your face. I drove out here in a pouring rain to keep a date with her. Everything just fine. Her husband was away on a trip and she was just itching for a piece of tail. . . . I'm trying to think now where I picked her up. I know this, that I had a hell of a time persuading her to let me visit her. Well, anyway, I had a wonderful time—never got out of bed for two days. Never got up to wash even—*that was the trouble*. Jesus, I swear if you saw that face alongside of you on the pillow you'd think you were getting the Virgin Mary. She could come about nine times without stopping. And then she'd say —'Do it again, once more. . . . I feel *depraved*.' That was a funny one, eh? I don't think she knew what the word meant. Anyway, a few days later it began to itch and then it got red and swollen. I couldn't believe I was getting the clap. I thought maybe a flea had bitten me. Then the pus began to run. Boy, fleas don't make pus. Well, I went round to the family doctor. 'That's a beauty,' he said, 'where did you get it?' I told him. 'Better have a blood test,' he said, 'it might be syphilis.' "

"That's enough of that," groaned Tess. "Can't you talk about something pleasant for a change?"

"Well," says MacGregor, in answer to that, "you've got to admit I've been pretty clean since I know you, *right?*"

"You better had," she answered, "or it wouldn't be healthy for you."

From "America" (Big Sur)

"If you do not know where you are going, any road will take you there."*

There are days when it all seems as simple and clear as that to me. What do I mean? I mean with regard to the problem of living on this earth without being a slave, a drudge, a hack, a misfit, an alcoholic, a drug addict, a neurotic, a schizophrenic, a glutton for punishment or an artist *manqué*.

Supposedly we have the highest standard of living of any country in the world. Do we, though? It depends on what one means by high standards. Certainly nowhere does it cost more to live than here in America. The cost is not only in dollars and cents but in sweat and blood, in frustration, ennui, broken homes, smashed ideals, illness and insanity. We have the most wonderful hospitals, the most gorgeous insane asylums, the most fabulous prisons, the best equipped and the highest paid army and navy, the speediest bombers, the largest stockpile of atom bombs, yet never enough of any of these items to satisfy the demand. Our manual workers are the highest paid in the world; our poets the worst. There are more automobiles than one can count. And as for drugstores, where in the world will you find the like?

We have only one enemy we really fear: the microbe.

---

* M. N. Chatterjee, *Out of Confusion* (Yellow Springs, Ohio: Antioch Press, 1954).

But we are licking him on every front. True, millions still suffer from cancer, heart disease, schizophrenia, multiple sclerosis, tuberculosis, epilepsy, colitis, cirrhosis of the liver, dermatitis, gall stones, neuritis, Bright's disease, bursitis, Parkinson's disease, diabetes, floating kidneys, cerebral palsy, pernicious anaemia, encephalitis, locomotor ataxia, falling of the womb, muscular distrophy, jaundice, rheumatic fever, polio, sinus and antrum troubles, halitosis, St. Vitus's Dance, narcolepsy, coryza, leucorrhea, nymphomania, phthisis, carcinoma, migraine, dipsomania, malignant tumors, high blood pressure, duodenal ulcers, prostate troubles, sciatica, goiter, catarrh, asthma, rickets, hepatitis, nephritis, melancholia, amoebic dysentery, bleeding piles, quinsy, hiccoughs, shingles, frigidity and impotency, even dandruff, and of course all the insanities, now legion, *but*—our men of science will rectify all this within the next hundred years or so. *How?* Why, by destroying all the nasty germs which provoke this havoc and disruption! By waging a great preventive war—not a cold war! —wherein our poor frail bodies will become a battleground for all the antibiotics yet to come. A game of hide and seek, so to speak, in which one germ pursues another, tracks it down and slays it, all without the least disturbance to our usual functioning. Until this victory is achieved, however, we may be obliged to continue swallowing twenty or thirty vitamins, all of different strengths and colors, before breakfast, down our tiger's milk and brewer's yeast, drink our orange *and* grapefruit juices, use blackstrap molasses on our oatmeal, smear our bread (made of stoneground flour) with peanut butter, use raw honey or raw sugar with our coffee, poach our eggs rather than fry them, follow this with an extra glass of superfortified milk, belch and burp a little, give ourselves an injection, weigh ourselves to see if we are under or over, stand on our heads, do our setting-up exercises—if we haven't done them already—yawn, stretch, empty the bowels, brush our teeth (if we have any left), say a prayer or two, then run like hell to catch the bus or the subway which will carry us to work, and think no more about the state of our health until we feel a cold coming on: the incurable coryza. But we are not to despair. Never despair! Just take more vitamins, add an extra dose of calcium and phosphorus pills, drink a hot toddy or two, take a high enema before retiring for the night, say another prayer, if we can remember one, and call it a day.

Appendix

Chronology of Miller's Life

1891 Born in Yorkville, New York City, December 26th, of American parents (German ancestry). Transplanted to Brooklyn in first year.

1896–1900 Lived in the streets: "the old neighborhood," Williamsburg, Brooklyn, known as The 14th Ward.

1901 Transplanted to Bushwick section of Brooklyn (Decatur Street): "the street of early sorrows."

1907 Met first love, Cora Seward, at Eastern District High School, Brooklyn.

1909 Entered City College of New York and left after two months—rebelled against educational methods. Took job with Atlas Portland Cement Company, financial district, N.Y. Began period of "athleticism" lasting about seven years: rigorous discipline. Took up with first mistress, woman old enough to be mother (Pauline Chouteau of Phoebus, Virginia).

1913 Traveled through the West. Worked at odd jobs in endeavor to break with city life. Met Emma Goldman in San Diego: turning point in life.

1914 Returned to New York, working with father in tailor shop; tried to turn business over to the employees. Met here first great writer, Frank Harris.

1917 Married Beatrice Sylvas Wickens of Brooklyn, a pianist.

1919 Daughter born, named Barbara Sylvas, now known as Barbara Sandford. Took many odd jobs.

1920 Became employment manager of the messenger department, Western Union Telegraph Company, N.Y., after working several months as a messenger.

1922 Wrote first book (*Clipped Wings*) during three weeks' vacation from Western Union duties. (Began March 20, 1922.)

1923 Met June Edith Smith in Broadway dance palace.

1924 Left Western Union, determined never to take a job again, but to devote entire energy to writing. Divorced from first wife and married June Smith.

1925 Began writing career in earnest, accompanied by great poverty. Sold prose-poems (*Mezzotints*) from door to door.

1927 Opened speak-easy in Greenwich Village with wife June. Worked for Queen's County Park Commissioner. Compiled notes for complete autobiographical cycle of novels in 24 hours.

1928 Toured Europe for one year with June on money donated by a "victim."

1930 Returned to Europe alone. Left New York with ten dollars loaned by Emil Schnellock. Befriended by Richard G. Osborn and Alfred Perlès; stayed with Osborn during the winter and spring of 1930–31 at Rue Auguste Bartholdi.

1931 Met Anaïs Nin in Louveciennes. Began writing *Tropic of Cancer* while walking the streets and sleeping where possible. Worked as proofreader on the Paris edition of the *Chicago Tribune*. Taught English at Lycée Carnot (Dijon) during winter.

1933 Took apartment with Alfred Perlès in Clichy. The *Black Spring* period: great fertility, great joy. Began book on Lawrence. Saw June for the last time.

1934 Entered Villa Seurat (No. 18) same day *Tropic of Cancer* came out: a decisive moment. Original Ms. three times size of published book; rewritten three times. Met Blaise Cendrars. Visited New York from December 1934 to March 1935. Divorced from June in Mexico City by proxy.

1935 *Aller Retour New York* published in October. Met Conrad Moricand, the astrologer. Began the *Hamlet* correspondence in November.

1936 Visited New York for the second time—January to April. Practiced psychoanalysis.

1937 Met Lawrence Durrell. Went to London during the winter for a few weeks to visit Perlès. Met W. T. Symons, T. S. Eliot, and Dylan Thomas.

1938 January, the publication month of *Money and How It Gets That Way*. Second edition of *Alf* appeared in June: *Max and the White Phagocytes* published in September.

1939 *Tropic of Capricorn* published in February. Left Villa Seurat in June for sabbatical year's vacation. Left Marseilles for Athens on July 14, arriving at Durrell's home in Corfu, Greece, in August.

1940 Returned to New York in March and visited friends in the South. Met Sherwood Anderson and John Dos Passos. Wrote *The Colossus of Maroussi, The World of Sex, Quiet Days in Clichy* and began *The Rosy Crucifixion.*

1941 Made tour of U.S.A. accompanied part of the way by Abraham Rattner, the painter, from October 20, 1940 until October 9, 1941. Met Dr. Marion Souchon, Weeks Hall, Swami Prabhavananda, Alfred Stieglitz, Ferdinand Leger and John Marin. Father died while in Mississippi. Returned to New York. Left for California in June, 1942. Continued with *The Rosy Crucifixion* (finished half of it) and with *The Air-Conditioned Nightmare* (finished about two thirds.)

1942 Offered home with Margaret and Gilbert Neiman at Beverly Glen, Los Angeles, where remained until 1944.

1943 Made two to three hundred water-colors. Exhibited at Beverly Glen (The Green House), American Contemporary Gallery, Hollywood, with success. Met Jean Varda, the Greek painter, and Geraldine Fitzgerald, the movie actress. Began correspondence with Wallace Fowlie.

1944 House guest of Lynda Sargent at Big Sur; offered home on Partington Ridge by Lt. Keith B. Evans, ex-mayor of

Carmel. Married Janina Martha Lepska, December 18, in Denver, Colorado.

1945 Returned to Big Sur, California in February.* Finished *Sexus* at Keith Evans' cabin, Partington Ridge. Started translation, which was never finished, of *Season in Hell.* Daughter Valentine born November 19.

1946 Moved to shack at Anderson Creek in January. Began work on *Into the Night Life* book with Schatz. Also began book about Rimbaud: *The Time of the Assassins.* Met Leon Shamroy who eventually bought over 30 of my water colors. Received news from Paris that 40,000 dollars had accumulated to my credit and which I neglected to collect. Jean Wharton offered us her home on Partington Ridge, to pay for whenever we could.

1947 Took possession of Wharton's house on Ridge in February. Began writing *Plexus. Into the Night Life* book completed.

1948 Wrote *The Smile at the Foot of the Ladder.* Son Tony born August 28.

1949 Finished *Plexus.* Began writing *The Books in My Life.*

1951 Separated from wife Janina Lepska; the children went to live with her in Los Angeles. Finished *The Books in My Life.*

1952 Eve McClure arrived April 1 to live with me. Began writing *Nexus.* Divorced from Janina Lepska. Left for tour of Europe with Eve on December 29. Arrived in Paris for New Year's Eve.

1953 Big year—best since Clichy. Visited Rabelais' house outside Chinon, then to Wells, England, to see Perlès and wife. Returned to Big Sur at the end of August. Married Eve McClure in Carmel Highlands, chez Ephraim Doner, in December.

---

* The chronology up to this point is taken from *Happy Rock: A Book About Henry Miller,* Bern Porter, ed. (Belfast, Maine: Bern Porter, 1970), pp. 152–154. All subsequent entries through 1971 are taken from *My Life and Times by Henry Miller* (Chicago: Playboy Press, 1971), end pages.

1954 Alfred Perlès arrived in November to write *My Friend Henry Miller*. Traveling exhibition of water colors in Japan. Began writing *Big Sur and the Oranges of Hieronymus Bosch.*

1955 Barbara Sandford, daughter by first marriage, came to see me; hadn't seen her since 1925. Wrote *Reunion in Barcelona.*

1956 Left for Brooklyn in January with Eve to take care of my mother who was dying. Returned to Big Sur. Finished *Big Sur and the Oranges of Hieronymus Bosch* book.

1957 Rewrote *Quiet Days in Clichy* upon recovery of ms., which had been lost for 15 years. Resumed work on *Nexus.* Elected member of National Institute of Arts and Sciences.

1958 Continued work on *Nexus.*

1959 Finished *Nexus* in early April. Left for Europe with Eve and children on April 14. Rented studio on Rue Campagne-Première, Paris, for two months.

1960 Wrote *To Paint Is to Love Again.* At Rowohlt Verlag, Reinbek, wrote preface to new edition of Elie Faure's *History of Art* (Gallimard). Over Christmas holidays wrote first draft of *Just Wild About Harry,* chez Renate Gerhardt.

1961 Toured Germany, Austria, Switzerland, Italy, Portugal and Spain. Returned to Pacific Palisades from London in November. In this year Grove Press published *Tropic of Cancer.*

1962 Began volume two of *Nexus* while in Pacific Palisades. Received final decree of divorce from Eve in June. Back to Pacific Palisades in July. Left for Edinburgh middle of July to attend Writers' Conference.

1963 *Cancer* published in England by John Calder—great success. *Capricorn* issued in paperback by Grove Press.

1964 *Henry Miller on Writing* published by New Directions, New York.

1965 Water color exhibition at Westwood Art Association, Los Angeles. Death of Eve, my third wife. Production of the opera *The Smile at the Foot of the Ladder* in Hamburg, Germany, in April. *Letters to Anaïs Nin* published by G. P. Putnam's Sons, New York.

1967 Married Hoki Tokuda on September 10 in Beverly Hills. Opera, *The Smile at the Foot of the Ladder*, produced in Trieste, Italy, in Italian, in December.

1968 Lawrence Durrell visited me in Pacific Palisades in March. Water color show toured Japan. Began *My Life and Times by Henry Miller*, a visual history, with Bradley Smith.

1969 Took trip to Europe in June to observe progress on *Tropic of Cancer* film.

1970 *Tropic of Cancer* film opened in U.S. *Quiet Days in Clichy* film opened in U.S. *Insomnia or the Devil at Large* published by Loujon Press, Las Vegas, Nevada. Received Book of Year Award in Naples for *Come il Colibri* (*Stand Still Like the Hummingbird*). First and only prize I ever received for my literary work.

1971 *Just Wild About Harry* to be produced in Paris. Publication of *My Life and Times by Henry Miller* by Playboy Press.

1972 *In Conversation* published by Quadrangle, *On Turning Eighty* published by Capra Press, *Reflections on the Death of Mishima* published by Capra Press.

1973 *First Impressions of Greece* and *Water Reglitterized* published by Capra Press, and *Knud Merrild: A Holiday in Paint* published by Richard West.

1974 *Insomnia* published by Doubleday.

1975 *The Nightmare Notebook* published by New Directions.

1976 *Book of Friends* published by Capra Press.